Particle Physics for Non-Physicists— A Tour of the Microcosmos
Part II

Professor Steven Pollock

THE TEACHING COMPANY ®

PUBLISHED BY:

THE TEACHING COMPANY
4151 Lafayette Center Drive, Suite 100
Chantilly, Virginia 20151-1232
1-800-TEACH-12
Fax – 703-378-3819
www.teach12.com

ISBN 1-56585-624-4

Steven Pollock, Ph.D.

Associate Professor of Physics, University of Colorado, Boulder

Steven Pollock is associate professor of physics at the University of Colorado, Boulder. He did his undergraduate work at MIT, receiving a B.Sc. in physics in 1982. He holds a Master's and a Ph.D. in physics from Stanford University, where he completed a thesis on "Electroweak Interactions in the Nuclear Domain" in 1987. Professor Pollock did postdoctoral research at NIKHEF-K (the National Institute for Nuclear and High Energy Physics) in Amsterdam, Netherlands, from 1988–1990 and at the Institute for Nuclear Theory in Seattle from 1990–1992. He spent a year as senior researcher at NIKHEF in 1993 before moving to Boulder.

Professor Pollock's research work is on the intersections of nuclear and particle physics, with special focus on parity violation, neutrino physics, and virtual strangeness content of ordinary matter. Professor Pollock was a teaching assistant and tutor for undergraduates throughout his years as both an undergraduate and graduate student. As a college professor, he has taught a wide variety of university courses at all levels, from introductory physics to advanced nuclear and particle physics, including quantum physics (both introductory and senior level) and mathematical physics, with an intriguing recent foray into the physics of energy and the environment. Professor Pollock is author of Thinkwell's Physics I, a CD-based "next-generation" multimedia textbook in introductory physics.

Professor Pollock became a Pew/Carnegie National Teaching Scholar in 2001 and is currently pursuing classroom research into student attitudes toward physics in large-lecture introductory courses. He received an Alfred P. Sloan Research Fellowship in 1994 and the Boulder Faculty Assembly (CU campus-wide) Teaching Excellence Award in 1998. He has presented both nuclear physics research and his scholarship on teaching at numerous conferences, seminars, and colloquia. Professor Pollock is a member of the American Physical Society, Nuclear Physics Division, and the American Association of Physics Teachers.

Table of Contents
Particle Physics for Non-Physicists—
A Tour of the Microcosmos
Part II

Particle Physics for Non-Physicists—
A Tour of the Microcosmos

Scope:

The buzzwords appear with regularity in newspapers and magazines—*quarks, neutrinos,* the *Higgs boson, superstrings...* It's the lingo of particle physics, the study of the deepest, most fundamental constituents and interactions of the physical world. This course will offer a tour of the particle zoo and the ideas and phenomena involved in qualitatively understanding current concepts of modern physics. No math involved! What's so strange about strange quarks? Why didn't we build a superconducting supercollider? Should we believe in particles that no one has ever seen—and never will? We'll learn about the most fundamental constituents of nature and the forces they feel—the history and discoveries, the apparatus and ideas, some of the curious characters involved, and the research and mysteries that are still being pursued today.

We begin on a fairly historical track. From the ancient Greek philosophers, we jump to Renaissance scientists whose work formed the starting point of physics. The scientific method developed by Isaac Newton more than 300 years ago continues to serve us well. Many of the physical insights Newton had, although now deepened and improved by modern physics ideas, are still relevant for understanding how the world works, which is the goal of this course and, indeed, of all physics. We jump again, to the start of the twentieth century, when new discoveries forced a radical shift in thinking about the behavior of matter—the dawn of quantum mechanics. We will not cover (or assume) any detailed knowledge of these laws of physics, discussing only the key ideas we need for the rest of this course. A "classical" approach to particle physics, although not technically correct, will serve us quite well. Students will find that understanding the basic elements of particle physics using common sense and classical intuition is possible, provided that we keep our minds open for the occasional quantum weirdness!

We will follow the early developments, both theoretical and experimental, and see how they lead us to an organizing scheme for matter at the smallest possible scale. The idea of seeking the fundamental constituents and the forces they feel will guide us through the rest of the course. We will learn about the growing "particle zoo," with just enough vocabulary to talk sensibly about the fundamental objects discovered from the early 1900s up through the most recent findings. This will lead us to quarks and neutrinos, force carriers and Higgs bosons, squarks and Zinos. Along the way, we will learn qualitatively about the theories required to describe such creatures—quantum fields, virtual particles, and all!

All this leads to what is now known as the *standard model of particle physics*—really the standard *theory*—a complete and self-consistent description of the apparently fundamental, point-like building blocks of everything, their interactions with one another, and the "rules of the game." We then move to more modern questions: Do we really have a fundamental theory at hand? Does that question even make sense? What is going on today in the world of particle physics? What are the central issues? What's hot these days? As we move through the course we will continually ask ourselves two key questions: Why is this idea interesting, and how do I know that it is true? Both are at the heart of appreciating science.

Lecture Thirteen
Symmetry and Conservation Laws

Scope:

What does the word *symmetry* mean to a physicist? Almost what it means to you: an aesthetic property of a system, a pattern that appears the same when viewed from a different perspective. The role of symmetry in our understanding of the universe has evolved considerably with time to become a guiding theme of physics. Emmy Noether's theorem played some role in this development; we'll learn how she connected symmetry to *conservation laws*, which are of enormous practical value. Spatial symmetries are easy to picture, but the more abstract, "internal" symmetries are not. How do we work these into a theory? What do they tell us about the world? Why are physicists so enthralled with symmetry?

> Symmetry seems to be absolutely fascinating to the human mind. We like to look at symmetrical things in nature, such as perfectly symmetrical spheres like planets and the sun, or symmetrical crystals like snowflakes, or flowers which are nearly symmetrical. However, it is not the symmetry of the objects in nature that I want to discuss here; it is rather the symmetry of the physics laws themselves.
>
> —Richard P. Feynman
> (*The Character of Physical Law*, Chapter 4)

Outline

I. In the next two lectures, we turn from the constituents to the laws of physics and the tools that physicists use to understand how the world works. One of the most powerful of these is the principle of symmetry.

   A. The meaning of the word *symmetry* in physics is fairly close to the meaning that you might think of but a bit more general. To a physicist, *symmetry* relates to looking at an object or a system from a different perspective. If an object looks the same from two different perspectives, then we say that it is symmetrical.

B. A snowflake has six-fold symmetry, which means that if it is rotated by one-sixth of a turn, it looks the same as it did at the start.

C. We can also talk about more abstract symmetries. If we say that a mathematical theory has symmetry, we mean that even if we make some change in perspective, the answers remain the same.

D. The mathematics of symmetry is called *group theory* and was once obscure. We now think of it as simply the mathematical formalism that describes the different kinds of symmetries that exist in the world.

II. Let's begin by looking at some perfect symmetries.

A. Imagine that you see a group of children on a field playing some sort of game. Some of them are wearing green shirts and some are wearing red shirts. What is the nature of their game? You might try to answer that question in a number of ways.

1. If all the children change into green shirts and continue to play in the same way, you learn that the game has symmetry, because a change in color is completely irrelevant to the rules.

2. This fact teaches you something about the game; that is, it probably doesn't involve teams. You don't know everything about the game, but symmetry is one tool that helped you learn one aspect.

3. If the children change shirts, then don't know what to do, you learn that the game probably does involve teams, and that color matters. Lack of symmetry has taught you something about the game.

B. That analogy was a bit of a stretch, but it is a good one for a discussion of the strong nuclear force, which involves protons and neutrons combining to form a nucleus.

1. Remember that in the 1930s, scientists were trying to understand the strong nuclear force. As in the game analogy, they discovered that the label "proton or neutron" was irrelevant. The forces of attraction held true whether the particles in question were protons or neutrons.

2. In other words, protons attract protons, protons attract neutrons, and neutrons attract neutrons. There was no change in the rules when the nature of a particle was changed from proton to neutron.

3. The strong force has a proton/neutron symmetry, which taught us something about the nature of protons and the nature of the strong force. Later, we came to understand that this force was further explained by the existence and nature of quarks.

C. What does symmetry teach us? In this case, we learned something about the nature of the nuclear force. Symmetry simplified our worldview. It reduced the number of degrees of freedom that we had to account for in describing a nucleus mathematically.

D. Think back to the snowflake example, which is geometrical. If we rotate a snowflake by 60 degrees, it looks the same. That fact teaches us something about the crystals that build the snowflake; in this case, we learn something about what goes on inside the structure.

III. We can also look for symmetry in theories, such as in Emmy Noether's mathematical theorem of symmetry and conservation laws from 1915.

A. Emmy Noether was raised and lived most of her life in Germany in the late 1800s through the early 1900s—a difficult time for a woman to be a mathematician. She met many challenges in her life to get her Ph.D. in mathematics and secure a position at a university.

B. Noether developed a theorem to connect symmetry to conservation laws. Generally, it argues that if we have a specific symmetry, then we are guaranteed to have a conservation law associated with that system.

1. Remember that a conservation law says that if we start with some quantity and it undergoes any number of changes, in the end, we will still have the same original quantity.

2. For example, if we start with some energy, we might change its form or create matter/antimatter, but we will always have the same total energy in the end. The same is true of electric charge.

C. Noether's theorem connected an abstract principle of a theory, its symmetry, to a practical benefit. Let's look at some specific examples.

1. Imagine that I am doing a physics experiment in which I knock billiard balls against one another to tabulate the laws of physics.

    a. If I do the same experiments in a different location, the laws of physics are the same. The laws are unchanged when the system is viewed from a different perspective, which is the definition of symmetry, in this instance, *translational symmetry*.

    b. Noether's theorem states that every symmetry of nature has an associated conservation law. We can't guess what will be conserved, but we can use the theorem to derive it.

    c. We discover that translational symmetry leads to conservation of momentum. If an object is moving to the right and it crashes into something, whatever is left of the object after the crash will still have some motion toward the right.

    d. Knowing about translational symmetry and conservation of momentum, we can test these ideas in the laboratory. How far can I take my equipment and still have the laws of physics be the same? As far as we know, the laws of physics operate the same as they do here even in the Andromeda Galaxy.

2. If I do my experiments today, then I do them tomorrow, I also find that the laws of physics are the same. This symmetry is *time translation*. At different times—which would be from a different perspective—the laws of physics are the same. The conservation law associated with time translation is conservation of energy.

IV. Let's discuss one more symmetry of nature that is very abstract and ties in with Noether's theorem—*gauge symmetry.*

    A. Gauge symmetry arose in the theory of electricity and magnetism. In the 1800s, people observed that the laws of electricity and magnetism were symmetrical. They were invariant under a certain change.

        1. Think of a simple electrical circuit. If we have a car battery and some wires going to a light bulb in the headlight of the car, when we hook them up, the light bulb glows.

        2. The laws of electricity and magnetism allow us to make predictions about how bright the bulb will be, how long it will burn, how hot the wires will become, and so on. These are consequences of the laws of electricity and magnetism.

        3. To do the calculations to make these predictions, we need to know that one side of the battery is at 0 volts and one side is at 12 volts. Physicist A does his calculations from the premise that the left side of the battery is at 0 volts and the right side is at 12 volts. Physicist B does her calculations from the premise that the left side of the battery is at 12 volts and the right side is at 24 volts. The numbers are different, but the difference is 12.

        4. Does Physicist B come to the same conclusions about the observables as Physicist A? The answer is yes. It's completely irrelevant what numerical value is assigned to the left pole and the right pole; all that matters is the difference.

        5. That's the essence of gauge symmetry: No matter what point is picked to be 0, the results are the same.

    B. The conservation law associated with gauge symmetry is conservation of electric charge, which is quite useful in a wide variety of experiments, not just those in particle physics.

V. We'll conclude this lecture by returning to the development of QED.

    A. Remember that Feynman, Schwinger, Tomonaga, and others were trying to come up with a quantum mechanical theory that would take into account the nineteenth-century understanding of electricity and magnetism and make it consistent with quantum mechanics.

    B. These scientists already knew that their quantum theory must obey the law of gauge symmetry.

    C. To ensure that the quantum theory was gauge symmetric, the mathematics forced scientists to introduce a new particle of nature, the photon.

        1. The photon comes out of the *principle of gauge invariance*, which is another term for *gauge symmetry*.

        2. All the properties of the photon also follow from the requirement that the theory be gauge symmetric.

    D. Once we have a gauge symmetry that we believe is present in nature, we can start to predict not only the existence of particles, but their properties.

    E. In later years, when people began thinking about the strong force between the quarks, the color force in QCD, they didn't have an earlier understanding to work from. They had to create the theory from scratch, and they used gauge symmetry as a guiding principle.

    F. These scientists started from the idea that if gauge symmetry is true for electricity and magnetism, it might also be true for the color force. Further, if gauge symmetry is true for the color force, then there must be a particle of nature that carries the strong force. We now call this particle the *gluon*, and we know that it has certain properties, which all come out of the theory.

    G. Even later, when scientists were trying to understand the weak force of nature, which was even more complicated, they again asked if it was related to gauge symmetry and again predicted the existence of a particle. This particle, the carrier of the weak force, is the Z particle.

Essential Reading:

Weinberg, *Dreams of a Final Theory*, chapter VI.

Barnett, Muhry, and Quinn, *The Charm of Strange Quarks*, chapter 5.

't Hooft, *In Search of the Ultimate Building Blocks*, chapter 10.

Recommended Reading:

Krauss, *Fear of Physics*, chapter 5, first half, up to "Symmetry breaking."

Greene, *The Elegant Universe*, pp. 124–126.

Lederman, *The God Particle*, chapter 7, section on "Conservation laws."

Calle, *Superstrings and Other Things*, chapter 25, first half, up to "The color force."

Wilczek and Devine, *Longing for the Harmonies*, Eighth Theme (through chapter 25).

Questions to Consider:

1. The laws of physics have many invariances; for example, they are the same no matter what your position is in the lab or what time it is in the lab. Are there more?

   (a) Do the laws of physics change depending on your orientation in the lab, that is, which way you are facing?

   (b) Do the laws of physics change depending on your speed as you walk across the lab, assuming that you walk in a straight line with a steady speed?

   (c) Do the laws of physics change depending on whether you sit still or accelerate across the lab? (This is a subtle one!)

2. Do you agree with the U.S. Patent Office policy that perpetual motion machines (which explicitly violate energy conservation) should be dismissed out of hand, without any further investigation? Why or why not?

3. Can you think of a symmetry in the world of particle physics that is exact? How about one that is approximate but not exact?

Lecture Thirteen—Transcript
Symmetry and Conservation Laws

I want to shift gears here a little bit for the next couple of lectures, and talk—not about the constituents, the particles and quarks and electrons that make up the world—but to talk a little bit more abstractly about the rules, the laws of physics. The tools that physicists use to try to understand how the world works. Both are important for particle physicists—to know what we're made of, and also how those things fit together in a theoretical framework—to understand the workings of the microscopic world. One of the most powerful tools that particle physicists use nowadays is the principle of symmetry. It's very useful. It has both practical consequences and aesthetic consequences. And, I want to spend this entire lecture just talking about what physicists mean by symmetry, and why and how it's useful if you want to understand the world of particle physics. In fact, it's much more general than just particle physics. Any kind of physicist, or even a biologist, or a chemist, any kind of scientist nowadays, is going to know about symmetry and care about symmetry. As you'll see, it's a very powerful guiding principle.

Physicists often use words in ways that are unfamiliar. When I talk about a force, I mean something very definite. It's a push or a pull. In the English language, the word force can mean, I don't know, forces of nature, the great force of an army, or "may the Force be with you". In English, these words have lots of meanings. And, in physics, we always make a definition and it's usually mathematically based. The word symmetry is pretty much what you think it is; it's just a little bit more general. To a physicist, symmetry means when you take an object, or a system, or anything, and you look at it from a different perspective. If it looks the same from the two different perspectives, then we say it's symmetrical. So think of a snowflake: A snowflake has a six-fold symmetry, and that means that if you rotate it by one-sixth of a turn, it looks exactly the same as when you started, or you could tilt your head by a sixth of a turn; it would look the same. So, that's a symmetrical object, because when viewed from a different perspective it's unchanged. Now, you can talk about symmetries of objects, but you can also talk about more abstract symmetries. You can talk about the symmetry of a mathematical theory; and you don't mean that if you tip your head, the symbols look the same. What you mean is that if you make some change in perspective, some change in how you look at that theory, the answers come out the same. We'll talk about some concrete examples of symmetry in theories coming up very shortly.

The mathematics of symmetry is called group theory. And, once upon a time, this mathematics was very obscure. It became important for physicists to learn about group theory in the early 1900s, when quantum mechanics was developing. And, group theory is really just the mathematical formalism that describes what different kinds of symmetries there are in the world; turns out there's different sorts, there's geometrical symmetries and more abstract kinds. And nowadays, it's an essential ingredient in the toolbox of pretty much any working scientist. We're not going to learn group theory in this course, but I want to talk about the basic ideas, the underlying principles behind the story.

The snowflake is a nice concrete example, because you can visualize it. Geometric symmetry is pretty easy to visualize. Another symmetry is left/right symmetry on my body. This side, and that side, look pretty much the same. We'll talk a little bit more about imperfections, or breaking of symmetries in the next lecture, when we start looking in fine details. But for today, I just want to focus on perfect symmetries. So I want to make a, a kind of, first a metaphor, or—I don't know—some sort of a concrete example of a symmetry which is not geometrical in character. And I'm stretching a little bit here, but I want you to imagine that you're in a foreign country, on a holiday, and you see a bunch of kids out on a field, and they're playing. It's obvious that there's some sort of game going on; they're in a confined area, and you're watching and you notice that some of the kids have green shirts and some of the kids have red shirts. And otherwise, you don't know what's going on down there. There's just a whole bunch of screaming and fun activities. There are various ways you could try to figure out what's going on—what is the nature of this game? Well, if you can't speak the language, you can't ask somebody what the rules are. Now, supposing you notice there's a pile of extra shirts off on the side, and so, you know, you sort of do the foreign-language pantomime thing, and you get all the kids with red shirts to put on green. So now everybody's wearing green shirts. Okay?

This is an experiment that you just did to learn about the symmetry of the situation. So, now you let them go. Watch what happens.

There's various possibilities. One is that they continue to play just the way they were before. They're still running around and screaming, and now you've learned that there is a very deep symmetry in this game; that color is completely irrelevant. So, my definition of symmetry was, you change something, but then the result looks the same. Here we changed the color of half of the players, and the end result is the same. This is a complete symmetry of color in this game. And what have you learned? Well, it can't be a competitive game, unless the kids know each other so well that it doesn't matter what the color of the shirt is; but one possible conclusion is it's one of those new-fangled cooperative games, where it doesn't really matter, there's not teams. The kids just wear whatever shirt they feel like; and it was just coincidence, when you first looked, that it was fifty-fifty, and they're playing some game that's not competitive. So you learn something; and of course, it's not going to teach you everything about the game. Symmetry is just one tool among many. There's another possibility, which is that everybody's green, and then they just all kind of stand around. They don't know what to do. Then it's more likely that the game was competitive, and you need to have two teams, and now the kids are confused because they don't know who's on what teams. So again, by looking either at symmetry or a lack of symmetry, you can learn something about the rules of the game.

Now, you might continue to do further symmetry experiments. For example, instead of just making everybody green, you could swap, so all the reds become green and all the greens become red. And again, there's various possible outcomes. It's possible that the game will proceed just as before. So now you would say there is "a symmetry." It's not the deepest possible symmetry; but there's a nice symmetry, which is under color interchange. The rules of the game are unaffected. So, apparently color doesn't matter. Most games are like that; in a soccer team, it doesn't matter if your team is red or green, all that matters is that you have two different colors. And so again, you've learned something about the nature of the game.

Now, you could imagine a situation where you flipped the colors and the game changes in some way. It might be that blue-eyed kids have to wear red shirts, and if they don't they're all confused, because that's the way it's always been. That's what, maybe even the rules say. It would be a slightly unusual situation, but you would learn something. This is a little bit of a stretched example of symmetry, but

I wanted to come up with something that wasn't just geometrical, where you rotate an object, or flip it, and it looks the same. And in fact, this analogy is a good one for the strong nuclear force, where you have protons and neutrons that combine together to form a nucleus. So we'll take one step back up from the quarks for a moment.

In the 1930s, people were busily trying to understand the nature of that force. How does a proton attract another proton, or another neutron? How do neutrons attract one another? That was nuclear physics, and people were very interested; it's the essence of the strong force. And it was, in a certain sense, like my little game analogy. What you discovered was, color was completely irrelevant; or in this case, whether you're a proton or a neutron, which team you're on, didn't matter. Protons attract protons, protons attract neutrons, neutrons attract neutrons; there's no change in the rules of the game when you change the nature of a particle from proton to neutron. So there's a proton/neutron symmetry of the strong force, which we were observing, and that taught us something very important about the nature of protons and the nature of the strong force. Later, we come to understand that more deeply, as a connection that says up quarks and down quarks are almost the same object, and the strong force doesn't care about whether you're an up quark or a down quark; it really only cares about the strong color charges inside, which is something totally different than whether you're a proton or whether you're a neutron. Now, it's also true that what I said is only approximate. There's a slight difference between proton-proton and proton-neutron, and that slight breaking of symmetry is also going to teach us something. That will be the subject of the next lecture, where we look at what violations, or breaking of symmetry, teaches us.

But for right now, I just want to continue to focus on what symmetry teaches us. So in this case, we've learned something about the nature of the nuclear force. It has simplified our worldview. If you're a nuclear physicist, and you're trying to describe a nucleus mathematically, you don't have to label each particle proton or neutron—at least at some crude level you don't have to—because it doesn't matter. So you've simplified your job, you've simplified the mathematics; you have reduced the number of degrees of freedom that you have to keep track of. And that's a very useful and powerful goal, in any science; to simplify the explanation of phenomena. So that's one value of symmetry. Think back to that snowflake example, which is geometrical. If you rotate a snowflake by 60 degrees, it looks the same as it did before, and that teaches you something about the individual crystals that are building up the snowflake. I'm not saying that all snowflakes look the same, but they have this general property of symmetry, which is always common. And, the fact that essentially all snowflakes have that symmetry teaches us something about the shape of the crystals inside. Even before we were capable of looking with electron microscopes, or the laws of quantum mechanics, to figure out exactly what an ice crystal looks like, we already knew something about it, just by looking at this macroscopic object that had symmetry. So sometimes, rather than saying it simplifies, you can say that symmetry teaches you about what's going on inside; another powerful use of symmetry.

There's more. Symmetry has many, many functions and values in the world. Of course, it's also nice to look at something that's symmetrical. Something about our nature as human beings; when I look at a snowflake, it just looks beautiful to me. And in part, it's because of that symmetry. It seems like it makes the object feel simpler to me. And so, when we're looking for theories, I think there's a just kind of a natural human desire to look for symmetrical theories in some way.

There was a mathematical theorem, which was published in 1915 by a mathematician named Noether, and it's quite a famous mathematical theorem. I usually don't want to teach math in this course, but in this one, without going into the details, again we can talk about the essence, and it's had a lot of implications in particle physics. Emmy Noether was raised, and lived most of her life, in Germany in the late 1800s—early 1900s; and it was a very difficult time for a woman to be a mathematician. The German institutions were incredibly sexist. She was, in principle, not allowed to take college courses, or get her Ph.D.; and she kind of did it by going to professors who were a little bit more liberated than the institutions themselves, and they allowed her to sit in on the classes. So she basically worked her way through to a Ph.D. in mathematics against the, sort of desires of some of the higher-ups. And even after that, when she had her Ph.D., she took a position at a university, and it was essentially an assistant professor position; she was teaching, she was doing research, and she didn't get paid. It took her many, many years before she could finally convince people to pay her for this job.

But despite all of this adversity, she was a fantastic mathematician. She was a mentor to many, many young students—unfortunately mostly men—who later became great mathematicians as well.

And this theorem in 1915 was a mathematical statement that connected symmetry to something a little bit more concrete, which are conservation laws. Now, the details are a little fancy, and in fact, the theorem is probably a little bit less general than what I'm going to imply here. You really need some fairly special assumptions and special cases for this theorem to hold. But the general statement is this, Noether's Theorem argues: If you have a very specific symmetry, then you are guaranteed to have a conservation law associated with your system. Let me remind you what a conservation law means. Conservation law means that you start with some quantity, and then all sorts of complicated stuff can happen; and then, in the end, you've still got the same amount of that original quantity. For example, energy, you start out with some energy. It might change forms, $E=mc^2$; you might create matter and anti-matter, it might re-annihilate; but in the end, you always will have the same total energy as what you started with. Or electric charge, that's also conserved. If you start off with an interaction of particles, it doesn't matter what the nature of that interaction is: electrical, magnetic, strong, weak. It's always true that whatever charge you begin with— it could be a big blob, and a big mess, and lots of confusion—and then when the dust settles, whatever comes out has the same charge as what you started with.

Conservation laws are wonderful for physicists. We teach them to freshman students, and we keep reminding them, over the years as they go on, there are more and more sophisticated and complex kinds of conservation laws. They make understanding complicated systems very easy, because it eliminates from consideration an enormous amount of physically impossible outcomes. When you've got particles smashing together, you might throw up your hands in dismay and say, "Anything could happen. It's quantum mechanics probabilities. Right? Anything could happen." And the answer is, well, anything that can happen will happen; but, many things can't happen. You can't create charge out of nowhere. So physicists love conservation laws, and it's practical. You know, police go to an accident scene, and they use conservation of momentum—looking at the tire tracks—to conclude whether the original driver was speeding; and, so, they can decide whether to give somebody a ticket by using a conservation law. This is, you know, real-world stuff.

What Noether's Theorem has done is, it's connected an abstract principle of a theory, its symmetry, to this practical benefit. And let me give you some specific examples of Noether's Theorem, because it really is pretty deep mathematics, and a little bit hard to visualize. Example number one: I sit at this table and I start doing physics experiments. Okay, I knock balls against one another, billiard balls; and I start tabulating laws of physics, Newton's Laws, and the laws for electricity and magnetism, and the laws for the strong force and the weak force, just by doing experiments. Okay? I'm not talking about the details of the experiment. I'm talking about the laws of nature that I'm concluding from them. Now I pack up my gear, and I move next door, and I do the experiments again. People have done this, and the laws of physics next door are the same as the laws of physics here. Newton's Laws are true in Australia, and Japan, and the United States; they're the exact same laws of nature. So this is "a symmetry." Okay? When you look at a physical system, the laws are unchanged when you view it from a different perspective. In this case, your perspective is looking at it from a different place. We call that translation symmetry. Translation not having to do with language, but just meaning translating yourself along some line. This is "a symmetry" of nature; and Noether's Theorem says, when you have "a symmetry" of nature, there must be an associated conservation law. Now what you can't do is to just guess what is going to be conserved. But Noether's Theorem is really a mathematical theorem, and you can derive what is conserved. And when you do the math, you discover that this particular symmetry, translational symmetry, leads to conservation of momentum. When objects are moving along, and you have a crash, if they started off with some motion to the right, to my right, then in the end, they—the mess, the blob of stuff that's all crashed together—will still be moving to the right, unless there's an external force. But that's a complication to the story.

Conservation of momentum, very useful; connected to symmetry of where you where looking at the laws of physics, very abstract. And, now you can test conservation of momentum in the laboratory; but you can also test for translational symmetry, and it's indirectly doing an experiment for you. So, for instance, how far can I go and still have the laws of physics be the same? It's an interesting question.

Astronomers have looked at galaxies far away. The Andromeda galaxy is the nearest one, but it's extraordinarily far away, millions of light-years; and yet, I'm going to argue that the laws of physics in the Andromeda galaxy are apparently the same as the laws of physics here. Now, how do I know that? There are no aliens who've told me the laws of physics there. But, I can look at a star in the Andromeda galaxy, and it's got the same colors, and the same light, and the same temperature, and the same distributions. All of the laws of physics, and pretty much all laws of physics, have to be put together to explain something as complicated as a star. That ultimate object is the same in the Andromeda galaxy as it is here. So this is very powerful evidence that the laws of physics are the same all the way over there; so conservation of momentum seems to be an incredibly, well-proven fact of nature, and it's well proven through this mathematics. It's kind of a wild concept.

The connection between position and momentum is definitely not obvious. I'm not implying that you should understand Noether's Theorem intuitively. Why momentum? And, as I said, the answer comes out of the math. There's a hint from quantum mechanics. The Heisenberg Uncertainty Principle says, an uncertainty in position is related to an uncertainty in momentum. So already, you can sort of imagine that momentum and position are, in some interesting way, hooked together. Noether's Theorem has really provided that hook in a rigorous way.

There are other symmetries of nature where Noether's Theorem applies. For example, I do my experiments today, and then I come back tomorrow and I do them—and I already did them yesterday—and the laws of physics aren't changing. There is "symmetry". The symmetry is time translation. At different times, that's a different perspective. The laws of physics are the same. So, what is the corresponding symmetry—sorry, corresponding conservation law? Noether's Theorem tells us the answer. You work through the mathematics; the conservation law associated with time-translation symmetry is conservation of energy. So you can check conservation of energy in the laboratory, or you can verify that the laws of physics are not changing with time; they're coupled together. And once again, if you look at the Andromeda galaxy, think about that for a second. The light that was emitted from those stars was emitted millions of years ago, traveling through space all this time, and now we see it. So not only are the laws of physics the same far away, they were also the same long ago. So this is a very, very powerful argument, and we've seen now out to billions of light-years; and the laws of physics appear to be completely unchanged, even from then to now. This is a powerful confirmation of this law of conservation of energy. So, it's not just physics experiments that make us believe that, it's also this mathematical theorem.

And I think this is why the U.S. Patent Office refuses to consider patents where you plug—well you don't plug something in, and energy comes out. A perpetual-motion machine has been dismissed by the U.S. Patent Office as clearly unscientific. It violates the principle of conservation of energy. And you might say, "Well, but what if somebody's really clever? Can't you get around the conservation of energy?" And my answer is, well, I don't think so; because (a) we've tested it directly, and (b) we know that the laws of physics aren't changing with time. If you build such a machine, then it also means that the laws of physics are changing with time, so maybe your machine isn't going to work tomorrow, and I'm certainly not going to buy it. So this is Noether's Theorem. Albert Einstein loved this idea, he was very impressed with Emmy Noether's theorem; and it became a part of his general theory of relativity, where he was looking at deep symmetries of space-time, and this theorem allowed him to connect these to very powerful conservation laws, which are useful in the mathematical statement and application of relativity.

I want to tell you about one more symmetry of nature, which is very abstract, and it's going to hook in with Noether's Theorem, but it also has a, sort of a story to tell all of its own. This is the toughest part of this lecture, for sure, so if you don't get it, just roll with it. Okay? Try to absorb what you can because I can't describe the symmetry to you in, sort of, obvious terms. This is a very abstract symmetry of nature. It's got the name "gauge symmetry;" and even the name, it's some historical name, has something to do with railroad tracks and the gauge of the railroad tracks, but I don't have any idea why that word is associated with this symmetry. "Gauge symmetry." Let me try to give an example that kind of hints at what gauge symmetry is. It arose in the theory of electricity and magnetism. In the 1800s people observed that the laws of electricity and magnetism were symmetrical, they were invariant under a certain change. So let's think of a simple electrical circuit. You've got a car battery, and some wires going to a bulb, like the front light bulb of your car. And you hook it up and the light bulb glows. The laws of electricity and magnetism allow you to make predictions: how bright will the bulb be, how long will it burn, how hot do the wires get, and so on. These are consequences of the laws of electricity and magnetism. Now, when you have a battery, one side's at zero volts and one side's at 12 volts; and you need to know that in order to do the calculations. So Physicist "A" does their calculations, saying, "This side of the battery, the left side, is at zero volts, and that side of the battery, the right side, is at 12 volts." Now Physicist "B" comes along and says—they don't know what Physicist "A" has done—Physicist "B" says, "The left side of the battery is at 12 volts, and the right side of the battery is at 24 volts." Okay, the difference is still 12, but they've picked different numbers. And now here's the big question: Does Physicist B come to the same conclusions about the observable, the light bulb and the wires? And the answer is yes. It's completely irrelevant what numerical value you assign to the left pole, and the right pole. All that matters is the difference. So the number doesn't matter; that's "symmetry" of nature. You can pick this point to be zero, or a different point to be zero; that doesn't matter. You can change that and the end results are the same.

So as I said, it's a rather abstract symmetry of nature. That's the essence of gauge symmetry. Gauge symmetry is a little bit deeper than that, but that's the idea. You could also think about analogs with gravity. Okay, I put an object like my fist at the top of the table and I say, "How high is that fist?" Well, I could say it's zero; it's zero above the table. Or, I could say it's two feet high, it's two feet above the ground. Or, I could say it's 150 feet above sea level. It really doesn't matter what number I associate with how high this object is; because, in the world of physics, what matters is always changes in height. As I lift it up, how much work did I have to do? I either go from zero to one, or I go from three to four, or I go from 150 to 151, or whatever numbers I'm using. It really doesn't matter. That's kind of like gauge symmetry. It's "a symmetry" of nature, so Noether's Theorem says there must be an associated conservation law. And, as usual, you'll never guess it; you've got to work through the math. And the conservation law that springs out of the mathematics is quite spectacular. Gauge symmetry in electricity corresponds, according to the theorem, with conservation of electric charge. So, that's one of those eye-opening surprises in a junior-level physics class, when you first teach Noether's Theorem, that makes people kind of get excited about this theorem. Because conservation of electric charge is so powerful, and so useful, in a wide variety of experiments, not just particle physics. And, it comes from this abstract mathematical symmetry of the starting theory that doesn't really seem to have necessarily anything to do with counting up charges.

Gauge symmetry goes much beyond Noether's Theorem, however; and that's where I want to finish up today's lecture. We constructed a theory—we, Feynman, and Schwinger, and Tomonaga, and the various other people like Dyson who were many people involved in the discovery and elaboration of quantum electrodynamics. Remember what they're doing. They are trying to come up with a quantum-mechanical theory that takes all of the 19th-century understanding of electricity and magnetism, including the concept of fields and electric charge, and make it consistent with quantum mechanics. So, when they tried to do that, they already knew that gauge symmetry was a good symmetry of electricity and magnetism. They knew that, whatever quantum theory they were going to write down, it must obey the law of gauge symmetry. That is to say, it must be symmetrical. Whether you call this point zero volts or ten volts doesn't matter, only differences matter. That's got to get built into their theory. So as they're constructing the theory of quantum electrodynamics, they have to be very careful—they're modifying it to be consistent with quantum mechanics—they have to be careful not to modify it in such a way that you lose gauge symmetry. And what they discovered—this is very difficult to grasp the first time through—is that, in order to make sure that the quantum theory is going to be gauge symmetric, they have to introduce a new particle of nature, the photon. It's not that you stick it in the theory because you know they're there. You have to put it in, in order to preserve gauge symmetry. It comes out from the Principle of Gauge Invariance. That's the fancy word for gauge symmetry.

So think about it. Not only does the existence of the photon come out, but its properties: it has no mass, it has no charge, but it does have spin. The photon has spin one; it's a boson. All of those facts about the photon are coming out, simply from the requirement that the theory be "gauge symmetric". Think of the power here. Once you have a symmetry that you believe is present in nature, you are starting to predict not only the existence of particles, but also their properties. And, so in later years, when people began thinking about the strong force between the quarks, the color force in quantum chromodynamics, people are struggling at first to construct a theory. They don't have electricity and magnetism—classical electricity and magnetism—to work from; now you've got the harder job of creating the whole theory from scratch, and gauge symmetry is a guiding principle now. You say, "Gosh. Gauge symmetry was true for electricity and magnetism; what if it's true for the color force as well?" It's an idea, and now you work out the consequences. If gauge symmetry is true for the color force as well, then there must be a particle of nature that carries the strong force—we now call it the gluon—it must have certain properties. It has no mass. It has spin one. It carries color. All that comes out of this theory. So, not only the existence, but also the properties of the gluon are forced upon you.

So when people discovered this, and it was matching with the theory and the data, people got really excited and they said, "Hey, gauge invariance is a great thing!" So then, later, when they started trying to understand the weak force of nature—which was even more complicated and even more esoteric and even more bizarre—people said, "Well, what if gauge symmetry is a principle of nature?" And this time around, they predicted the existence of a particle—the carrier of the weak force, not the W but the Z particle—which nobody had ever seen, nobody had ever thought of. It was just because of this principle of symmetry that they were able to predict the existence of a new particle; and a new particle means a new force of nature. It was a new aspect of the weak interaction that nobody had ever thought about before. And, it was real. It was there. They went out in the laboratory, took about ten years, and they found it.

So I think at this point, symmetry, as a general principle, is deeply required and deeply admired. It's useful. It's powerful. It's part of the way that physicists look at the world. As we reach out and try to understand new physics, physics beyond the standard model of particle physics—because we're still working on our understanding of the world—symmetry is still, and probably always will be, now, a guiding principle. You look for symmetries, and when you find them, you use them as a tool to understand the world.

Lecture Fourteen
Broken Symmetry, Shattered Mirrors

Scope:

Imperfect symmetry is called *broken symmetry*, which can be either slight or extreme. In either case, we inevitably learn something useful about the world. What is *mirror symmetry* (also called *parity*), and what would it mean if it were broken? We look at the surprise of parity violation and the role of broken symmetry in modern particle physics. This topic is difficult but significant to particle physics; we will accept some confusion without ending our exploration.

> I heave the basketball; I know it sails in a parabola, exhibiting perfect symmetry, which is interrupted by the basket. It's funny, but it is always interrupted by the basket.
>
> —Michael Jordan (former Chicago Bull)

> A broken symmetry breaks your heart.
>
> —Abdus Salam (The World Treasury of Physics, Astronomy, and Mathematics, p. 669)

Outline

I. In the last lecture, we noted that symmetry can serve as a simplifying principle. If we find that a complicated system is symmetrical, our description and understanding of the system can be made easier. We can also make predictions using symmetry, as we did with Noether's theorem and the laws of conservation.

    A. In the real world, many times, symmetry is broken. Consider your own body. Are your hands the same? In some respects, yes, but in other ways, no. You can't put a right glove on a left hand, for example.

    B. Think again about watching children play a game, this time, soccer. The team of boys is wearing blue uniforms, and the team of girls is wearing pink. If we have the teams switch uniforms, we should find that an exact symmetry exists between uniform colors.

1. Suppose that after watching many games, we observe that the pink team seems to win more often. That's a breaking of symmetry.

2. We might conclude that in America, young girls mature faster than boys and tend to be more coordinated and stronger. Thus, the pink team may beat the blue team more often if they're second graders, but not when they're tenth graders.

3. This subtle breaking of symmetry teaches us something about the players and the culture they live in.

4. If the players are high school students and the boys are forced to wear pink, the girls might laugh at them and the game might fall apart. This is a more radical breaking of symmetry. We didn't expect to swap the two colors and stop the whole game.

C. Physicists often look at systems first for symmetry, which is easy to find when the symmetry is exact or almost exact. Often, if we find a slight break in symmetry, we notice it and it teaches us something.

1. For example, as we've noted, the laws of the strong interaction are independent of whether a particle in a nucleus is a proton or a neutron. This is a deep symmetry of nature, but it's not exact.

2. A nucleus with a proton and a neutron is stable, but one with two protons is not. Swapping a neutron for a proton changes electrical properties. Because electricity is very weak compared to the strong force, it doesn't have a big influence, but it can play a role.

3. We can point to another symmetry between protons and neutrons that is also broken, very subtly: If they were completely symmetrical, they would weigh exactly the same, but a neutron weighs about 0.1 percent more than a proton.

4. This breaking of symmetry teaches us that the down quark might have a slightly different weight than the up quark. After all, a neutron is made of two downs and an up, and a proton is made of two ups and a down. A tiny difference between the quarks, then, could lead to a tiny difference between the two objects.

5. We can also use this breaking of symmetry to learn something about electricity. At first, we might say that the role of electricity inside a nucleus is insignificant. The strong force binds everything together tightly.

6. However, electricity exists inside the nucleus. Positive charges repel, but the neutrons are not repelled, because they're neutral. Again, we learn about the connection between electricity and the strong force in the nucleus by looking at the differences between nuclei that have different numbers of protons and neutrons.

II. We also need to look at some situations in which symmetry is so badly broken that we hardly recognize it ever existed.

   A. For example, imagine that you're at a fancy dinner and you sit down at a large, round table. In front of each seat is a plate and in between the plates is a glass of water.

      1. When you sit down, there's a glass of water on your left and a glass of water on your right. You might think that because the table is perfectly symmetrical, you are free to choose either glass.

      2. Sooner or later, however, somebody around the table will reach for a glass. If the first person picks up a glass with his or her left hand, the symmetry is broken. You no longer have a choice.

      3. A latecomer might arrive and see a full glass on the left and an empty glass on the right. This latecomer believes that the table has no symmetry.

   B. Let's look at another example that is more related to physics.

      1. Suppose you look inside a kitchen magnet. Physicists understand magnetism as arising from the magnetism of individual atoms, but let's just take for granted that an individual atom acts like a tiny magnet with a north pole and a south pole.

      2. The atom can be oriented in any direction, and if it's warm, it moves around. First, it points north, then west, then east.

      3. Now suppose that you have a crystal, which is a large number of atoms. If all the atoms are pointing in different directions, the result is just a crystal, not a magnet.

4. What happens if all the atoms in the crystal are magnetized in the same direction? If the atoms are pointing in opposite directions, they cancel, but if they're pointing in the same direction, they add up. Thus, a kitchen magnet is a material in which all the atoms are pointing in the same direction.

5. Let's think a little bit more about why this happens. If you warm up your kitchen magnet, it will demagnetize, because the thermal energy results in the atoms pointing in different directions. If you cool it down, the atoms will tend to begin lining up again in a sort of chain reaction, and the magnet will remagnetize itself.

6. A tiny physicist living inside the magnet might deduce that north and all the other directions of the compass are radically different, because all his experiments tend to point toward north. He might conclude that the laws of nature are not symmetrical. If another tiny physicist comes along and heats up the world around them, she could prove that their world has broken symmetry, but that the laws of nature do not.

C. Let's go back to mirror symmetry, in which you notice that your left hand and your right hand are nearly the same, but they're opposite. Physicists call mirror symmetry *parity*, or *p symmetry*.

1. Remember that a human body is almost, but not quite, left/right symmetric, but that's not a law of nature. A human body is an object.

2. The breaking of symmetry of a human doesn't break any symmetry of laws of nature.

D. To further understand this idea, imagine that you are using a pool table to do physics experiments in a room that has a big mirror on the wall. Instead of watching the table, however, you watch the mirror and take all your data from the mirror-image balls.

1. When you watch the laws of physics in a mirror world, you find that they are exactly the same as they are in our world. You could check electricity, magnetism, and the strong nuclear force, and you would find that the outcomes are identical but reversed in the mirror and on the pool table.

2. Any physicist would agree that the laws of physics are unchanging with time or space. In fact, in 1956, two physicists, Lee and Yang, wrote a paper in which they observed that this fact of mirror symmetry had been verified countless times for gravity, electricity, magnetism, optics, and the strong nuclear force.

3. But nobody had ever checked the weak interaction. What if we look at a beta decay? That's a weak nuclear reaction. Is it true that the reaction and its mirror reaction both occur with the same probability in the real world? Lee and Yang posed this question.

4. Of course, most physicists believed that parity symmetry would be unbroken. A year later a physicist named C. S. Wu set up an experiment to test mirror symmetry.

   a. Let me try to summarize the idea for you: If we have a nucleus that is spinning in the clockwise direction, we might say that it has a certain "handedness." If a particle is moving away from me and spinning clockwise, I call it a right-handed particle. Similarly, a left-handed particle would be spinning in a counterclockwise direction from my point of view.

   b. Wu examined some nuclei that had a certain handedness and were in beta decay. After the decay, she was left with a nucleus that had been transformed, and beta rays (electrons) go flying out.

   c. Imagine watching this experiment in a mirror. If the nucleus in the real world is spinning clockwise, the mirror nucleus is spinning counterclockwise. If the real nucleus is labeled north and south, the mirror nucleus is the opposite, south and north.

   d. If the world is mirror symmetrical, we would expect that the outgoing electrons would be equally likely to go north as to go south, or east or west. If all the electrons went north in the real world, that's what we would call south in the mirror world and would be a drastic breaking of mirror symmetry.

   e. Wu's experiment found that *almost* every electron goes to the north and none of them goes south. It was almost the maximal breaking of mirror symmetry imaginable.

5. As we know, the weak interaction is already rather odd; it changes the strangeness of particles; it transforms neutrons into protons; and apparently, it knows the difference between something spinning right-handed and something spinning left-handed.

6. Many, many experiments were done after Wu's, and they all verified that in any weak interaction, left-handed spinning particles and right-handed spinning particles behave differently.

7. In fact, when we start doing experiments with neutrinos, we would expect that right-handed and left-handed neutrinos would be equally likely to exist in the universe, but there are no right-handed neutrinos. To an excellent approximation, the neutrino massively breaks mirror symmetry.

8. We have also found that matter/antimatter symmetry is broken, although more subtly than parity symmetry in this instance.

E. In physics, we look at these broken symmetries and ask: Is that an accident, or is there a reason that this symmetry is broken? Does it have some fundamental origins? Can we learn something from it?

Essential Reading:

Weinberg, *Dreams of a Final Theory*, chapter VIII.

't Hooft, *In Search of the Ultimate Building Blocks*, chapter 7 (slightly hard going).

Recommended Reading:

Lederman, *The God Particle*, "Interlude C."

Krauss, *Fear of Physics*, chapter 5, second half, after the introduction of "Symmetry breaking."

Wilczek and Devine, *Longing for the Harmonies*, chapter 26.

Questions to Consider:

1. When you look at a mirror image of a map of the United States, it is hardly recognizable. Is this an example of parity violation;

that is, does it demonstrate that the laws of physics are not mirror symmetric? Why or why not?

2. Consider an idea from Richard Feynman: Suppose you could have a radio conversation with a distant alien race. We have no visual connection, audio only. The members of this race are so distant that we can't even see the same stars. After much effort, you might learn to communicate with them. (Perhaps you could tap 1, then 2 so that they could understand how we count. Then you might say "hydrogen" and tap 1, then "helium" and tap 4, and so on, tapping the atomic weights of the elements. They might then figure out the names of elements.) Imagine, ultimately, that you could converse freely with them. Then one day, they ask you to describe yourself, and you say, "My heart is on my left side." The aliens reply, "We don't know the word *left*. Which side is left?" Think carefully about this: How could you possibly explain this to them?

(Hint: If parity was not violated, I don't believe that there is any conceivable way that you could!)

Lecture Fourteen—Transcript
Broken Symmetry, Shattered Mirrors

Our last lecture was about symmetry. It was a little bit rough going in spots. There were some heavy-duty mathematics, Noether's Theorem and the principle of gauge symmetry. And today's lecture is going to also be about symmetry. About the breaking of symmetry and what that can teach us about how the world is made, and as a guide for learning about laws of physics and our understanding. Sometimes, when the going gets really abstract in a colloquium, I get a little frustrated. I go to colloquia all the time. And, if it's about nuclear and particle physics, oftentimes I can kind of nod my head and follow the whole time. And if it's—especially if it's another branch of physics, or some other science—I can get completely lost in parts of colloquia. And, I want to remind you that it's okay to get lost from time to time, as long as I can bring you back at some point, either in this lecture or an upcoming lecture. Oftentimes, when you get lost, it's because you're learning about some brand-new topic that's a little bit abstract, and as you continue along you will learn some principles and some ideas, so that when you go back and look at what you had heard before, and it was confusing, it all begins to tie in together. There's not always a starting place when you're learning about some complicated thing. It's just a big old mess, and you just have to jump in somewhere, and begin to learn more and more of it, and then the big picture begins to appear. So, having said that, I want to talk about the breaking of symmetry today; and we're going to talk about how that fits in with the world of particle physics.

Let me start off just by reminding you of why symmetry is such a lovely principle. Not just its aesthetic appeal to us as human beings, it can serve as a simplifier. If you look at a complicated system, but it's symmetrical, then your description of the system, and your understanding of it, can be made easier, simplified. For example, a neutron-proton system, like a nucleus, is not quite as complicated as you thought. You could just call them all nucleons, and work out a theory that really only has one object in there. It can also teach you about microscopic details. Think of a crystal, where the six-fold symmetry of ice teaches you something about the shape and character of the individual molecules, which might otherwise be invisible to you. And, it can lead to predictions, and understanding in a very deep way. For example, Noether's Theorem allows you to take "a symmetry" and predict a conservation law, which is practical, useful. Or even better yet, gauge symmetry, an extraordinarily abstract symmetry of nature, can lead you to predict the existence of a new particle, of new forces in the world. Symmetry is a wonderful thing.

And alas, in the real world, many times, symmetry is broken. Look at your body. Okay, it's got a left side and a right side, and it seems to be quite symmetrical. Look at your hands, in particular. Hold them in front of you. Are they the same? In many respects, they are the same—except, they're totally different! You can't put a "right" glove on a "left" hand. They're completely different, but they're also completely symmetrical. And then you look more carefully, and you notice, "You know, I've got a scar on one hand, and not on the other; my body has a heart on one side and not on the other." So there are small, subtle "breakings" of this symmetry, and many of them are accidental. Sometimes, symmetry begins and then some accident of nature breaks it, and that's a common situation, and that might teach you something. By looking at a scar on my hand, you learn something about the history of my life. It can also be that you learn much deeper principles, and that's where we're headed today.

Let's think again about watching games, and thinking about the colors of the uniforms as a slightly stretched metaphor for thinking about symmetries. So, let's go now to an American game, soccer, and we've got two teams; and imagine that one of the teams is wearing pink, and one of the teams is wearing blue, and they're a bunch of little kids and they're playing soccer. Now, the question is, is there an exact symmetry between swapping the color pink and blue? In principle, there should be. The rules of the game are exactly symmetrical; if you look in the rulebook, it's going to tell you it doesn't matter what color you are, and if everybody on one team swapped with everybody on the other team, nothing should change. So now you watch this game, and let's suppose that after watching many games you observe that the pink team seems to win more often. Okay? That's a breaking of symmetry. It might just be a subtle breaking of symmetry, and what you might learn then is, in America, that little girls in the second grade mature a little bit faster than little boys, and they tend to be more coordinated and stronger. And so, the pink team may, in fact, beat the blue team more often, if they're second graders; and when they're tenth graders, maybe it's the other way around. So this is a subtle breaking of symmetry that teaches you something about the players, and maybe the culture, that they live in.

And, you could also imagine playing that game I described last lecture, where you swapped the uniforms. If you take a bunch of high school students, and you swap the pink for the blue, the game might just fall completely apart. Because all the little girls are laughing at all the little boys, and they can't play soccer anymore. Because in our culture, it's a little bit bizarre, boys aren't supposed to wear pink. And so again, by looking, this would be a more radical breaking of symmetry. You swap the two colors and now the whole game falls apart. It's not at all the way you expect it.

So physicists are often looking at systems, and looking first for symmetry. It's easiest to find symmetry when it's exact, and it's pretty easy to find when it's almost exact. In fact, sometimes it sticks out more when it's almost exact. I think artists have really mastered this. Many, many paintings will have some symmetrical aspects; but, they are almost never perfect. Geometrical. Exact. And, it's that slight "breaking of symmetry" that kind of draws you in, and gets your attention. So, I think, many times in physics when we're looking at situations where there's a slight breaking of symmetry, we notice it. Not only does it point us towards the symmetry, but it also teaches us something. For example, I've talked about neutrons and protons in a nucleus, and I said, the laws of the strong interaction are independent of whether you're a proton or a neutron. It's a deep symmetry of nature. That it doesn't matter which you are. But it's not exact. In fact, a nucleus with two protons is not a stable nucleus; a proton and a neutron, is. It's a very subtle difference in most cases. Swapping a neutron for a proton changes electrical properties. Electricity is very weak, compared to the strong force, so normally it doesn't have a big influence; however, it can play a role. There's another symmetry that's broken between protons and neutrons, very subtly: if they were completely symmetrical, they would weigh exactly the same. And in fact, a neutron weighs about 0.1 percent more than a proton. It's a tiny breaking of symmetry, and it's very interesting. Where does it come from? Well, it comes from a couple of places. It teaches us, for example, that the down quark might weigh just a little bit differently than the up quark. Because, after all, a neutron is made of two downs and an up, and a proton is made of two ups and a down; so a tiny difference between the quarks would lead to a tiny difference between the two objects. You can use this small breaking of symmetry to learn something about the quarks that build up the objects, even if you can't see them directly.

You can also use this breaking of symmetry to learn something about electricity. What is the role of electricity inside of a nucleus? At first, you might say, "Never mind: the strong force is so strong, everything is tightly bound who cares about electricity?" But, it's there. It's real. Positive charges repel, but the neutrons are not repelled, because they're neutral. And again, you can learn about the connection between electricity and the strong force in the nucleus by looking at the differences, between nuclei that have different numbers in protons and neutrons. So, when symmetry is slightly broken, it's easy to find, it teaches us lots of things; and, we can use both the symmetry and the breaking to learn stuff.

Life gets tough when symmetry is badly broken. When the symmetry is so broken that you'll hardly even recognize that there was any symmetry there to begin with. Let me try to make this concrete with a couple of examples: the first one, a little bit more metaphorical, and the second one, a little bit more physical. Imagine that you're at a fancy dinner, and you sit down at a very large, round table, and there's a bunch of seats; and in front of each seat there's a plate, and in between the plates is a full glass of water. Now, when you sit down, there's a glass of water on your left side, and there's a glass of water on your right side; they're between the plates. And you say, "Ah, this is a perfectly symmetrical table. I am completely free to choose left, or right, to grab the glass of water." Now, there might be a social convention, I never know, so what I do is, I just wait. And, sooner or later, somebody around the table is going to grab their glass—and I'm paying attention, everybody else is doing the same thing. If the first person reaches out with their left hand and takes a sip, everybody's obligated. The symmetry is broken. You no longer have a choice. Because if one person goes left, and another person goes right, somewhere around the table—think about it—somebody is not going to have a glass of water. And so, this is a case where symmetry is broken. Imagine a latecomer who sits down, and now everybody at the table, except for them, has taken some sips. So, the newcomer sits down, and they see a full glass on their left side and an empty glass on their right side. They say, "This table has no symmetry whatsoever; completely broken symmetry of water glasses." And they might, if they're not so bright, they might not even be able to fathom the idea that the table began symmetrically.

And they might think, "Well, gee. You have no choice in life. You have to drink from the left glass, because that's where the water is." This analogy is not mine; it was actually invented by Abdus Salam, who is one of the co-winners of the Nobel Prize for his understanding and explanation of the weak force of nature, which manifests some very serious broken symmetries. And we'll come back later, and talk more about Salam's understanding of the symmetries of forces, which are analogous to this left/right choice that you have to make at the dinner table.

Let me give you another example that's a little bit more physics-y. Supposing that you look inside of a kitchen magnet. So, a kitchen magnet is a small chunk of metal, and when you stick it to the refrigerator, it sticks. Why? What's going on? Well, physicists understand magnetism as arising from the magnetism of individual atoms. And I don't want to, you know, go on this detour to talk about why an individual atom is itself magnetic. We need a course on electricity and magnetism to talk about that. But let's just take for granted that an individual atom is acting like a little teeny magnet, and it's got a north pole and a south pole, and it's an atom; so it can be oriented any which way. So, it's like a little, randomly oriented atom—a little randomly oriented magnet—and in fact, if it's warm, it's jiggling around. First it's pointing north, and then it's pointing west, and then it's pointing east. Now, supposing that you have a crystal, which is a whole bunch of atoms. There are various possibilities. One is that all of the atoms are pointing every which way. Then you just have a crystal. It's not a magnet at all. But what happens if all of the atoms in the crystal are magnetized in the exact same direction? Well, magnetism adds up. If they're pointing in opposite directions they cancel; but, if they're pointing in the same direction, they add up. And so a kitchen magnet is a material where all the little atoms, all the little mini-magnets, are all pointing in the same direction.

Okay, now let's think a little bit more about why this happens. If you have a magnet, and it's warm—if you warm up your kitchen magnet, it will demagnetize because there's so much thermal energy in there, all the atoms are pointing every which way. Now imagine cooling it down. Maybe one of the atoms will be pointing in some direction, and its neighbor will say, "Hey, you know, magnets love to be pointing in the same direction. Compass needles love to point up with the Earth's magnetic field. That's what magnets do, they like to line up." So if one atom is pointing in some direction, its nearby neighbors—if they're close enough and if they are strongly enough interacting—may momentarily line up. Now imagine a neighbor of that pair. So you've got two that lined up, and now there's a nearby third one who says, "Hey, two of my neighbors are lining up. I definitely want to line up," because now there's an even stronger local field. So, it's kind of a chain reaction. Once a couple starts to line up, then it spreads. Everybody lines up. It's like lemmings. Once somebody does it, everybody wants to do it. And this is, then, the spontaneous magnetization of the magnet; and magnetic materials are materials where the atoms are close enough, and strongly enough coupled, that they can do that.

Now, imagine that you're a little teeny-weeny physicist, and you live inside the magnet, and it's magnetized. Right? You're living on the refrigerator, and you've spent your whole life in there, and you're trying to deduce fundamental laws of physics inside the magnet. At first you're not too bright, and you're making observations, and trying to come up with rules, and it seems like many, many experiments that you do point north, and it's special. For example, if you build a little compass needle, it always points in one direction. Always. And it doesn't matter where you go in your universe. Right? You're really small. Your whole universe is inside this magnet, even if you get far away from your home. Right? It's like a human being leaving Earth. If you left Earth, your compass needle would point in a random direction, but not if you live inside Magnet World. North is special to you. And furthermore, if you take little charged particles, and you make them travel, you make beams when they're going north. They go in straight lines. But, when they're going west, they go in circles. So north and west are radically different directions to you. So, maybe you become religious and you say, "God is to the north." And maybe you're a physicist, so you say, "The universe is not symmetrical. The north direction is the special direction. And the laws of physics reflect the rule that, if you're going north, life is simple; but, if you're going west, life is complicated." And, then comes along a little genius mini-physicist, a little micro-Salam who says, "No, no, no. I believe that the world is truly symmetrical, that atoms can point any which way. It was an accident of history that they happened to line up northwards. And really, when we describe the laws of nature, they should not care about which way is north and which way is west. It's just that our world is a broken-symmetry world."

So this metaphor implies that you live in a world that's complicated, and some direction is special. It requires some insight to realize that the fundamental laws are truly symmetrical. And this little mini-physicist could prove that he or she is correct by heating up the world around them; and, if you heat up the world around you, then all of a sudden north is no longer special. And now the symmetry becomes manifest. It becomes obvious.

This kind of completely broken symmetry, shattered symmetry, is one that exists in the real world; and let me give you an example. This one is, again, slightly difficult to picture. But, it's the way the world is. So let's go back to mirror symmetry, where you look at your left hand and your right hand and you say, "Pretty much the same thing, only opposite. Left and right have been swapped." Physicists have a fancy word for mirror symmetry. It's called "parity symmetry." And, I actually don't have any idea why we call it parity; the etymological origins of that word don't seem to connect with mirrors. But anyway, that's what we call it, parity or "p" symmetry. And I'm not talking about human bodies now. A human body is an object. My body is not left/right symmetric, but that's not a law of nature. You could imagine, in some genetically engineered future, that human beings have a heart on the left and a mirror heart on the right. It would be nice. Then you could have a heart attack, and it wouldn't matter, because you've got a spare. So, you could imagine a world that's the same as ours, the same laws of physics, where human beings were exactly symmetrical. So, the breaking of symmetry of a human doesn't break any symmetry of laws of nature. I'm talking about something much deeper.

I do some experiment on the table, like I bang billiard balls. Playing pool is a good physics experiment. Physicists like to play pool because, in principle, if you know the laws of conservation of energy, and conservation of momentum, and angular momentum, you can predict exactly what's going to happen. Now it's just the physical skill of getting the balls to do what you know they're supposed to do. It's a metaphor for doing an experiment testing fundamental laws of nature. Now, imagine that you're in the pool hall doing your physics experiments, and there's a big mirror on the wall. And, instead of watching the table to write down your data—to verify that energy is conserved, and F equals ma, and all the laws of physics you're trying to derive—suppose that instead, you watch the mirror and you're taking your data from the mirror-image balls. Now there's some weird aspects, like the three ball has this funny symbol on it that's a backwards three; but that's just a human convention, you can get used to that. There's not a law of physics that says threes have to be one way. And indeed, when you watch the laws of physics in Mirror World, the laws of physics over there are exactly the same as they are in our world. You check mechanics. You check electricity, and magnetism, and the strong nuclear force. And you discover, in experiment after experiment: you do the experiment, you do its mirror image, the outcomes are identical, but mirror reversed. There's no difference in the laws.

So you say, "Ah; this seems pretty reasonable. Just like the laws of physics are the same in different places, the laws of physics are invariant under translation. And, just like the laws of physics are the same at different times, so to the laws of physics are also invariant under mirror reversal." So this looks like a good symmetry of nature. And, if you could go back in time and chat with Albert Einstein, and you said to him, "Albert, do you believe that mirror symmetry is an exact symmetry of nature?" He would say, almost certainly, "Of course it is! It's obvious! It's as obvious as the fact that the laws of physics are unchanging with time, or with space." To almost any physicist—you can't even imagine—I mean, how could it be that mirror billiards spontaneously fly up into the air? No. I don't think so. It just doesn't make any sense.

In 1956, two physicists, by the names of Lee and Yang, wrote a paper in which they observed that this law of—this fact of—mirror symmetry had been verified countless times for all the forces that I've mentioned. In fact, gravity, electricity, magnetism, optics, and strong nuclear force were all mirror symmetric. But, apparently, nobody had every actually checked the weak interaction. What if you have beta decay? That's a nuclear reaction. Is it true that the reaction, and its mirror reaction, both occur with the same probability in the real world? Lee and Yang just sort of posed this. They suggested that, maybe not; because there were some puzzles in bubble chambers that were a little bit confusing, and this was a possible way out. Now at first, I don't think they were suggesting that it had to be. They were just asking, could it be? And most physicists said, "Oh, come on! For goodness sakes, it's obvious, parity is a good symmetry." I have a quote from Wolfgang Pauli: "I am prepared to bet that the experiment will be decided in favor of mirror invariance, in spite of Yang and Lee. I don't believe that God is a weak left-hander." Okay, what does he mean by that? God is the metaphor for laws of physics. And, calling him a weak left-hander means that, in the weak force, your left hand and your right hand would be fundamentally different beasts. They wouldn't just be mirror images of one another.

Well, Mr. Pauli was wrong. The experiment was done just a year later. It was done by a physicist at Columbia by the name of C.S. Wu; and, Madame Wu was a brilliant experimental physicist, expert in beta decays. She set up an experiment to test mirror symmetry. Let me try to summarize the idea for you; the details are a little bit complicated. Take a nucleus that spins. Okay, maybe it's spinning in the clockwise direction. So, it's got a certain "handedness". Let me say why left hand and right hand is a nice metaphor. If I take my right hand and I point my thumb forwards, my fingers naturally curl in a particular direction. From behind, they seem to be curling clockwise. So, when a particle runs away from me, and it's spinning clockwise, I call it a right-handed particle. Similarly, my left hand, they go the other way; if I point my thumb away from me, like the direction of travel, a left-handed particle would be a particle that is spinning in the counter-clockwise direction, as viewed by me. So we can talk about left-handed particles or right-handed particles. So, C.S. Wu has taken some nuclei which are spinning in a certain direction, they have a certain handedness, and they beta decay. That's the weak force in action that makes them spontaneously, after a certain amount of time, fall apart. And, what comes out? Well, you're left with a nucleus that's been transformed; and beta rays, electrons, go flying out.

Now imagine watching this experiment in a mirror. If the nucleus in the real world is spinning clockwise, the mirror nucleus is spinning counter-clockwise. So, if the real nucleus is labeled north and south, your mirror nucleus is exactly the opposite, south and north. So now, what would you expect if the world were truly "mirror symmetrical?" I would expect that the outgoing electrons would be equally likely to go north as to go south, or east, or west. They should be equally likely to go in different directions. Because, if all the electrons went north in the real world, that's what we would call south in the mirror world. That would be a drastic breaking of mirror symmetry.

Now you could imagine that mirror symmetry is just slightly broken. Maybe, out of every hundred, fifty-one go north and 49 go south. That would be a very small breaking of mirror symmetry. And, what Wu's experiment found, was radical. Okay? Every electron goes out to the north, and none of them goes out to the south—almost. It was almost the maximal breaking of mirror symmetry that you could imagine.

Mr. Pauli wrote afterwards, "After the first shock is over, I begin to collect myself. It was very dramatic." In fact, Mr. Feynman also made a bet—he made a fifty-dollar bet. This is in the 1950s. I'm guessing that was a lot of money back then. He bet that parity would be a good symmetry of nature, even in these weak decays. Everybody expected that. So, it was really a big surprise. And, our understanding of the world shifted. Now comes this weak interaction, which is already kind of an oddball: it changes the strangeness of particles; it transforms neutrons into protons; and apparently, it knows the difference between something going, spinning, right-handed, and something spinning left-handed. God is a weak left-hander, if you want to make that metaphor.

Many, many experiments were done after this, and they all verified that, in any weak interaction, left-handed spinning particles and right-handed spinning particles behave differently. In fact, when you start looking at experiments with neutrinos, it's an intrinsically weak interaction now, because the neutrino can only interact via the weak force. So, if any particle of nature is going to be the kind of most obvious place to look for parity violation, or breaking of mirror symmetry, the neutrino is where you want to go. And even today, with neutrino physicists, one of the things that they're trying to understand is mirror symmetry.

It turns out that every neutrino in the world is left-handed. Remember, neutrinos are particles. They don't have electric charge, and they don't have mass, but they do have spin. If a neutrino runs away from me, it's spinning in the left-handed sense; it's spinning counter-clockwise as it's running away from me. And, if mirror symmetry was a good symmetry of nature, well, shoot; you would expect half the neutrinos in the universe would be left-handed, and half would be right-handed. They should be equally likely. And, in fact, it's as unlikely as can be. There are no right-handed neutrinos. I make a very strong statement about that; and actually, there's some current research that is hinting that maybe there's a tiny, tiny possibility of right-handed neutrinos. That's a branch of physics we'll come to in one of the last lectures, to talk about this sort of exotic idea. But to an excellent approximation, the neutrino massively breaks mirror symmetry. They're all left-handed.

Now, what about the anti-neutrino? The anti-neutrino is right-handed. Every anti-neutrino that we've ever found, or measured, has always been right-handed. So, the mirror image of the particle, in this case, is the anti-particle. That's not normally true. The mirror image of a billiard ball is not an anti-billiard ball. It's just another billiard ball. The mirror image doesn't change electrical charge. So, there's something very unusual, and very special, about neutrinos and the weak force.

And now, I told you at the beginning of this lecture that when you find a broken symmetry—and this one is as massively broken as can be—you might ask yourself, "Is it really true that nature has some beautiful left/right symmetry, and that, as the universe cooled down from the original big bang, somehow, left froze out by accident?" Kind of like in my little magnet world, it started off completely symmetrical, and then, as it cools down, one direction, north, kind of freezes out as being special. The answer is, we don't know. This is a branch of theoretical physics research that people are interested in today. We would love to be able to construct a deeper theory of nature in which left and right are completely symmetrical because it just seems so nice and elegant. It's an accident of something, history for example, that the left hand became special. I mean, otherwise, why is left, in a certain sense, better than right? It's crazy.

So, we're working on it. We don't have a deep explanation at the present time; but, what we do have, is a description. So, we're kind of like Johannes Kepler. We have observed behavior in the subatomic world. We have observed that all neutrinos are left-handed. We have constructed a model. I keep referring to the standard model of particle physics. That's the name for everything that I'm trying to build together here. A quantum-mechanical, relativistic theory that describes the quarks, and the leptons, and all the forces of nature, at least all the subatomic forces of nature: strong, weak and electromagnetic. And this standard model exists;

you can write it down on a piece of paper. You can do calculations with it. And, built into that theory, is the fact that the weak interaction violates parity symmetry. And, it's not an explanation; it's just a description. So we're hunting for that.

There are other examples of broken symmetry in the world, which we're going to want to come back, in future lectures, to talk about. One of them is the symmetry between matter and anti-matter. Forget about handedness. Forget about parity. Just think about a proton and an anti-proton. Okay, at first glance, you would say those are completely symmetrical particles. They have the same properties, except for the sign of their electric charge. That's the difference. But, they have the same mass. They obey the same laws of physics. Well, we thought that was true. We thought that matter and anti-matter was a perfect symmetry, until some experiments, about 20 or 30 years ago, that showed that, in fact, just like parity is broken, so is matter/anti-matter symmetry, in a very subtle way. We have to come back and really devote more time to talk about the ways in which matter/anti-matter symmetry are broken. This is not an egregious breaking. This is a very small breaking. And, it turns out, to have many important consequences in our understanding of where the world came from.

When you have a spontaneous breaking of symmetry—like one person picking the left-hand glass and then everybody does—or a magnet cooling down, and all of sudden there's one direction, north, that's special—it's very interesting to ask, "Was it really an accident, or was there a reason?" Maybe there is a social convention, I don't know what it is, but maybe you're supposed to reach for the right-hand glass, and that's what people do, if they're savvy. Maybe, if you've got a magnet in the real world, where we live next to planet Earth, that is a magnet, that points north; well then, when you cool this hot magnet down, it's probably going to point in the same direction as the Earth's magnetic field, because there's an external reason for everybody to line up in that particular direction. It's not exactly an accident.

Now why is the Earth's magnetic field pointing the way it does? We have to look and see if there are some deeper reasons. Sometimes broken symmetry has some deep reasons, sometimes it really appears to be a true accident; and it's one of the goals of theoretical researchers, when you see a broken symmetry, to try to ask, "Where did it come from? Does it have some fundamental origins? Is it an accident? Can we learn something from it?"

Lecture Fifteen
The November Revolution of 1974

Scope:

In November 1974, two simultaneous experimental discoveries rocked the world of particle physics. A new quark had been found. It came from two radically different places—a cutting-edge detector at Stanford and a challenging experiment at a powerful facility in Brookhaven. The new charmed quark had been anticipated (at least, by a few) and fit so well into the quark model and the new theory of QCD that it changed the scientific paradigm for many physicists nearly overnight. In some sense, this event was the dividing line between early particle physics and modern high-energy physics.

> The man was tired, for he had diligently worked the area for weeks. He stooped low over the pan at the creek and saw two small glittering yellow lumps. "Eureka!" he cried, and stood up to examine the pan's content more carefully. Others rushed to see, and in the confusion, the pan and its contents fell into the creek. Were those lumps gold or pyrite? He began to sift through the silt once again.
>
> —Harvey Lynch (SPEAR Logbook, Nov. 9, 1974)

> BJ, I think you'd better go down to the lab now.
>
> —James Bjorken's wife (on the evening of the discovery of the psi particle at SLAC)

Outline

I. By the early 1970s, the quark model was definitely established, but it was by no means dogma in the world of physics. As we've said, particle physicists were aware of the model, but many believed that it might be just a mathematical framework, not a reflection of a real object.

   A. At the same time, the theory of quantum chromodynamics, the mathematical framework for understanding the strong force, was in development. This theory showed why quarks were not being observed in the laboratory, but it had not been widely disseminated.

B. The experiment that revealed that quarks were physically real occurred in the mid-1970s, at a time now called the *November Revolution*.

II. The November Revolution is a play with two acts. Experiments were going on in parallel at two large experimental facilities in the United States.

   A. We'll begin with the facility on the West Coast, the Stanford Linear Accelerator Center (SLAC).

   1. Using this accelerator, electrons are accelerated up to an energy of a couple of billion eV, then smashed into targets.

   2. The physics community had debated whether smashing electrons was productive. Why not accelerate protons? When a proton hits a target, it interacts strongly, but the electron does not.

   B. The competing philosophy was manifested on the East Coast by an accelerator at Brookhaven National Lab on Long Island.

   1. This facility accelerated protons up to a much higher energy, closer to 30 billion eV. These experiments produced many more events, because the interactions were strong.

   2. This interaction is also more complicated, because the object being smashed is more complicated and results in much more debris. The interpretation was more difficult on the East Coast.

   C. At Stanford, the director of one of the research groups, Burton Richter, had an interesting idea.

   1. Richter knew that when energy is pumped into a small region of space to smash electrons into a target, e+/e– pairs can be produced.

   2. Richter wondered what would happen if the positrons were channeled by some sort of magnetic field and trapped. He proposed accelerating the positrons further and running them in the same circle with electrons. Because they have opposite charges, they would run opposite each other, and at a certain point, they would collide.

3. The result of this experiment would be, for the first time, matter/antimatter collisions right in front of a detector. The electron and the anti-electron would annihilate. Pure energy would exist for a brief moment, then the energy would be converted into creating new particles of nature.

D. Brookhaven was using its high-energy proton beam to produce large numbers of new particles, including new matter/antimatter pairs.

1. A physicist there named Samuel Ting was looking at all the debris coming out of the smashed protons to find a muon and an anti-muon coming out back-to-back.

2. What would make a muon and an anti-muon appear out of this debris? Presumably, they would be created from some small bundle of energy, maybe a particle, for example. Imagine that a particle is created; it lives for a short time, then decays. One of the things that it might decay into would be matter/antimatter.

3. Muons leave a distinctive signature in a detector. Remember that the muon is like a heavy electron; it does not interact strongly.

4. In the summer of 1974, Ting's research assistants noticed something interesting in the data. According to conservation of energy, total energy going in must equal total energy going out. As they graphed the data, the researchers noticed a number of events at one particular energy. Many muon pairs were being produced with the exact same total energy. Such an event is now called a *bump*.

5. This bump indicates, most likely, that there is a fundamental particle of nature with that energy. In this case, it was a very unusual signal for a variety of reasons. Ting understood that he had made a radical discovery of a particle that was super narrow and super strong, but he did not immediately publish his data.

E. On the West Coast, Richter's group now had an e+/e− collider and was analyzing data from a reverse of Ting's experiment. Instead of looking for a particle/anti-particle pair coming out, they were starting with a particle/anti-particle pair, then looking for what was produced.

1. The procedure is to tune the energy of the beams to know exactly how much energy is coming in to the system, then to look at all the particles that come out; most of the time, not much happens.

2. If you hit a resonance—the energy where a particle could be created—then you'll create that particle. It will exist for a moment, then it will fall apart and other particles will come out.

3. Experimenters at Stanford had been steadily ramping up the energies in the accelerator and collecting data. Earlier, some researchers had noticed an unusually high count rate of events in the detector at around 3 billion eV. The decision was made to back down to that energy to see what was happening.

4. On November 10, 1974, SLAC was running at 3.12 GeV. When they changed the beam energy a little bit, the count rate exploded. Particles were appearing everywhere. When they adjusted the beam energy again, they saw hundreds and hundreds more events than the regular event rate.

F. At this point, the two stories converge; the particle that was being discovered at Stanford was the same particle that Ting had discovered earlier at Brookhaven. Ultimately, the particle came to be called the *J/psi*, a combination of the names given to it at both laboratories.

III. Why was the discovery of this particle so exciting?

A. First of all, its narrowness was a big surprise. In this context, *narrowness* means that it has an extremely definite energy or, if we're thinking quantum mechanically, it lives for a very long time.

1. If we think about the Stanford experiment, we note that e+/e– pairs annihilate, and a new particle is formed. We can determine its quantum numbers, including its mass, which was 3 GeV.

2. We would expect that the J/psi would decay immediately because all the other particles in the zoo decay very rapidly, and the more massive they are, the more rapidly they decay. This particle lived for a very long time. Of course, its lifespan is still fractions of a second, but in the particle physics world, that's a long time.

3. No one had ever seen a meson like this one, but almost immediately, physicists figured out what it was. In fact, some scientists had predicted what it was before it was even seen.

B. In the years preceding this discovery, two predictions had been made.

1. Remember the quarks that we've talked about. We have up quarks and down quarks, which are similar. They're both quite light and they make up most of the ordinary world. One of them, the up quark, has charge 2/3. The down quark has charge –1/3.

2. We also have the strange quark, which has a charge of –1/3. It's just like a down quark, only heavier and unstable.

3. The two light quarks and one heavy quark make a sort of funny pattern. If we want to have symmetry, we ask why we don't have a heavier version of the up quark with a charge of 2/3.

4. Even in 1964, physicists had thought about that question as soon as the three quarks had been proposed. Sheldon Glashow and James Bjorken published a paper in 1964 suggesting that this particle existed. In fact, they thought that the existence of such a particle would be charming because it would make the picture so elegant. Thus, they called it the *charm quark*.

C. As the years went by, stronger arguments were made for the existence of a charm quark. Glashow, along with two other scientists named Iliopoulos and Maiani, made a subtle theoretical argument for what came to be known as the *GIM mechanism.*

  1. Physicists had been looking for some events in bubble chambers that were not occurring, but everybody thought they should. A kaon particle, for example, can decay in many different pathways. It might turn into a pion, an electron, or something else. But one of those pathways did not occur, and it should have.

  2. Glashow, Iliopoulos, and Maiani came up with an explanation that involved the use of Feynman diagrams. Remember that we have to draw every possible Feynman diagram and add them up before we know the probability for some event.

  3. If we include virtual charm quarks—if we imagine creating a charm quark, then having it disappear again very quickly—mathematically, that event would cancel all the other Feynman diagrams and the final answer would be nearly 0. That would explain why there were no occurrences of a certain kaon decay in the bubble chamber.

  4. This theory pins down the math of the charm quark. In order for the math to work out, a certain mass must be predicted for the charm quark. In retrospect, after the J/psi particle was found, its mass was exactly twice the predicted mass of the charm quark.

D. What is the J/psi particle, then? It's a charm/anti-charm meson. It's a new meson that is built out of the fourth quark, the charm quark, and its anti-quark.

  1. In a certain sense, this object doesn't have net charm. We call it *hidden charm.* What's called *naked charm* would be if we produced a meson that was charm and anti-up or charm and anti-down. We might have naked charm in a baryon if we produced, for example, a charm up, up; or a charm down, up; or any of the quark combinations that we could imagine involving charm.

  2. Thus, a new industry began in particle accelerators. Physicists began to look for all these new possibilities that could be seen in the laboratory, the new mesons and the new baryons.

3. The fact that new particles appeared just as expected from the quark model clinched the idea of quarks. In the November Revolution, the idea of quarks was transformed from an abstract and slightly radical proposition to a mainstream, well-established philosophy. The discovery of the J/psi was the critical event in confirming the physical reality of quarks.

Essential Reading:

Barnett, Muhry, and Quinn, *The Charm of Strange Quarks*, chapters 1, 6.1–6.4.

't Hooft, *In Search of the Ultimate Building Blocks*, chapter 15.

Recommended Reading:

Riordan, *The Hunting of the Quark*, chapters 11, 13, and especially 12.

Lederman, *The God Particle*, chapter 7, from the section on "The November Revolution" up to "The third generation."

Questions to Consider:

1. In the quark model, how would you describe the J/psi particle? Is it a meson or baryon? A fermion or boson? A hadron or lepton?

2. Why do you suppose Sam Ting waited so long to publish his discovery of the J/psi?

3. These days, we might sometimes feel that small scientific discoveries receive a lot of "hype." Could the November Revolution have been one of the first public relations hypes of physicists—an attempt to excite the public and ensure continued funding? What arguments can you make against such a suggestion (or for it?)

Lecture Fifteen—Transcript
The November Revolution of 1974

The quark model, in the early 1970s, was definitely established; however, it was by no means dogma in the world of physics. I think all particle physicists were aware of the model. They were thinking about it; however, there was a sense that these things might just be mathematical. It might just be a framework for understanding the complexity of the world; but, not necessarily, a reflection of some real object. And you have to appreciate, on the one hand, there's this zoo of particles, a hundred particles with all sorts of complicated properties, that all make sense. It all fits in, at least to a crude quantitative level, if you believe in quarks; but nobody's finding a quark in the laboratory. You never see the trail of a particle in a detector that you can identify as a quark.

Now, at this same period of time, the theory of quantum chromodynamics, the rigorous mathematical framework for understanding the strong force, is in a process of development. And, the people who are working on it are not completely disseminating those ideas, so most of the physics community has a kind of a crude model with which to work, and they're not seeing the detailed mathematical formalism. The formalism is beginning to show that there's a reason why you wouldn't see a quark all by itself; but that idea hadn't really spread so much, and I think the physics community, in order to believe in quarks as something physically real, was in need of some concrete experiment. And, that experiment finally occurred in the mid-1970s. So in today's lecture, I want to talk about what physicists now refer to as the November Revolution of 1974.

To talk about this, it's really a play with two acts. There are two big experimental facilities in the 1970s in the United States where experiments were going on in parallel with one another. They looked quite different, and we need to talk about both of them, because they both contributed to this big discovery.

Let me start on the West Coast, at Stanford. We've talked a little bit about the Stanford Linear Accelerator Center, SLAC: this is a long, two-mile long, linear accelerator that takes electrons, accelerates them up to an energy of a couple of billion electron-volts. It's a couple of GeVs. So that's a pretty darn high energy, and what they had been doing with those electrons is smashing them into targets, primarily, and then looking to see what comes out. There had been some debate in the community about whether that was really such a great idea. Why not accelerate protons? Because when a proton hits a target, it interacts strongly, and you'll get a whole bunch of stuff happening. It interacts, almost, with a hundred-percent probability— not quite true—but it interacts very strongly. The electron does not interact strongly. It's a lepton, so it only will interact electrically; and that's a hundred times weaker, at least; and so, many of your electrons just go flying right through your detector and just get wasted, they get absorbed by some beam dump. So I think when SLAC was constructed, there was some debate in the community about whether there was going to be very many good experimental discoveries made here. And I think SLAC proved, by the number of Nobel prizes that were awarded for what they did over the years, that indeed it was a great idea. The nice thing about SLAC is that an electron is a very, very simple particle. It's just a little point-like electric charge. So, although it doesn't have such a great probability of interacting, when it does, you understand in great detail what's coming in, and you can focus your attention only on what comes out.

The competing philosophy, which was manifested physically in the East Coast by a big accelerator at Brookhaven National Lab—that's on Long Island—they accelerated protons; and they accelerated the protons up to a much higher energy, more like 30 billion electron-volts, almost ten times as much energy; and now you smash the proton into a target—and lots more energy, many more events happening, because it's a strong interaction—but now you've got a complicated object coming in. If you believe in the quark model, you've got three quarks coming in, and then you have to figure out, well, which one interacted? And, right. There are all sorts of debris coming out, some of which is from the event, some of which is just coming from what you started with. So the interpretation is a little bit more difficult on the East Coast; however, you've got more energy, and more events to work with. So it's two complementary experimental approaches.

On the West Coast, at Stanford, they had this machine. They'd been running it for several years. And the director of one of the research groups, Burton Richter, had a great idea. He knew that when you smashed electrons into the targets at the end, you produce a lot of new particles. You're dumping a lot of energy into a small region of space, and some of the particles that come out are anti-electrons, positrons. Because, when you put energy into a small region of space, you can produce e-plus/e-minus: electron and positron pairs. So, what would happen if you could take some sort of magnetic field and channel those positrons, and trap them, or store them? This was the idea. It was technologically feasible in that era. And so, Burton Richter wrote a proposal to the U.S. government to upgrade the Stanford facility, to get some of these positrons and make them run around in a circle. At first, he proposed accelerating them some more, and you would have some electrons running around in that same circle—because they have opposite charges, they run around opposite one another—and at a certain point, you could run them head-on into one another. Okay, think of this: for the first time, you could have matter/anti-matter collisions right in front of your detector. Very, very clean, very pure. The electron and the anti-electron will annihilate; you will have pure energy for a brief moment, and then, particles will come flying out. E=mc2. You can convert that energy into creating new particles of nature. What a great way to learn if there's new particles out there.

So, he submits this proposal to the governmental funding agency. You know, it takes a lot of money to build a new facility like this; and it's quite normal, at national research laboratories, after they've been running for a while, to propose upgrades. It's like, you know, I've got a mountain bike, and after four or five years, I go out and I buy some front shocks for the mountain bike. It's some money, and it's a little bit extra weight; but, it really improves the character of the bike, and I can do all sorts of new things with it that I couldn't do before. It's the same idea with the facilities. The U.S. government had to approve this construction project, and they liked the project. It was a great idea. But, there were various technical problems, and there were some other projects that they needed to fund, so they put it off. And Burton Richter kept, year after year, reapplying, improving his design. At first, it was going to be a twenty-million-dollar upgrade, and he was cutting corners and figuring out ways to make it cheaper. But, you know, this was the late '60s, early '70s: there was a new accelerator being built in Cambridge, and another one later in Chicago, and there was the Apollo mission going on, and there was the Vietnam War; and, it never got funded. Burton Richter kept on trying.

And the amazing thing is, the hero of this story is a bureaucrat, a comptroller in the U.S. government. His name was John Abbadessa, and at a certain point, he said to Burton Richter, "You know, technically speaking, you have to go through this review process if you want new construction. But, if you just want to take existing operating funds and re-channel them to upgrade a detector or something, we don't need to give you official approval for that. That can be an internal SLAC decision." So, Burt Richter went to the laboratory director, Panofsky was his name—they called him Pif— and Panofsky agreed. So, basically, instead of getting official approval, and lots of new external money, they just channeled some of their existing operating funds, and they built this thing. You know I don't want to imply that it was illegal, it was definitely legal; however, it was a little bit on the sly. And, if you look at this machine that they built, it's like cinderblocks on the parking lot. They ended up spending about 5 million dollars, instead of the original 20, and they got their particle/anti-particle rings that would collide.

Now, it had been very frustrating for Burt Richter, because the Europeans had taken this idea and run with it several years earlier. So by the time they had their machine, the Europeans, who—is it competition or cooperation between the United States, and Europe, and Japan, and everybody who's got particle detectors? I don't know. It's both. It's all of the above. Everybody wants to make the discoveries themselves, and of course, we also work all together. But it's a little frustrating when you have this great idea, and then other people are building it, and getting to run their detectors. So we were a little bit behind.

Now let me leave the Stanford story and tell you about the East Coast story. We've got Brookhaven Lab, which is this thirty-GeV proton beam; and so the protons smash into a target, and they produce a whole bunch of particles. You knock chunks of nuclei out, you create new matter/anti-matter pairs; so there's a whole spray of particles. You've got these gigantic detectors trying to collect all the data, in order to analyze what's going on. And the physicist there, in the experiment that I want to talk about, his name was Samuel Ting. He's a professor from MIT working at Brookhaven for his research; and his idea, his experimental program, was to look amidst all this complicated debris, all the stuff that's flying out, for a muon and an anti-muon that come out, in a certain sense, back-to-back. Okay, what would make a muon and an anti-muon appear out of all this debris? Well, it's matter/anti-matter; and if they're coming out back-to-back in some reference frame, then presumably they were created from some little bundle of energy, maybe a particle, for example.

So imagine, you create a particle, it lives for a short time and then it decays; and one of the things that it might decay into would be matter/anti-matter. So, the muons leave a very distinctive signature in your detectors, because they're so different. Remember the muon, that's that "who ordered that?" particle; it's like a heavy electron. It's the particle that does not interact strongly. It's just like an electron. So the tracks that it leaves are very, very different from the tracks of almost all the other particles in the zoo, which very quickly decay.

So Mr. Ting is analyzing these muon pairs, and in the summer of 1974, his graduate students notice something very interesting in the data. So, here's how you analyze this data, one of the ways. You measure the total energy of the muon pair, the total energy of your system. Okay, conservation of energy says that total energy must equal to the energy that you started with; and what you do is, you sort of draw a little graph, a histogram. And on the one axis, the horizontal axis, is the total energy that you observed; and the vertical axis is just, how many times did you see an event like that. So, you see a couple of events at this energy and a couple of events at that energy, and all of a sudden, at one particular energy, they saw a whole bunch of events. Many, many muon pairs, over and over again, were being produced with the exact same total energy. Nowadays, we call this a bump. It's a bump in the graph, and it indicates, most likely, that there is a particle of nature, some fundamental particle of nature, with that energy. So it's created, it's a resonance, so it's easily created; and then when it falls apart, it always produces a muon pair with that energy. It was a very unusual signal, for a variety of reasons. One of the reasons was, it was super-narrow. People talk about "binning" their data, which means how much energy—there's always some uncertainty in the energy that you measure—and so you're going to have some range of energies that you're going to put into your plot, and they could make that range very, very narrow; and still they were seeing a bump. It was a very definite energy that they were seeing.

Now, this is very exciting. You have to appreciate that Sam Ting understands that this is a pretty radical discovery. Even though there have been hundreds of particles discovered by 1974, there's something really special about this one, because it's super-narrow and super-strong. Many, many orders of magnitude different than anything anybody had ever seen before. Okay. This is Nobel Prize material that you're looking at. So the big question is, why didn't Sam Ting jump up and down and publish his data? Because, you know, that's what physicists do when they discover some spectacular data, they let everybody know, and they publish.

Sam Ting was an unusual fellow. He's a brilliant physicist, very well respected, very serious, and very critical. He had, for many years, been very good at being able to point out what was wrong with everybody else's experiments. So, I think, he maybe had some physicists who weren't exactly friends of his; and so, perhaps part of the story was that he really wanted to be super-cautious about this. It would be humiliating if you published and it turned out to be an accident; maybe a glitch, maybe a statistical fluke, maybe just a mistake in your analysis. So, you might argue that he was being extremely cautious, and he just wanted to be darn sure.

So, they began running again, and they changed their detectors. They fixed, they changed, and his graduate students are working very hard. He was known as a tough advisor. People were working long hours. And, I think, there was a lot of pressure on him to publish. Of course there's another idea, another possibility—you can read stories about this whole November Revolution business, and it's fascinating to think about the characters and personalities involved here—it may be that Sam Ting realized that he was probably the only person in the world with this data. Okay? There were other accelerators where, in principle, if this particle existed, you could find it. But, it was so narrow, finding it would require an incredible stroke of luck. It was a stroke of luck for him, and he figured, "I've got time. It's like finding a needle in a haystack. I've got months before anybody else even has the slightest chance of finding this thing." So, given that, he could collect all sorts of data, and really figure everything out about this particle. So, that when he finally did publish, it would be a sort of a complete explanation of what he had, which would really guarantee fame and glory; or, at least, some scientific success. In any case, he continues analyzing this data, and September goes by, and October goes by, and they're continuing to collect data—no publications.

Let me go back to the West Coast. Burt Richter's group now has this machine with the e-plus/e-minus collider, and they're now analyzing data. So what do you do? It's kind of the reverse of Sam Ting's experiment. In Sam Ting's experiment, you put a whole bunch of junk together, and you look for a particle/anti-particle pair coming out. At Stanford, you're putting a particle/anti-particle pair in; they're annihilating and forming energy, and then you're looking for all the junk that comes out. So it's kind of like the same experiment, only backwards. And what you do is, you tune the energy of your beam—so you know exactly how much energy is coming in—and then you just look at all the particles that come out; and most of the time, not much happens. They swing by each other. Maybe they bounce. Maybe they produce another particle/anti-particle pair. At most energies, there's not much interesting going on. But, if you happen to hit a resonance, if you happen to hit the energy where a particle could be created, then you'll create that particle. It'll sit there for a moment, and then it'll fall apart, and all sorts of stuff will come out.

So that's what they're looking for. You ramp up the energy, and you collect data for a little while. Ramp up the energy some more, collect data for a while. They'd been actually doing this for a year, by the fall of 1974. And, there was a strong temptation in the laboratory to upgrade to higher energies, because the Europeans—in particular in Germany, there was a facility called DESY, it's a German acronym; Deutsche Electron something or other—the DESY accelerator was planning on having a higher-energy electron/positron collider. And so, SLAC really wanted to get there first. So there's some political pressure in the laboratory to fix up your magnets, make them a little stronger so you could have higher energies, and ramp up to higher energies.

There was another conflicting opinion in his group, because the summer before, they had been collecting data, and at about three billion electron-volts at around three GeV, there had been a slightly, unusually high count rate of events in their detector. So some people were saying, "You know, we should really go back and check out what was going on at three GeV, just to see if there was something that we missed. And it might also help us to calibrate our machine." So, Burt Richter weighed the possibilities and finally compromised and said, "We'll spend a few days going back down in energy to three GeV"—going down in energy, sort of a scary political decision. But, he says, "We'll do that, but just for a couple of days; and if we don't see anything, then we'll ramp up to the higher energies." So they went down to three GeV.

Let me get the numbers and dates straight. On November the 10th, 1974, they're running at 3.12 GeV; and what they saw, on their computer screen, was a sort of a real-time image that showed the events that they were collecting. So, the screen would light up every now and again, you know, indicating that something interesting had happened; and it was lighting up a little bit more frequently than their usual baseline. So it did look, indeed, like there was something there. When you're a particle physicist, you have to be careful. You're kind of flipping coins, right? It's quantum mechanics. There's some randomness associated with the production of particles. You've got energy. It will produce anything that it can produce, but only with a, sort of a statistical distribution.

So, if you're tossing coins for a living, and you toss six heads in a row, you know, do you get excited and think that you've got an unusual coin? Well, not if you've been tossing coins thousands and thousands of times; six in a row is not all that unusual. So they really had to check their data, and run for a longer amount of time. They changed the beam energy a little bit. They went from 3.12 to 3.11, and now the count rate just started exploding. The display was like a fireworks display—flash, flash, flash! Particles were just appearing like crazy. So, they had found something. They changed the beam energy again, from 3.11 to 3.104, right? They're honing in on something. And now it's just crazy—hundreds and hundreds of times the regular event rate.

And here's where the two stories converge, because this particle that was being discovered at Stanford was exactly the same particle that Sam Ting had discovered months earlier at Brookhaven. Of course, there's no communication between the two labs—yet—because Sam Ting had been keeping a lid on his data in the hopes of putting it all together and getting—making absolutely sure that it was right before he announced it. The climate at Stanford was very different. Stanford is—was really one of the archetypes of the kind of modern sociology of particle physics. Extremely open laboratory; physicists there were highly collaborative, the teams were international. Everybody's on the phone. It was the most expensive telephone bill in SLAC's history up to that date. They're calling all their physics buddies in

Europe, and on the East Coast, and throughout the whole world, telling them about what they had, because they were very excited. It was obviously a big discovery. And I think this is more in keeping with the usual climate of scientific discovery in particle physics today. This collaborative nature is, in fact, what created the World Wide Web—not in 1974, but at a later time. CERN, in Europe—that was the European center for nuclear research, which was kind of the European version of our big laboratories—they, along with the big American laboratories, really wanted to share data as rapidly and easily as possible. I remember, as a particle physics post-doc, using the World Wide Web before there were any commercial websites; all that you had on the web were physics laboratories, where you could look up data and collect information, pretty much on the fly.

It just so happened, by sheer coincidence, Sam Ting was in an airplane on that day, on his way to Stanford. Because every year, maybe even a couple of times a year, physicists get together—it's a kind of a working group—to discuss what's going to happen at the National Laboratory. It's kind of a business meeting, and Sam Ting was part of that collaboration. And, so he was on his way for this regularly scheduled meeting when this discovery was happening at Stanford. Now, the graduate students and post-docs at Brookhaven start hearing telephone calls, because everybody's talking about this thing. And, they're just freaking out: I mean, imagine how you would feel if you've just spent the last several months of your life, spending, you know, eighteen-hour days collecting this data, thinking this is your big break, and now somebody else is going to scoop you! So, they're all frantic. And, how do you reach Sam Ting? He's on an airplane. There are no telephones on airplanes in those days. So, they left a message for him at the TWA gate, so that when he got off the plane he would get this message.

He gets the message late in the evening, and realizes—I think probably to his horror—that he's about to be scooped. So he goes to his hotel room. He hasn't even gone to SLAC yet. He doesn't really know any of the details. And, he starts making telephone calls himself, which he probably should have done much earlier. You know, I don't want to criticize Sam Ting, he's a great physicist, and he had, in fact, made the discovery first; and, it was well analyzed and ready for publication by this point. But in any case, he made telephone calls to his colleagues at Brookhaven, and at MIT; and really wanted to make it clear that this discovery was his.

And the story goes that the next day, Sam Ting walks into Burton Richter's office, and Sam Ting says, "Burt, I have some interesting physics to tell you about." And Burt says, "Sam, I have some interesting physics to tell you about!" And so they're, of course, each sharing the same physics, and they're both incredibly excited about it. Both of these papers ended up getting submitted to the journal at the same time, and they were published back-to-back; and a few years later they shared the Nobel Prize, Sam Ting and Burt Richter. It's sort of interesting to hear all this kind of human aspects, which is always present; and the physics story often, kind of misses out on this interesting character stuff.

There's one more element to the human nature of this story. If you discover a particle, you get to name it; and it's kind of a big deal for physicists. So Sam Ting wanted to name the particle the "J". Now, that's not the usual convention—people usually use Greek letters for new particles—but J, it turns out, is very close to the Chinese character for his name. And, you know, he's a physicist—like many physicists, kind of a big ego, maybe—and so that's what he wanted to call it. That's what his team had been calling it. At Stanford, they had been calling it the psi, the Greek letter; and it just so happens that P-S are two of the letters in the name of their ring. It was called SPEAR. The Stanford Positron-Electron Accelerator Ring. So they liked the name psi particle. And so there was, for many years, some sort of an East Coast/West Coast thing, where if you went to talk about this particle on the West Coast, it was the psi, and on the East Coast it was the J. Nowadays. The official name of this particle is the J/psi; so, that was the compromise.

Why was this so exciting? Why is this a revolution in physics? Well, you might just say, "Come on—it's another particle. You've just been telling me about, you know, hundreds of particles that are produced." There was something extraordinarily special about the J/psi. First of all, its narrowness was a big surprise. Narrowness, meaning it has an extremely definite energy; or, if you're thinking quantum-mechanically, it lives for a really long time. If you're thinking about the Stanford experiment, e-plus/e-minus annihilate, you form a new little particle; you can figure out its quantum numbers, it has no electric charge, and you can figure out its spin, it's a boson. So it's a meson; it's a strongly interacting particle, of very high mass. 3 GeV. You expect that it should decay immediately, because all of the other particles in the zoo decay very,

very rapidly; and, the more massive they are, the more rapidly they decay. But this thing lived for a really, really, really long time. Of course, it's still fractions of a second; but, in the particle-physics world, that's forever. It's practically stable. So what is going on? This is a meson like no one has ever seen before. And, there was sort of a buzz in the physics community; but almost immediately, people figured out what this thing was. In fact, some people had predicted what it was before it was even seen. Let me tell you about two predictions that had been made in years before.

First of all, I want you to think about the quarks that we've talked about. There's an up quark and a down quark. They're both quite similar, they're both quite light, and they make up most of the ordinary world. One of them, the up quark, has charge two-thirds; the down quark has charge minus one-third. So if you're imagining a little table, you've got an up quark and a down quark next to each other; and then there's this heavier version of the down quark. It's also got charge minus one-third, just like the down quark. That's the strange quark. It's just like a down quark, only heavier, and unstable.

So, there's this sort of funny pattern. You've got two light quarks, and only one heavy quark. So if you want to believe in symmetry, you ask yourself, "Well, how come there's not a heavy partner to the up quark? How come there's not a heavier version of a quark with charge two-thirds?" And right away, in 1964, people had thought about that, as soon as the three quarks had been proposed. Shelly Glashow and James Bjorken were the physicists who published a paper in 1964 suggesting that maybe this would exist. And in fact, they thought it would be very charming if such a particle existed, because it would sort of make the picture so elegant; so they called it the charm quark. You've got the strange quark; now you've got the charm quark. It's the '60s. People are being a little bit silly in their naming conventions. It was a nice idea; but shoot—people hardly even believe in quarks in those years. It's so speculative. And now you're speculating about a quark that nobody's even seen or has any evidence for whatsoever, based on theoretical symmetry grounds. So, I think the idea was out there, but not really very well accepted.

As the years went by, there were stronger arguments made for the existence of a charm quark. Glashow, again the same Glashow who had proposed the charm quark in the first place, along with a fellow named Iliopoulos, and a fellow named Maiani—and these names are hard to pronounce, so people referred to the three of them as G-I-M or GIM—the GIM paper, or the GIM mechanism, was a kind of a subtle, theoretical argument. They were looking at some events in bubble chambers that were not occurring, but everybody thought they should. You have a kaon particle, and it can decay, and it decays in many different pathways. It might turn into a pion, it might turn into an electron; there's all sorts of possibilities for how the kaon might decay, and one of those pathways didn't occur. It should as there was no violation of any obvious conservation law. And Glashow, Iliopoulos and Maiani came up with an explanation. It involved drawing Feynman diagrams. You have to draw every possible Feynman diagram, and add them up, before you know the probability for some event. And, if you include virtual charm quarks—if you imagine creating a charm quark and then having it disappear again very quickly—it turns out, mathematically, that they would cancel all the other Feynman diagrams, and you would get zero as your final answer. So, that would explain why you were getting no such events.

Very esoteric. At the time, it actually pins down the math of the charm quark. In order for the math to work out you would have to predict a certain particular mass for this charm quark. And sure enough—in retrospect—after the J/psi particle was found, the mass of the J/psi was exactly twice of the predicted mass of the charm quark. So what's the J/psi particle? It's a charm/anti-charm meson. It's a new meson, which is built out of this brand-new quark, the fourth quark, the charm quark, and its anti-quark. Now, you've got charm and anti-charm; so in a certain sense, this object doesn't have net charm. We call it naked, sorry; we call it "hidden charm". "Naked charm" would be if you produced a meson that was charm and anti-up, or charm and anti-down. Or, you could have naked charm in a baryon, if you produced, for example, a charm/up/up, or a charm/down/up, or any of the quark combinations that you could imagine involving charm. So now, a whole industry begins in particle accelerators. Let's go look for all these new, possible things that you can see in the laboratory: the new mesons and the new baryons—and they were all found.

So you have to appreciate the significance of the J/psi. It's a new quark, so that's exciting. And, I think in a certain sense, the reality of these quarks—the fact that all the new particles appeared just as expected from the quark model—really clinched the idea of quarks.

So, in this November Revolution, it wasn't that it was a completely new idea. The ideas had been all around. But what was really exciting, and radical, and transformational, in the physics community was that, all of a sudden, the idea of quarks went from a sort of an abstract, and slightly radical, proposition to pretty much a mainstream, well-established, almost orthodox philosophy. I think the discovery of the J/psi was the big critical event in making us really believe in the physical reality of quarks.

Lecture Sixteen
A New Generation

Scope:

The last of the great surprises in particle physics was a new layer of particles with the discovery of the tau lepton. As we know, once we find one new particle, symmetry arguments compel us to look for others, which we found—the tau neutrino and the bottom and top quarks. What do we learn when particles are predicted before they are discovered? We conclude by revisiting the periodic table of particle physics, including all the new particles.

> Inventions have long since reached their limit, and I see no hope for further development.
>
> —Julius Sextus Frontinus
> (highly regarded engineer in Rome, first century A.D.)

Pastore: Is there anything connected in the hopes of this accelerator that in any way involves the security of the country?

Wilson: No, sir; I do not believe so.

. . .

Pastore: Is there anything here that projects us in a position of being competitive with the Russians, with regard to this race?

Wilson: Only from a long-range point of view, of a developing technology. Otherwise, it has to do with: Are we good painters, good sculptors, great poets? I mean all the things that we really venerate and honor in our country and are patriotic about. In that sense, this new knowledge has all to do with honor and country but it has nothing to do directly with defending our country, except to make it worth defending.

—Excerpt from testimony before the Congressional Joint Committee on Atomic Energy, April 16, 1969

Outline

I. Some older physicists might look back on the 1970s as a golden age of particle physics. The discovery of the J/psi during the November Revolution was the highlight, but many other discoveries were also made, some of which we will discuss in this lecture.

    A. The quark model had at first been tentative but was later fleshed out. This was followed by the theory of QCD, which transformed the idea of quarks into a mathematical framework that could be used to make quantitative predictions about quarks.

    B. The significance of the J/psi particle was that its behavior and properties made sense in relation to the theory of QCD.

        1. Think, for example, about the most distinctive characteristic of the J/psi particle: It is "narrow," which means it lives for a long time. Why? It is a charm and an anti-charm. Why don't the two particles annihilate, like matter and antimatter? The answer comes from the mathematics of QCD.

        2. QCD says that when two quarks are far apart, they attract each other very strongly, but if they're close together, they don't feel a strong attraction. The closer they get, the freer they become. Further, in quantum mechanics, the more massive the quarks in the meson are, the smaller the effective distance between them becomes.

        3. The charm and anti-charm quark are, in a real sense, very close to each other in the J/psi particle. Because they are so close, they are almost completely free particles.

    C. After the discovery of the J/psi, the theory of QCD began to spread rapidly and become well established in the physics community.

II. Experimentalists began working to prove or disprove the theory of QCD, which led to some "big surprises" in the field. Ultimately, these surprises fit beautifully with the theory of quarks and QCD.

A. A couple of years after the discovery of the J/psi, a physicist named Marty Perl at Stanford discovered a new lepton.

    1. Obviously, we knew about the electron and the muon, which was a heavy version of the electron. Perl had now found a third lepton. It had electric charge, just like the electron. It had spin 1/2. It did not interact strongly. It was truly a lepton, just like the electron and the muon. It was like a third generation of these other lighter leptons. Perl called this particle the *tau lepton*, or *tau particle*.

    2. What does the discovery of this particle tell us? Imagine trying to organize the fundamental particles into a kind of periodic table.

        a. Because the quarks and leptons are so different, we'll keep them separate. The lightest quarks, the up and the down quarks, are in a row by themselves. They're distinct from each other. They have different charges. Next, we have the two lightest leptons: the electron and the electron-flavored neutrino. Those four particles compose the world we live in.

        b. Next, we've got a kind of photocopy, or second generation. The strange quark is a heavy version of the down quark. It has the same charge and the same spin, but it's heavier and radioactive. In 1974, we also discovered a heavy version of the up quark, which is the charm quark. Our table now has up and down quarks and charm and strange quarks.

        c. What is analogous in the lepton sector? There, we have the muon and the muon-flavored neutrino. We have a complete second generation of quarks and leptons.

    3. This second generation of particles is still kind of mysterious. They come raining down on us in cosmic rays—strange quarks, muons, and muon neutrinos but not so many charm quarks. They also exist fleetingly as virtual particles. They may exist in certain unusual astronomical phenomena, such as massive neutron stars.

4. Perl now discovered one more lepton. Imagine that beneath the electron and the muon in our table is a new particle, the tau particle. This discovery led us to expect the discovery of a row of new particles corresponding to the tau neutrino. Further, if we have a new generation of leptons, we should be able to find a new generation of quarks, heavier still and even more radioactive.

B. The discovery of the third generation of quarks came quickly by Leon Lederman and a team at Fermilab.

1. Fermilab is a giant ring, similar to the Brookhaven facility, but it is no longer a cyclotron. It is made up of a number of magnets that guide protons around in a circle. There are also electric fields so the protons gain more and more energy as they go around the ring.

2. In 1977, this facility could produce protons with an energy of 200 GeV. Aiming that amount of energy into a target should enable production of a new particle of nature.

3. Think about our periodic table. We have an up and a down quark in the lightest generation, and the down quark, in a certain sense, is a little bit lighter than the up quark. In the next generation, the strange quark is quite a bit lighter than the charm quark. If the pattern continues, the new quarks should match the known ones in charm and spin, but be heavier still.

4. These new heavy quarks in our chart are now called top and bottom, or occasionally, truth and beauty. Lederman found the lighter of these, in the form of a bottom and an anti-bottom quark bound together in a meson, now called the upsilon. This is analogous to the discovery of the J/psi, also a meson (a charm and an anti-charm quark bound together).

C. These new bottom quarks are so massive that the theory of QCD could start to make some quantitative predictions about the lifetime and the decay products and the quantum numbers—almost everything that could be measured—about this bottom/anti-bottom meson.

D. Thus, we had discovered a third generation of electron-like particles, or lepton, the tau. We had also discovered a third generation of quark. What would be the next? We should find a tau-flavored neutrino, which would be difficult to detect but was found a couple of years ago. We should also be a final quark that comes under the up quark and the charm quark, with charge 2/3; this would be the top quark.

  1. The top quark was expected to be heavier than the bottom quark, but nobody knew exactly what its mass should be.

  2. Remember that the theory of QCD is a renormalizable quantum field theory, meaning that in making calculations from it, some infinities arise mathematically, and some properties, including the mass of fundamental particles, cannot be computed.

  3. QCD can't predict the mass of a top quark, but we can make some educated guesses about it by looking at data.

    a. Physicists already had an idea for the mass of the charm quark by considering events in which a charm quark might appear virtually, very briefly, then disappear again.

    b. We can create a charm quark out of nothing if we give it back again, even if we don't have enough energy to actually make it come free. The act of pulling the charm quark, or any quark, out of the vacuum affects observables.

    c. If we calculate with Feynman diagrams, we must include every possible splitting of the vacuum into particle/anti-particle, which will change the probability a little bit. This kind of calculation is called *precision particle physics*.

    d. If we make a highly precise measurement, then make a careful calculation, we can compare the measurement with the calculation, and we may be able to deduce the mass of this one last unknown quark, the top quark.

E. The top quark was finally found in 1995 at Fermilab, which is now called the Tevatron, because its energy has been upgraded from billions of eV to trillions. That's the energy required to produce these ultra-massive top quarks and anti-top quarks.

III. Let me tell you a little bit about the sociology of modern particle physics and these gigantic physics facilities.

    A. The accelerators at Fermilab and SLAC are gigantic. The area where the collisions take place has detectors the size of buildings and teams of as many as 500 physicists working on these experiments.

    B. At Fermilab, two very narrow beams counter-rotate in the accelerator. The protons go one way; the anti-protons go the other way. The goal is to make the protons and anti-protons run into each other.

        1. These particles have a probability of interacting, but the probability is not 100 percent. Some of them will interact, and some of them will pass on by and continue to circle.

        2. The rings of the accelerator are designed to be slightly off kilter so that most of the time, the protons and anti-protons pass by each other. In a couple of spots, the rings cross paths; those are the interaction regions where the detectors are set up.

        3. At the time of the search for the top quark, two teams were working at Fermilab completely independently. Both teams ultimately came up with data, and their two publications agreed, within experimental uncertainties, on the mass of the top quark.

    C. We are now in a period of consolidation.

        1. The tau neutrino was really the last discovery to be made, and it clarified and consolidated the standard model of quarks and leptons. We now believe that we have a complete list of particles, with no evidence that there is a fourth generation.

        2. In fact, we have now seen hints that a fourth generation does not exist. A fourth-generation neutrino could be very light and, if it existed, we would already have found evidence of it.

    D. We now seem to have a well-established framework for understanding the world, including six fundamental quarks, up and down, charmed and strange, top and bottom, and six fundamental leptons, electron and electron neutrino, muon and its neutrino, tau and its neutrino.

E. However some people are wondering how many fundamental particles we can account for before we start to ask if the story goes even deeper. Someday, we might be able to go beyond the current standard model.

Essential Reading:

Schwarz, *A Tour of the Subatomic Zoo*, chapter 7.

Kane, *The Particle Garden*, chapter 5, to p. 8.

Barnett, Muhry, and Quinn, *The Charm of Strange Quarks*, chapter 7.

Recommended Reading:

Riordan, *The Hunting of the Quark*, chapter 14.

Lederman, *The God Particle*, chapter 7, section called "The third generation"; chapter 8, section called "Search for the top."

Questions to Consider:

1. Is it possible that we might someday find a totally new *fourth* generation of particles? What arguments can you make for and against this possibility?

2a. Why did it take so long to find the top quark and the tau neutrino? Both were discovered at Fermilab within the last several years. Do you think that the difficulties associated with discovering these particles were fairly similar or totally different?

2b. The top quark mass is about 170 GeV, compared to a proton mass of about 1 GeV. What element in the periodic table has a mass that large? (Bear in mind, the top quark is still considered a fundamental, elementary, pointlike object.) How many constituents does the "mass equivalent" element you found have?

Periodic Table of Particles

PERIODIC TABLE OF PARTICLES

LEPTONS

| ν_e electron neutrino | ν_μ mu-neutrino | ν_τ tau-neutrino |
| e electron | μ muon | τ tau |

QUARKS

| d down quark | s strange quark | b bottom quark |
| u up quark | c charm quark | t top quark |

Lecture Sixteen—Transcript
A New Generation

I think some physicists, especially older physicists, might look back at the 1970s kind of wistfully, as a golden age of particle physics. There were a lot of big discoveries being made, the J/psi November Revolution kind of being the highlight; but there were many others, some of which we're going to be talking about today. It was not just surprises; it was also a sense that it was all beginning to come together. The quark model, which at first had been tentative, had become fleshed out. And then a theory, quantum chromodynamics, had been developed, which really took what was effectively a model, an idea about quarks, and turned it into a rigorous, mathematical framework, where you can do calculations, and make quantitative predictions; and they were starting to come true. One of the most impressive things about the J/psi particle was not just that we had discovered a new quark, a charm quark and its anti-quark; it was, the behavior and property of the J/psi really made sense, if you look at the theory of quantum chromodynamics.

Think, for example, about the most distinctive characteristic of this new J/psi particle: it lives for a long time, it's very stable. Why is that? It's a charm quark and an anti-charm quark. Why don't they just annihilate like matter and anti-matter, and the thing disappears right away? And the answer is, it comes from the mathematics of quantum chromodynamics. QCD says, when you have quarks that are far apart, they attract each other very strongly; but if they're close together—it's kind of like a rubber band force of nature—they don't really attract one another very strongly at all. They become free the closer they get. And in quantum mechanics, the more massive a particle is, in a certain sense, that means distance is very small. The charm and anti-charm quark are, in a real sense, very, very close to one another in the J/psi particle; and because they're very, very close, they feel each other almost not at all. They're essentially completely free particles. They don't suck each other, one into the other, and annihilate, for a long time, because of the properties of quantum chromodynamics.

QCD was just a fledgling theory in 1974. There was a small community of theoretical physicists who knew about it, some of whom had even, really, predicted the existence of a particle like this with its properties. In fact, there was one theorist who had bet his hat, at a conference a year or two before the discovery of the J/psi, that such a particle, something like it would be discovered. I think that as soon as the particle, the J/psi, was discovered, the word of quantum chromodynamics began to spread very rapidly, because this was now a great success, a quantitative success for this new theory. And so, not only is the quark model well established by the November Revolution; but also, the theory of quantum chromodynamics becomes well established. Now, to physicists, when a theory is well established, it doesn't mean you quit thinking about it; in fact, physicists are the most skeptical, cynical, and aggressively challenging conservatives that you can imagine. If you say, a theory's out there and it's correct, all the experimentalists want to do is prove you wrong; and they're working really hard to try to find some data that proves you wrong. Of course, in the process, if they keep agreeing with the theory, it's just stronger and stronger and stronger evidence that, in fact, the theory really is correct.

So today I want to talk some more about the final, what we might call "big surprises." Okay, we just talked about the big surprise of finding a charm quark, which wasn't really such a surprise after all. In fact, it fit in, in a nice way, with the scheme that we're developing. And the same goes for the new big surprises that I want to talk about today. They were surprises, they weren't expected, but they fit in beautifully, into the theory of quarks and the theory of quantum chromodynamics. So, instead of getting everybody all upset, because they were unexpected; instead, it made everybody feel more confident and satisfied that their theory was indeed an accurate description of nature.

The first surprise came at Stanford, again. A couple of years after the discovery of the J/psi, a fellow named Marty Perl, at Stanford, was doing an experiment, and he discovered a new particle. And, it took a while for him to convince himself, and then convince the world, that this new particle that he was seeing was real. But it's very real, and since those days it has been seen many, many, countless times in lots of accelerators. It was a new lepton. Okay, we had the electron, and we had the muon, which was like a heavy version of the electron; and now Marty Perl finds a third one. It's got electric charge, just like the electron; it's got spin one-half; it does not interact strongly. Okay, it's not another meson, it's not another strongly interacting particle. It's truly a lepton, just like the electron and the muon. It's like a third generation, or a photocopy, of these other, lighter mesons. Of course, it's very radioactive, it decays very rapidly, leaving some characteristic signature; in fact it produces some new neutrinos—and that's a story that we'll come back and talk about. It's the third generation, so he gives it the Greek letter tau. It's the tau lepton; some people call it the tauon, but that's too hard to say, so we just call it the tau particle. And this was Nobel Prize material; Marty Perl got the Nobel Prize for the discovery.

But, in a certain sense, what is this telling us? I want you to try to imagine organizing the fundamental particles that we know about now in a little table, kind of like a periodic table of the elements; but now it's a periodic table of fundamental particles. So, the periodic table of the elements, you start with light ones and you work your way to heavier and heavier ones. Now, we have a slightly different scheme here. These aren't atoms we're talking about. I would say you've got quarks, on your one hand, and leptons on your other; and they're really quite different in many respects, so we'll keep them separate.

The lightest quarks are the up and the down, so I think they should get a row to themselves. They're distinct from each other; they have different charges. And then there are the two lightest leptons: the electron, and the electron neutrino, the electron-flavored neutrino. And those four particles really compose the world we live in. Right, your body is made of up and down quarks, which combine to form protons and neutrons—and maybe a few pions, which are still made of up and down quarks—and that's the nuclei; and then there's electrons; and the neutrinos, well, they're here, they're in the room. There's a hundred billion of them every square centimeter, every second passing through you, coming from the sun; although you don't feel them, or care about them, most likely, they are a part of ordinary, everyday life. It's just that that first generation, those lightest particles that seem to make up the ordinary world.

And then, we've got a kind of a photocopy, a second generation. Think about the quarks. We knew about the strange quark, which is like a heavy version of down: it's got the same charge and the same spin, but it's heavier and radioactive; and now, in 1974, we've discovered a heavy version of the up, the charm quark. So, we've got up and down, and then, charm and strange; and what about over in the lepton sector? Well, analogously, we've got the muon, and the muon-flavored neutrino. Now we have a complete second generation of quarks and leptons. And who ordered them? Well it's still kind of a mystery, although there are some arguments that we can make about why these particles are a necessary part of the world that we live in. They do appear naturally. They come raining down on us in cosmic rays—strange quarks for sure, muons for sure, and muon neutrinos—not so many charm quarks. They also exist, fleetingly, as virtual particles. They exist, perhaps, in certain unusual astronomical phenomena like massive neutron stars.

And now, what Marty Perl has discovered, is one more lepton. So, imagine, beneath the electron, and beneath the muon, now there's a new particle, the tau particle. So, you can think like a physicist now. If you found one new particle in a new generation, what do you expect? All right, I expect, by just sheer virtue of beauty and symmetry, that there should be a whole row. There should be a corresponding tau neutrino, right? Just like there was a previous generation of a heavy lepton and its corresponding neutrino. So I'm expecting that, if we go out and hunt, we should be able to find a tau-flavored neutrino. How about in the quark sector? Well, if nature is nice and symmetrical, if we've got a new generation of leptons, I'm thinking there's probably got to be a new generation of quarks: heavier still, even more radioactive. I think it's a natural guess, and everybody immediately started hunting. Okay, this was sort of a big, obvious project, starting right after this discovery in 1975 of the tau lepton.

It didn't take long. It was an experiment done by Leon Lederman and his team at Fermilab. Fermilab was, at that time, a fairly new nuclear particle-physics accelerator just outside of Chicago. It's still there; in fact, today it's the highest-energy facility in the United States. It's our premiere particle-physics facility, although we have others, including SLAC, which is still running and doing good stuff. Fermilab was not like SLAC. It was a little bit more like the Brookhaven facility: it was a giant ring. It's no longer a cyclotron. You, what you really have is a ring made up of a whole bunch of magnets, and the magnets are there to guide protons around in a circle; and you're whacking those protons all the time, giving them more and more and more energy as they go around. Fermilab is gigantic. It's four miles around, and if you every fly into the Chicago O'Hare airport, look out the airplane window and you'll probably see this big, very obvious from the sky, four-mile-round ring. When I first saw it, I was really psyched; it's very visible.

This was the accelerator facility where Leon Lederman was working. It's 1977, and the facility at that time could produce protons with an energy of 200 GeV—that's two hundred billion volt electrons. So, that's a lot of energy. And, if you dump that energy into a target, you should be able to produce new particles of nature. So, if you're visualizing this new periodic table, what are you going to see? You have an up and a down quark in the lightest generation, and the down quark, in a certain sense, is a little bit lighter than the up quark. And in the next generation, the strange quark is quite a bit lighter than the charm quark. You're always more likely to produce something that's lighter, because it's just easier to produce something that's lighter, and tougher to produce something that's heavier. So, if there's going to be a new generation of quarks down there—first of all, what are we going to call them? People actually made up the name before they found these particles, and there were actually two competing schools of thought. The first thought was, "Well, we have up and down, how about calling them top and bottom—it's just a name, and it's kind of analogous and reminds us of the sort of symmetry of this picture of the world that we have—or T and B." And, as soon as people thought of T and B, the more whimsical characters wanted to call them truth quarks and beauty quarks, just like charm and strange. So there was a little bit of a dispute in the physics community—and I think today, top and bottom have won out. Everybody refers to the quarks in that way, and every now and again you'll somebody talking about a beauty quark. Mostly it's just T and B, or top and bottom.

If the pattern follows, the new quark that has charge negative one-third, the one that goes underneath the down quark and the strange quark, the bottom quark, is going to be the lighter of the two. And so, the guess is, that most likely, if this model of nature is correct, and if we're really going to find a third generation, that's what we are likely to find. And indeed, that's exactly what Leon Lederman found. It was completely analogous to the discovery of the J/psi, in the sense that Sam Ting had found evidence of a particle with definite energy by looking at protons smashing into a target, and investigating the debris that came out. The J/psi particle was a meson, a charm and an anti-charm quark bound together; and so, what Leon Lederman found was a bottom and an anti-bottom quark bound together.

And now, these quarks are so massive that the theory of quantum chromodynamics can really start to make some quantitative predictions about the lifetime, and the decay products, and the quantum numbers. Everything that you could imagine, that you could measure, about this bottom/anti-bottom meson is now theoretically predicted. So you might, you know, ask, "Well, did he get the Nobel Prize for that?" He did get the Nobel Prize, but for another experiment that he had done in his career. He didn't get the Nobel Prize for this one. It's kind of interesting: it's almost the same discovery as the J/psi, which got a Nobel Prize; but I think at this point, now you're just confirming what everybody's expecting. It's not such a big shock. And, you know, shoot, it's now quark number five—I mean, how many Nobel prizes are we going to give for new quarks? So, too bad.

Lederman named this quark the upsilon; it's another Greek letter, and at first I wondered why he picked upsilon; but I think, you know, upsilon sounds a little bit like Leon, which is his first name. And in fact, there's a humorous story: When they were looking for this particle—you know, what are you doing? You're collecting data, and you're looking for a large number of events that occur at one particular energy. And, at first, they begin to accumulate some events at one particular energy, so they said, "Aha! We found the upsilon." Of course they're good physicists, and they're cautious. It's like tossing that coin and you get ten heads in a row and you say, "I think we've got a weighted coin," but you should keep tossing for a while. If you discover that it was just a fluke, you have to apologize. And, in fact, it turned out that that first discovery was a mistake, it was just a statistical fluke; so, many people called it the Oops, Leon particle. And nonetheless, they very quickly did find the true upsilon.

There's another name for these particles, by the way. If you have a bottom and an anti-bottom quark in orbit around one another, like a little binary star system, you'd call it bottomonium. So, the charm/anti-charm quarks, which we call the J/psi, you could also call charmonium. Charmonium is sort of a generic name. You could imagine, if it's a little planetary system, that you could also have a particle where they spin a little faster—if you like, in a higher orbit. And in fact, you could predict the properties of that particle. And that would be an excited state, and that does exist. In fact, it was found at Stanford just within weeks of the discovery of the J/psi, exactly where you expected it. So a similar story happens with bottomonium, and in fact people have made electrons and anti-electrons go in orbit around one anther, and that's called positronium, just another naming convention.

So now, we have a situation where we've discovered a third generation of electron-like particles, a third lepton, which is called the tau; and we've discovered a third generation of quark. So now I think everybody's completely confident in the framework, in the reality of these objects; and so what do you predict? There's two particles left, in 1977. There should be a tau-flavored neutrino—which is going to be really tough to detect, because it's a neutrino. And you need lots of energy to produce a tau neutrino, because tau neutrinos are always produced as partners with the tau, which means you're not going to have very many of them; and if you don't have very many neutrinos, it's going to be a nightmare to try to detect them, because most neutrinos just go flying through detectors. So people knew right away: it's real, but it's going to take us a long time to find. And they were right. In fact, we only found the tau neutrino, directly, just a couple years ago. It's a 21st-century discovery.

So, the next particle that people are expecting to be able to find is the last, final quark, the one that sits underneath the up quark and the charm quark, the one with a charge of two-thirds. That would be what we would call the top quark. And everybody expects it, so—this is, you know, 1977, but everybody also expects that it should be heavier than the bottom quark; and nobody knows exactly what its mass should be. I want to remind you that the theory of quantum chromodynamics is a rigorous, mathematical framework; you can make calculations of almost anything, but it's a renormalizable quantum field theory. That's a fancy word that means that there's some infinities that arise, mathematically, and to fix them, there's a couple of things that you cannot compute. One of those couple of things is the mass of the fundamental particles themselves. You just can't predict that from the theory. So, you can't predict, from QCD, what the mass of a top quark is going to be. You can make some educated guesses. You can make some educated guesses, not by looking at the fundamental theory, but by looking at data. Okay, how do I mean that?

I mentioned in the previous lecture that people already had an idea for the mass of the charm quark, by considering events where a charm quark might appear virtually, very briefly, and then disappear again. The fact that it is real, and it exists in nature, means that you can sort of create a charm quark out of nothing, if you give it back again, even if you don't have enough energy to actually make one come free. And the pulling of the little charm quark, or any quark, out of the vacuum affects observables, even if you just scatter an electron against another electron and you look at the probability of them going off at some particular angle. If you calculate that with Feynman diagrams, you must include every possible intermediate state, every possible splitting of the vacuum into particle/anti-particle, and they will change the probability a little bit. So this is called precision particle physics. If you make a super-precise measurement, and then you make a very careful calculation, you can compare the measurement with the calculation; and you might be able to deduce the mass of this one, last, unknown quark, the top quark, by calculating the effects of—well, if it's there, then we should be able to produce a virtual top/anti-top. And if we do that, it's going to change any observable that you can think of, but by a very small amount.

So this was big business. Starting in 1977, people were looking at all of the data that they had, and at first it was very crude. People said, "Well, it's probably more than a hundred GeV and probably less than a thousand." It was that loose. As the years went by, I would go to conferences, and there was always a series of talks, "The Status of the Standard Model." And one of the things that they would always talk about is: "Okay, we've done these calculations, and we're honing in." And I remember, it was between 150 and 200 GeV, and then between 160 and 180 GeV; and this is now getting into the 1990s. I've gone through graduate school, and the standard model is now taught to graduate students. It's accepted pedagogy at this point, it's in textbooks; and you'll see a table of all the quarks and all the leptons with their masses; and then you get to the top quark, and there's simply a little question mark next to its mass. There's no questioning of the model—well, not much—but it's just assumed that this particle's got to be there and we just don't know quite where it is—yet. It was not until 1995 that the top quark was found. So that's a long time, almost 20 years, between the discovery of the bottom and the discovery of the top.

And yet, throughout that whole time, I think the physics community was not worried about it. We were beginning to expect where it should be, based on our precision measurements of unrelated experiments. It was finally found at Fermilab, once again. In the intervening years, Fermilab had been upgraded in energy. It's now called the Tevatron, because TeV is the acronym for trillion, or tera, electron-volts. So we've gone from billions to trillions now. The Tevatron now takes protons and anti-protons, accelerates them in this giant four-mile ring, and smashes them into one another. And so now you have matter/anti-matter annihilation of a proton with an anti-proton, a huge amount of energy, a trillion-volt collision. And that's the energy that's required to produce these ultra-massive top quarks and anti-top quarks.

I remember, in 1994, there was a colloquium at my institution. Some folks from Fermilab were claiming the first evidence for a top quark. So it was once again, kind of analogous to the discovery of the J/psi, this time at Stanford, where you had matter/anti-matter producing a particle and then you look at what comes out. They had a few events that were consistent with what you would expect if you produced a top/anti-top particle. And I remember playing my role as a physicist, and being skeptical. I thought, "Well, you know, it's a few events. Maybe they're tossing the coin enough times." And there's another thing that makes you nervous. Remember that these precision experiments have been homing in. We expect to find a particle somewhere between 160 and 180 GeV; and what they're claiming, now, is a particle at 170. That was the first evidence of the top quark. And I'm thinking, "Yeah, yeah; maybe they're finding what they want to find." And I think that's the right attitude. They needed to convince us, and they knew that too. It took another year of data collection before the folks at Fermilab would go from announcing hints of a discovery to actually writing a paper in which they discovered the top quark. So, you know, that's sort of part of the sociology of physics today. People are very much aware of the statistical nature of quantum mechanics, and there are criteria that you must satisfy. It's like tossing that coin; getting six heads in a row is definitely not going to be proof that a coin is unfair. It has to be repeatable; you have to be able to leave it and come back; it has to be discovered at other accelerator facilities.

The top quark requires so much energy to find that it's very difficult to duplicate this experiment. And, it's duplicated in a very interesting way. Let me tell you a little bit more about the sociology of modern particle physics. Okay, this is a huge machine. If you ever get to visit

Fermilab, or SLAC, or any of these facilities, you've got to go. They're impressive machines, gigantic in scale. You walk into the area where the particle/anti-particles collide, and there's detectors the size of buildings all around the region. And there are teams of physicists: we're now talking about five hundred physicists working together on the discovery of the top quark. When they published the paper, you know, they give you the name of the collaboration—there was a CDF collaboration, and another group, the DZero collaboration. Each of them had five hundred names, so the next two pages of the paper just list everybody's names. And these are all Ph.D. physicists, or graduate students—and some technicians—who are working, essentially, full-time together. It's quite a spectacular collaborative effort, and it's also extremely international. People from throughout the world work on these big projects.

You know, physicists—some of them, have rather big egos. So you can imagine what it's like to try to get five hundred people to work together; and everybody has to agree before you can publish this paper. So, you know, you really have to have extraordinarily convincing evidence before these things get published. And, it's quite spectacular that not only does it work, it really works very well.

At Fermilab, you've got these two beams counter-rotating: the protons go one way, the anti-protons go the other way; and you have to get the beams very, very narrow—it's very high-tech—and then you have to make them run one into the other. Now, even though they're matter and anti-matter, they're still quantum-mechanical particles, and so they have a probability of interacting, but it's not 100 percent. Some of them will interact, and some of them will pass on by, and continue to rotate. So what they do is they design the rings so they're slightly off-kilter, so most of the time the protons and anti-protons just pass by one another. And, there are a couple of spots around the ring where they cross paths and those are the interaction regions; and that's where you set up your detectors.

There were two major detectors at the Fermilab ring—CDF and DZero were the names of the collaborations working to search for the top quark—and they were completely independent. It's like two teams, and they're fighting each other. Everybody wants to be first. If you're first you get the credit, and the glory; you get to name it, and everything. And they'll talk to each other, but you definitely have independent apparatus, completely independent ideas about what would be the best way to find a top quark, what sorts of detectors do you build; so these experiments really are independent, even though they're occurring at the same facility, and highly competitive. Both of them, in fact, came up with data, and in the end, the two publications agreed, within experimental uncertainties, on the mass of the top quark. Again, nice, confirming evidence that what we're finding is not just wishful thinking.

Today, what's the story now? We've passed through what you might call this golden age, and it's really now a period of consolidation. The top quark—and in fact, the tau neutrino was really the last; it came after 1995, it was the final discovery which really clarified and consolidated this theory of the strong interaction. The particles, we believe we know what they are. We think we have a complete list. At least there is no hint of any evidence, whatsoever, that there's a fourth generation, another new quark or lepton. It's an interesting question to ask. Could there be? You might say, "Well, maybe we just haven't built a high enough energy machine," and there are physicists who want to build higher-energy machines, still. But there's no, not even a clue right now, not even a hint, that there should be another generation. In fact, there are even some hints that there might *not* be another generation. That hint has to do with the neutrinos. We'll come back and talk about neutrinos in future lectures some more.

But, basically, although it's hard to detect neutrinos, you can actually at least learn about their existence, because it's not so hard to produce neutrinos in certain events; and the neutrinos, unlike everybody else, are extremely light. So even though everybody else is getting heavier and heavier, we're guessing that the neutrino, in a fourth generation, would be light; and if it was there, we would have already had evidence for it: at Stanford, and in European accelerators, and at Fermilab. So, there are even hints that there really isn't another generation. Maybe we really do know the fundamental building blocks of the world we live in. It's a lovely and compelling idea.

We also have a theory, quantum chromodynamics, which allows us to compute the properties of this top/anti-top pair: what are they going to decay into, what do you expect for the behavior of the system? Everything is fitting; everything is working well. We continue to discover new particles in the accelerators, but they're not exotic. Maybe we find a charm quark paired with an anti-bottom quark. That's something new, but we expect it. We know where to look for it. And so people continuing to look, to kind of verify this model—it's very important that, if you have a theory, you have to look for cracks, and breaks, and see if there's anything wrong with it—but, so far so good. We really do seem to have a well-established framework for understanding the world.

Now, we have six fundamental quarks: up and down, charmed and strange, top and bottom. And, we have six fundamental leptons: electron and electron neutrino, muon and its neutrino, tau and its neutrino. That's a lot of fundamental particles. It was nice when we had three—in fact, I think everybody really wants there to be one fundamental particle; that would be the most elegant of all. When we had three—you know, I think we can accept that maybe nature has three fundamental particles. When we have 6 and 6 is 12, plus the force-carriers, and then there's the anti-particles, and then there's all the different colors of the quarks; you know, it's starting to look like there's an awful lot of fundamental particles. And it's a perfectly legitimate question to ask, "How many fundamental particles can you have, before you start to wonder if there's some explanation, some deeper story?" And that's an idea that I want to revisit.

We don't know the answer to that. Right now, it looks like we have a very beautiful, very consistent mathematical theory. It describes all the subatomic data very well; and so, it's kind of just a feeling, a thought, that some people have, that maybe we might be able to go further beyond the standard model some day.

Lecture Seventeen
Weak Forces and the Standard Model

Scope:

Progress in the 1960s and 1970s was not limited to understanding strong forces and quarks. We were also homing in on the weak force, the source of beta decays and the only force felt by the ghostlike neutrinos. It was a struggle at first. Scientists desperately wanted a field theory (like QED or QCD) for the weak force, but they couldn't make it work until the introduction of a novel particle called the *Higgs*. In this lecture, we cover the theory of Weinberg, Salam, and Glashow: the electroweak theory that unified the fundamental weak, electric, and magnetic forces. This has been one of the central goals of particle physics for a long time: to "unify" disparate laws into one single, simple, coherent whole. Just how unified are the forces now? At this point, we can summarize everything we know about particle physics: the players, the forces, and the rules! This is what we mean by the *standard model*. Do we now have the fundamental tools for understanding all microscopic phenomena?

> I will not try to define beauty, any more than I would try to define love or fear. You do not define these things; you know them when you feel them.
>
> —Steven Weinberg (*Dreams of a Final Theory*, p. 134)

Outline

I.   At this point in the course, we have almost all the ingredients—the history, concepts, and terminology—to talk about the standard model of particle physics, which we believe explains the fundamental constituents of our world. One important ingredient that we are still missing is the weak force.

   A.   The theory of the weak force that we've talked about so far is an old one, dating back to the 1930s. Enrico Fermi had tried to explain beta decays, in which a nucleus spontaneously transforms itself into a different kind of nucleus and loses an electron and a neutrino.

B. Fermi's theory was not a particularly deep one. Although it served to make useful calculations, it began to break down if people tried to push it to make highly accurate predictions. Feynman taught us the importance of accounting for vacuum fluctuations when studying the electric forces of nature. If we attempt to account for these fluctuations in Fermi's theory, the result is infinity and nonsense.

C. Fermi's theory also makes a prediction about weak interactions in particle collisions. In collisions, just as in decays, particles can come together, interact weakly, and transform. However, as higher energies are achieved, the weak force becomes stronger. The strong force becomes easier to predict at higher energies, but the weak force is exactly the opposite.

D. In the late 1960s, it became clear that a better theory of the weak interaction was needed to go along with QED and QCD. Many important physicists were involved in the development of this theory, including Steven Weinberg, Abdus Salam, Sheldon Glashow, Gerard 't Hooft, and others.

II. The goal was to construct a relativistic quantum field theory for the weak force, and one of the most important ingredients for this theory would be the concept of gauge symmetry.

    A. Gauge symmetry relates to the fact that in working with electricity, the measure of voltage we call 0 is arbitrary. No matter what point we choose to call 0, once we've made that choice, the equations, the experimental results, and the laws of physics are the same.

    B. Also remember the idea of the force carrier in electricity. The classical idea is that a charged particle, the photon, has an electric field that reaches out into space. Imagine jiggling an electric charge, causing (electromagnetic) waves to propagate outward, similar to what you see in a pond. In quantum mechanics, we think of that propagating wave as a particle of electromagnetic energy, a photon.

        1. QED, particularly gauge symmetry, tells us everything about the photon, that it's massless, has no electric charge, and so on.

2. QCD works in the same way. If we jiggle a quark that has color, it will propagate a gluon, and gauge symmetry tells us that the gluon is massless.

3. The single most important character in the story of electricity and magnetism was James Clerk Maxwell, a Scottish physicist in the 1800s. Maxwell took the idea of a classical field and formulated a mathematical field theory for electricity and magnetism, the precursor to QED. He recognized that electricity and magnetism are two facets of one universal underlying force of nature, which we now call the *electromagnetic force*.

C. As we said, in the late 1960s, physicists were trying to find an analog of this for the weak force, which is responsible for many radioactive decays, and neutrino physics. Every mathematician and physicist who tried working on this theory came to the conclusion that if gauge symmetry was a true principle of nature and they attempted to impose it on the weak force, then the weak force should have a carrier that is massless.

1. The carrier of the weak force, the particle that causes the weak force to travel from one place to another, is the *W particle*, or now, the *W* and *Z particles*.

2. The W particle is massive; it weighs almost 100 times as much as a proton. The mass of the W makes the likelihood of weak interactions improbable, because to have a weak interaction, we must, in a sense, excite the weak field. A W particle is an excitation of the weak field, a traveling wave of weakness. Thus, the weak interaction has its characteristics because its force carrier is so massive.

3. This leads to a dilemma. Gauge symmetry has helped us to understand electricity and magnetism. If we try to apply it to the weak force, however, we get results that are in direct contraction with the data. Gauge symmetry says that the W boson should be massless, but nature says that the W boson is massive.

D. Even as QED and QCD became successful, it was difficult to make all the ideas fit together. A physicist named Peter Higgs came up with the idea that made it all work.

1. Higgs proposed that there might be a new particle of nature that nobody had thought of before. Those who were trying to understand the weak interaction adopted Higgs's idea.

2. The theory started with a what-if game. What if this new particle is everywhere? It could be a field that was present in the early universe and has spread everywhere.

3. Imagine a particle that is similar to a photon. It is a massless weak-force carrier, and it's propagating along through space that's filled with Higgs particles. The weak-force carrier bumps into Higgs particles all the time, which makes it effectively slow down. It seems to have mass because it is trying to move through this swamp of Higgs particles.

4. This idea could explain how a particle that, for other reasons, should be massless appears to be massive. In 1967, Weinberg produced a paper in which he put together a coherent mathematical framework for the weak force that took into account gauge symmetry and the Higgs particle.

E. The theory matched the data at low and high energies. As Maxwell unified electricity and magnetism, Weinberg, Salam, Glashow, and others now unified the weak force and electromagnetic forces. The weak force, which seemed so different in every respect, is really just like electricity and magnetism, viewed from a different perspective.

III. When Weinberg, Salam, and Glashow were looking at this theory, they noted that gauge invariance not only predicts the existence of the W particle, which is electrically charged and becomes massive in the presence of the Higgs field, but also the existence of another force carrier, the *Z particle*.

A. The Z particle is a consequence of the mathematics of the new theory. It is a new force carrier, which means that a new force exists. Although the masses of the W and Z particles could be predicted, the accelerators of 1967 were not capable of producing these particles.

B. The worldview at the time was as follows: We have gravity, electromagnetism, the strong nuclear force, and the weak force—four fundamental forces of nature. Then, electricity, magnetism, and the weak force were simplified; all of them were really one. However, we also seemed to have something brand new, because the weak force can be manifested in a way that is different from what we have seen before.

1. The Z boson is electrically neutral; it's a non-transformative weak force. Electrons can bounce off each other electrically, and now we have a way that particles can bounce off each other weakly.

2. Such an interaction could have all sorts of experimental signatures. For example, physicists could look for neutrinos bouncing off particles.

3. Such an event was seen at CERN, the European Center for Nuclear Research, in 1973. Using neutrino beams, researchers saw *weak neutral currents*. The term *weak* was used because the events involved the weak force, and the term *neutral* was used because the Z-zero particle was being transferred virtually between the neutrino and the target. This was the new force of nature.

C. The next hurdle was the discovery of the W and Z particles, which was made in 1983 at CERN with an Italian physicist, Carlo Rubbia, as the lead in the project.

D. The name for this theory of Weinberg, Salam, and Glashow is the *electroweak theory*; it is a mathematical field theory that is the analog to QCD. It unifies electricity and the weak force so that QED becomes part of the electroweak theory.

IV. We can now take stock of what we have been talking about throughout the course. We have in our hands all the ingredients of the standard model, even though a better title might be the standard *theory* of particle physics. Let's quickly reiterate these ingredients.

A. We have the fundamental particles of nature, which appear to be point-like, to the best of our knowledge even today. They come in two classes: quarks and leptons.

1. The six quarks are all strongly interacting. They are colored objects that get progressively heavier. We start with up and down quarks; then, heavier are the strange and charm quarks; then we have a third generation, heavier still, top and bottom.

2. In the category of leptons, we have the electron and its neutrino, a muon and the muon-neutrino, the tau and the tau-neutrino. Again, these get heavier and less stable, that is, more radioactive, as we go down in our table.

B. The forces are the electroweak force, which is described by the electroweak theory, and the strong force, which is described by QCD. Those theories are consistent with everything we've ever learned in the last 400 years about science.

1. These theories include the principle of the field and all the logical consequences of having a field that also exists in a quantum mechanical world.

2. These theories predict new particles of nature, which we call force carriers. They predict the photon, the W+/W−, and the Z particle. These theories also predict the gluons, carriers of the strong force.

C. From these ingredients of the standard model, we can calculate the observable consequences of any imaginable subatomic physics experiment. In principle and in practice, we can calculate the properties and structure of fairly complicated particles.

D. The development of the standard model stands out as a grand human intellectual achievement, although certain interesting questions remain.

Essential Reading:

Schwarz, *A Tour of the Subatomic Zoo*, chapter 6.

Weinberg, *Dreams of a Final Theory*, Chapter V, pp. 116–end of chapter.

Recommended Reading:

Taubes, *Nobel Dreams.* (Take your time and read the whole book. It's interesting and quite different from the usual, somewhat "drier," readings.)

Riordan, *The Hunting of the Quark*, chapter 9.

Lederman, *The God Particle*, chapter 7, section on "The weak force revisited"; and chapter 8, up through the section titled "What are we talking about?"

Questions to Consider:

1. What is the difference between a "charged current" weak interaction, and a "neutral" weak interaction? Can you think of a specific example for each?

2. The mass of the W and Z particles is roughly (slightly under) 100 GeV. What can you say about the *range* of the weak interaction? (Either qualitatively or quantitatively, if you are so inclined)

3. Why do physicists make such a big deal about renormalizability? What does that mean again, and why does it matter?

Diagram of the Standard Model of Particle Physics

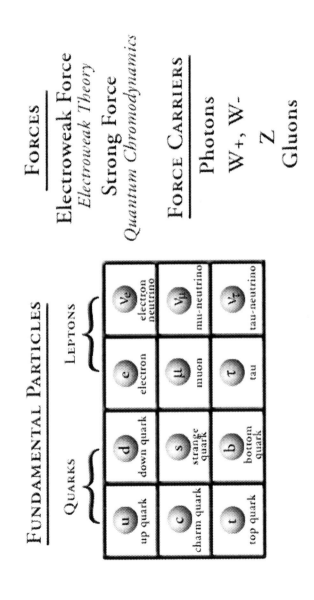

Lecture Seventeen—Transcript
Weak Forces and the Standard Model

We are rapidly approaching a turning point in this course. We have almost all of the ingredients, the history, the concepts, the terminology, to put everything together and talk about the standard model of particle physics, the coherent framework that physicists have today which, we believe, explains the bottom layer, the fundamental constituents of the world that we live in. But there's one very important ingredient that's still missing, and that I want to talk about today; it is the weak force. Okay? We've been talking an awful lot about the strong force, and the quarks that feel the strong force. We talked about the weak force when we introduced the concept of neutrinos and beta decays. But the theory of the weak force that we've been talking about so far is an old one that dates all the way back to the 1930s.

Enrico Fermi had tried to explain the phenomena of beta decays, where a nucleus spontaneously just transforms itself into a different kind of nucleus, and an electron would go flying out, and a neutrino would go flying out, usually undetected. And Mr. Fermi's theory was a mathematical one; you could make predictions about what the probability of such decay, and there were lots and lots of data. Beta decays are very common in nature; many radioactive decays involve the weak force, as well as processes in the sun. It's quite a ubiquitous force of nature, even though we don't usually feel it on a daily, personal basis. Mr. Fermi's theory was okay, but it was not a particularly deep theory. Although it served to make useful calculations, if you tried to push the theory to make really accurate predictions it began to break down.

For example, Feynman taught us, when he studied the electric forces of nature, that you have to worry about the possibility that the electric field can spontaneously split, for a very short amount of time, into a particle-anti-particle pair. That vacuum fluctuation, those virtual matter-anti-matter pairs, can modify the electric forces between any objects. It's a modification If you're trying to do precision calculations, if you really want to do better than ten percent or something, you start to have to worry about those sorts of fine details, and you can't do that with Mr. Fermi's theory. If you try to look at, for example, how the possibility for a beta decay would change if we take into account the possibility of vacuum fluctuations, using his theory, you would get crazy answers - infinity and nonsense. It just doesn't make sense.

Also, Mr. Fermi's theory makes a prediction about weak interactions in particle collisions. Just as in decays, you can also have particles coming together, interacting weakly, transforming and turning into something else; the theory works reasonably well. As you go to higher and higher energies, starting in the 1930s and working your way up through the 1960s, at accelerators, the details of the weak interaction depend on the energy. That's not unusual. We've talked about how the strong force of nature actually gets weaker if the particles get higher and higher energy. That's why the strong force gets easier to predict when you go to higher and higher energies and more modern facilities. The weak force, according to Fermi's theory, works exactly the other way. As you go to higher energies, the weak force gets stronger. And at a certain energy, around, oh—it's a little bit hard to be precise, because it depends on the process—but around 100 GeV, the weak force goes off kind of crazy. It starts to go to infinity. You start to get calculations that tell you probabilities are greater than one of some weak interaction occurring. This is clearly nonsense. That didn't worry anybody for a long time because there were no accelerators anywhere near that energy until the 1970s. Until then, Fermi's theory was working fine, but it was clear to just about everybody that we needed a better theory of the weak interaction. It was a shame; we had this lovely quantum theory of electricity (in fact, between 1964 and the early 1970s, quantum chromodynamics, the mathematical theory of the strong force, was developed) and it, too, became very well established experimentally. It was clearly a good theory of nature, so we could explain the strong force, we could explain electricity and magnetism, but what about the weak force?

There were a lot of people who became involved in this business. It is hard to point to just one name. It's not as though there's an Einstein or a Fermi who we can say invented the theory. The Nobel Prize went to three characters: Steven Weinberg, Abdus Salam and Sheldon Glashow. I've mentioned Shelly Glashow before. He was the one who proposed the idea of the charm quark, and in some sense, Steven Weinberg was the one who wrote the paper that pretty much put it all together; but each of these three guys made many contributions, and there were many other people as well. There was a young graduate student, 't Hooft, in the Netherlands, who wrote a theoretical paper which really established the theory, ultimately, as a mathematically rigorous one. He and his advisor, Veltman, received a Nobel Prize at a later time. I think this is a story that occurs more and more frequently in physics today, that it's a little bit harder to point to one genius who came up with the theory all by himself. It may even be true, if you go back in history, that lots of people didn't get enough credit for the work they did.

What are people looking for? Quantum electrodynamics is a lovely theory that has quantum mechanics in it; it has relativity in it, and it has fundamental particles in it. We can do all of those things for any force, so let's try to build a relativistic quantum field theory for the weak force. One of the most important ingredients, for both QED and QCD, was the idea of gauge symmetry. Okay? It's a very abstract concept. We've talked about it briefly. Gauge symmetry has something to do with the fact that, in electricity anyway, it doesn't really matter where you choose to call zero volts. It's pretty much an arbitrary human convention. No matter what you choose, once you've made your choice, the equations are the same, the laws of physics are the same, and the experimental results are the same. It's an abstract mathematical symmetry, which is a little bit more complicated than that.

Gauge symmetry leads us, in fact, to the theory of QED, as well as to the theory of QCD. Not only does it help you write down the theory, it makes a clear prediction about the force carrier. Let me remind you about this idea of the force carrier in a field theory. Think about electricity. You have a little charged particle, which has an electric field that reaches out into space. That's a classical idea. Now, what is the photon? What is the carrier of electricity? Well, imagine jiggling that little electric charge, so the field lines get a little kink; and that kink propagates outwards like the rings of water when you disturb the water surface. It's a little wave that travels outwards, classically. In quantum mechanics we think of that propagating wave as a little particle of electromagnetic energy, a photon. So it's a wiggle in the field that we call the photon. The theory, in particular the gauge symmetry, tells you all about the photon. It says it's without mass, it says it has no electric charge, in the case of the photon; it tells you everything that you could ever want to know about the photon. We see the same thing in QCD. If you wiggle a quark that's colored, it will propagate a gluon. That's the particle, and the gauge symmetry predicts that the gluon should be without mass. In fact, it's very much like a photon, in a lot of ways, except that it itself has color.

Michael Faraday originated the idea of a field. I've mentioned Faraday, but I've never mentioned the most important character in the story of electricity and magnetism, James Clerk Maxwell. This is pre-quantum mechanics. James Clerk Maxwell was a Scottish physicist in the 1800s, and if I had to pick the most important physicist, far and away, between Isaac Newton in the 1600s and Albert Einstein in the early 1900s, it would definitely be Maxwell. Maxwell took the idea of the field, a classical field, and turned it into a mathematical field theory for electricity and magnetism. It was the precursor to QED, and in the process, he understood the principle of gauge symmetry. He wrote down all the mathematical equations discovered that electricity and magnetism are unified. It was a grand intellectual achievement. It's one that even today physicists look back, with just amazement, that these two forces of nature, electricity. You know, it didn't seem, to a physicist in the early 1800s, as though they had anything to do with one another. Electricity, as you know, sparks when you comb your hair; and magnetism moves compass needles, but, if you hold a compass needle near a spark, it doesn't do anything. There's no obvious connection between electricity and magnetism. People were finding clues about it in the 1800s, but Maxwell was the one who really unified the two and recognized that, in fact, electricity and magnetism are two facets of one universal, underlying force of nature which we now call the electromagnetic force. That's what I've been calling it all along. It's like one force of nature and you look at it from two different perspectives. You see electricity if you're moving this way and magnetism if you're moving another way. That's a kind of a simplistic way of thinking about it, but it really is one fundamental, unified force. That unification led to his prediction of light.

That's the classical story. Then the quantum analog of that is in QED; again, electricity and magnetism are unified, and the principle of gauge invariance now makes the statements about the carrier of the force. So people are now hunting for an analog of this. We would like to do the same thing for the weak force of nature, responsible for these esoteric radioactive decays and neutrino physics. Every mathematician physicist who tried working on this came to the annoying conclusion that, if you believe in gauge symmetry as a principle of nature, and try to impose it on the weak force, you should have, by consequence, a carrier of the weak force, which is without mass. We've talked a little bit about the carrier of the weak force, the little particle that causes the weak force to travel from one place to another, the quantum field of the weak force; we called it the W particle. Nowadays we have the W and the Z particles, and the W particle is massive - super-massive. It weighs almost 100 times as much as a proton. It's so massive that it is what makes the weak interaction so weak. It makes it very improbable for weak interactions to occur, because for it to occur, you have to excite this weak field. That's what a W is, the excitation of the weak field, a little traveling wave of weakness; and, despite its name, it's very massive. It's very hard to borrow that energy from nature, so the weak interaction has all of its characteristics because the force carrier is so massive.

You have this dilemma. On the one hand you really believe in gauge symmetry; it's helped you to understand the other two fundamental forces of nature. On the other hand, if you try to apply it to the weak force, it tells you something that's in direct contradiction with data. Gauge symmetry says the W boson should be without mass, but nature says the W boson is very massive. People were, for many years, kind thought it was hopeless. Even as QED became successful, and QCD was already successful, it was rather difficult to understand how to make this all work. The idea that made it work came from a physicist working on something else, as often happens. His name was Peter Higgs, and we'll talk a lot about Mr. Higgs's idea because it's a little bit complicated. We'll devote a whole lecture to the Higgs particle.

Mr. Higgs proposed that there was a new particle of nature, one nobody had thought of before. The folks who were trying to understand the weak interaction took Mr. Higgs's idea and said, "Okay, suppose there's this new particle of nature. Let's just do a 'what if'; it's the usual game. What if this new particle is everywhere? It's like a field that's present already in the early universe, and it spreads out throughout the entire universe; it's everywhere. It's inside you, it's out in deep, dark, empty space." The Higgs idea is everywhere. Now imagine that you have a particle that's kind of like a photon. It's a weak-force carrier without mass, and it's propagating along through space that's filled with Higgs. The weak-force carrier keeps bumping into Higgs all the time, and that makes it slow down, and get sluggish. It's as though it acts as if it had mass because it's trying to walk through this goo of Higgs's particles. It's a crazy idea, it's a mathematical, formal idea; but it could explain how a particle that, for other reasons, should be without mass, appears to be massive. People started working out the details. In 1967, Weinberg was able to produce a paper in which he put it all together and had a coherent, mathematical framework for the weak force. You could have gauge symmetry, and all the beautiful things that gauge symmetry gives you, and you introduce the Higgs particle. This theory reproduces Mr. Fermi's theory at low energies, so that's good; it agrees with all the data so far, but at high energies, no problems. Okay? Everything's finite, everything works, it makes sense, you can compare with the data; it all works. It's a quantum field theory. You can add many, many more complicated Feynman diagrams, and calculate to as an accurate, high precision as you want.

Now, I mentioned the unification of electricity and magnetism that Mr. Maxwell had discovered in the 1800s, because the same thing happened again when we were constructing this weak theory. This was discovered by all of the characters—Weinberg, and Salam, and Glashow, and 't Hooft—that there was a unification between the weak force and the electromagnetic forces. So what did that mean? It meant that this weak force, which seemed completely different in every respect, was really just like electricity and magnetism, viewed from a different perspective. It's always beautiful and wonderful, when different things actually turn out to be unified, different facets of one fundamental, deeper, underlying object. Physicists love that, and I think this unification of weak and electromagnetic forces was one of the compelling arguments for people to pay attention to this theory and take it seriously. At first the theory, although it was highly predictive, wasn't at first making predictions that changed any connections to data; but as the years went by, the theory was more and more sort of seriously verified mathematically. Nowadays it's incredibly well tested, but in the early days I think people paid more attention to it because of its aesthetic character than anything else.

When you have a gauge field theory, you predict the existence of force carriers. When Weinberg and Salam and Glashow were looking at their theory, they said, "Gauge invariance not only predicts the existence of the W particle, which is electrically charged and becomes very massive in the presence of the Higgs field, but our theory also predicts the existence of another force carrier, which I (Weinberg) am going to call the Z particle." Weinberg called it the Z particle maybe because it has zero charge, or maybe, he says, because it's the last letter of the English alphabet. He thought, "This has to be the last new particle we're going to have to propose." It turned out there have been others since then, but it was a nice dream. So, the Z particle is a consequence of the mathematics of this theory; and what is it saying? It's a new force carrier, which means there is a new force. Okay? This is really wild.

You are not only predicting a new particle of nature, you can state with some mathematical certainty what its mass is. Unlike the fundamental quarks and leptons, whose mass cannot be predicted from the gauge field theory, the mass of the force carrier *can* be predicted from the theory because it comes from gauge symmetry. So you could predict the mass of the Z particle, and the masses of the W particles, so we have numbers that are too high to look for right away in an accelerator. We need higher-energy machines than were available in 1967, so this just goes into the literature as a prediction about how nature is.

It's even a bigger deal than that. It's not just one more new particle; it's a new force. Okay? Think about this. Particle physicists have this worldview that—what do we have? There's gravity, there's electromagnetism, there's the strong nuclear force, and there's the weak force. That's it—four fundamental forces of nature. Now what we're seeing is—the story is in some ways more beautiful, because electricity, magnetism and the weak force are really all one. So there's a simplification; but also there is something brand new, because the weak force itself can be manifested, not just in the way we had always seen, transforming one nucleus into another; this Z boson is electrically neutral. So it's a non-transformative weak force. It's like a neutrino could just whack into an electron and bounce off of it. Electrons can bounce off of each other electrically, and now we have a way that particles could bounce off of each other weakly; and nobody had ever thought about this before. It would have all sorts of experimental signatures; you could look for neutrinos bouncing off of particles. "People immediately said, "If this is real, then we have to be able to see this in an experiment," and it didn't take very long.

It was in 1973 when, at the European facility, CERN - (the European Center for Nuclear Research; the acronym uses the French words for its name)—they had neutrino beams by then, at CERN - they could beam those neutrino beams right into a big bubble chamber and see the events. They saw what they called weak neutral currents. They called it weak, because it's the weak force; neutral, because it's the Z (zero) particle being transferred virtually back and forth between the neutrino and the target. And why was it called "currents?" I don't know; it was just a word. So, "weak neutral currents" were the new force of nature.

You have to appreciate both the sort of sweet success of this theory, and also the hubris of the theorists who are proposing new particles. It's not like the old days. All right? Dirac discovers anti-matter, but he was sort of timid about proposing it because it was too wild. Pauli, with the neutrino, was, also, too timid about proposing it. Even with quarks, in the early 1960s, after Murray Gell-Mann published his paper, then he gave talks and said, "I don't really believe they're real, I just think they're a mathematical framework." But, you know, Steve Weinberg went out there and said, "Oh, you're going to find weak neutral currents, you're going to find the Z particle; you're going to find the W right where we predict because the math looks good. He was pretty confident." It came together in just such an elegant way. The theory was unified, and it looked just like QCD, so everything really seemed to tie together in a beautiful way.

So what about the discovery of the W and the Z? It took a while. The Americans had kind of taken over from the Europeans. Europeans had dominated this physics story in the late 1800s and the early 1900s; we were just puppies back then. It kind of turned around after World War II. We started building the big accelerators and were putting big money into particle physics. We were making all the big discoveries. I think the Europeans, at a certain point in the 1970s, thought they should be big competitors again, and they pulled together. It was a brilliant stroke. Instead of the Germans just building a German facility, all of the Europeans got together; they built a European national center. The ring actually runs between France and Switzerland, so the particles go back and forth across the border as they run through the giant accelerating ring at CERN.

There was a physicist, an Italian physicist named Carlo Rubbia, who took the lead in the project to find the W and find the Z. What we're talking about is to put enough energy into a small region of space that you don't have a virtual force carrier, but you actually produce one. You see a little track—evidence, direct evidence, in some modern analog of a bubble chamber that this particle is real, and it has the charge and the mass and everything that you expected. Carlo Rubbia is quite an interesting character. There was a book written about this story called "Nobel Dreams," which I enjoyed. It's not a technical book at all; it's about the very strong personality of Carlo Rubbia. He had to step on a lot of toes to put together multimillion-dollar projects like this. He had to convince a lot of people that it was the right thing to do; in the end, he was quite successful. The Europeans, and Carlo Rubbia, got their Nobel Prizes. The discovery was made in the 1980s; 1983 was the year of discovery of the W, and just six months later they produced a Z boson. Some people don't like the book about Carlo Rubbia; I think it's somewhat critical, just on a personal level, of this character. You know, when you're a strong personality, you always step on people's toes, but I suggest reading those kinds of books as a way of seeing the human aspect of this story, which so often is just impersonal and formal.

The neutral current has been seen now many, many times; and the Z bosons, in fact, have been seen so many times I would call it probably one of the most well-studied particles ever in the history of particle physics. Shortly after its discovery, the people at Stanford said, "You know, we could build an upgrade. It's the same idea of taking electrons and positrons and annihilating them, but this time we're going to up the energy, so that the total energy of the e-plus/e-minus pair exactly matches the mass—$E=mc^2$, the mass-energy of a Z boson. And we'll have a little Z factory. We're just going to be producing nothing but Z's after Z's after Z's, and we can see how they decay." That was the experiment that told us there apparently were only three types of neutrinos. Because when Zs decay, they love to decay into neutrino-anti-neutrino pairs, and you can see how likely it is for the Z to decay. After that, actually shortly after that - CERN built a Z factory, and now they are producing millions upon millions of Z particles. So, extremely well verified, and matched with this theory, which I haven't named, is electroweak theory. The electroweak theory of Weinberg, Salam, and Glashow is the mathematical field theory that's like the analog of QCD. It put together electricity and the weak force unified them, so there was no more QED all by itself; it's a part of the electroweak theory.

So now we really are at a state where we can just take stock of what we've been talking about throughout this entire course. What we have in our hands now are all the ingredients of the standard model. I wish it weren't called the standard model. It's the standard theory of particle physics. A model, to me, implies kind of a crude collection of ideas that give you qualitative understanding. A theory, to me, is a mathematical framework, with well-defined constituents and a set of rules for computing observable facts. In particular, a theory, a tested theory, is exactly what we have with the standard model. Nobody calls it the standard theory, but that's really what it is.

Let me try to sort of reiterate the ingredients. We have fundamental particles of nature, which appear to be point like, to the best of our knowledge even today. They come in two classes: quarks and leptons. The quarks are all strongly interacting. They are colored objects, and there are six of them: up, down, and then heavier, strange, charm; and then a third generation, heavier still, top and bottom. Over in the leptons, you have the electron and its neutrino; a muon, and the muon neutrino; the tau and the tau neutrino. Again, getting heavier, and less stable, more radioactive, as you go down in the table, or up in mass. Those are the ingredients. Those are the fundamental particles of the world.

The forces are the electroweak force, which is described by the electroweak theory; and the strong force, which is described by quantum chromodynamics. Those theories are consistent with everything we've ever learned in the last three or four hundred years about science. They're consistent with Isaac Newton, although they go deeper; they're consistent with Maxwell and his theories of electricity and magnetism, but they go deeper. They're consistent with quantum mechanics, and Albert Einstein's relativity. They include the principle of the field and all of the logical consequences when you have a field that also exists in a quantum-mechanical world. These theories predict new particles of nature, which we call, force carriers. They predict the photon, the W plus and minus— there're both charges - and the Z particle, they're the electroweak's force carriers. Then, you have the gluons, which are the carriers of the strong force, and that is the standard model.

From those ingredients, you can calculate the observable consequences of any imaginable subatomic physics experiment. In principle, it's not just sub-atomic physics. For example, if you take two hydrogen atoms and combine them together, it's just electrons orbiting around up and down quarks. The forces are all described by this theory, the standard model. So, in principle, and in practice, you can calculate the properties and the structure of, let's say, a hydrogen molecule. We can keep building now. We can argue what the properties and structures are of a more complicated molecule. The more particles you put together, the tougher it gets to work out the math, and solve for the detailed, final answer. Chemists nowadays use quantum mechanics in order to describe—and quantum field theory—to describe chemical reactions, and to help us to design and understand novel chemical elements. So this story really is tying in to more complicated sciences.

As a reductionist, you can at least imagine, in principle, following this chain on up. Maybe we could understand DNA and its properties by examining the quarks that make up the nuclei, and the electrons that are orbiting around them. In practice it's just too formidable a problem. DNA is a very complicated molecule with lots and lots of constituents, and it's just too tough to really go directly from the bottom level up to such a complicated level, but in principle, we should be able to. People are making progress, and you can imagine that all of the biological properties that arise from DNA can be understood, at some level, from this fundamental, underlying theory, the standard model of particle physics.

So I think we're talking about what is really a grand human intellectual achievement. It stands out in the history of the evolution of human thinking, along with Isaac Newton's understanding about force, and the nature of gravity, or Albert Einstein's insight into the nature of space and time. The standard model of particle physics is such an achievement. It's really a very elegant and closed mathematical system. You know, it's a shame it doesn't fit on a T-shirt. If the standard model fit on a T-shirt, then I'd say we're done, you know, we've got the fundamental theory of nature. Alas, it takes several pages of a textbook to write out all the details; and in fact, there are still some issues; I won't call them problems. We're going to be talking in future lectures about why we don't just close the book; you know, publish it, set it on the shelf, and go off and study other stuff. In fact, particle physics is still very much alive. There are lots of interesting problems and questions.

We are now struggling to understand this theory itself, at some deeper level. I don't think we're trying to prove it wrong anymore. It might happen. You know, we're not trying to prove Newton wrong either, 300 or 400 years later. He's correct, but Newton's theory has been improved and deepened, and I think that's the state we're in now with the standard model of particle physics. There are still a large number of quantities, like the charge of the electron, and the mass of the strange quark, and so on—in fact, if you count it up, there are about 23 such numbers that don't come out of the theory. You have to go in the lab and measure them, and put them into the theory because it's a renormalizable theory, and that's the price you pay.

Twenty-three numbers, six quarks, six electrons; it is a little bit complicated. It's simple enough that I sort of view it as a lovely, simple theory; but I can understand this sort of sense that maybe, someday, we will be able to understand even this level of complexity in terms of something simpler still. It's a nice dream.

Lecture Eighteen
The Greatest Success Story in Physics

Scope:

Make no mistake; the standard model of particle physics is an impressive accomplishment, an unprecedented artwork of mathematics and physics. It is a "minimalist" theory, composed in the 1960s with the simplest available framework, and guided only by the basic requirements of quantum mechanics, relativity, and the known data at the time on the fundamental particles. It is not fully unified, but it comes close, and it is an effectively complete description of subatomic particles and forces. The standard model has been the target of more than thirty years of intense efforts to find hidden cracks or problems in it—to no avail! The unparalleled success of the standard model includes qualitative and quantitative measurements, with years of increasingly precise tests. Still, many people are left with more than a slight discomfort with this theory. Could this really be the final story? Despite the descriptive successes, we are still missing a lot of explanations.

> The must incomprehensible thing about the universe is that it is comprehensible.
>
> —Albert Einstein

Outline

I. In the last lecture, we talked about the electroweak theory, which ties together electricity, magnetism, light, and the weak force of nature and all the associated particles and force carriers to form a coherent mathematical framework. This lecture consolidates everything we have learned thus far.

   A. Let's begin with a review of the standard model. We have a set of six quarks and a set of six leptons. Each one of these is considered to be a fundamental particle of nature. It has certain properties, including an electric charge, a weak charge, a mass, a spin, and not much else.

   B. Those are the fundamental building blocks of all the complexity in the world, everything from the hardness of a table to the softness of human skin; the colors that we see, the light that strikes our eyes, the sounds that we make—all these can be understood as coming from the rules and the players of the standard model.

C. The rules are the theories, QCD and the electroweak theory, or the Weinberg-Salam model as it's also called. The electroweak theory is a renormalizable relativistic quantum gauge field theory.

1. *Renormalizable* is a mathematical statement that says that if we include all the subtle quantum mechanics, the result is some infinities, in principle. If we add progressively smaller and smaller corrections, they add up to be infinitely large. However, if we measure a few things that the standard model cannot predict, everything else is completely finite and mathematically consistent.

2. *Relativistic* means that the theory must satisfy what Einstein has told us about the nature of space and time, including the symmetries that Einstein recognized.

3. *Quantum* means that the theory must satisfy all the laws of quantum mechanics that were first postulated in the early 1900s, then rigorously tested and proven by Heisenberg, Schrödinger, Pauli, Fermi, and many others.

4. *Gauge* refers to an abstract symmetry of nature that apparently all the fundamental forces have. Symmetry is observed when a change is made in an experiment or a theory, but all the answers come out the same. It is an invariance in a theory when viewed from different perspectives. Gauge symmetry was long observed to be true for electricity and magnetism, then later found to be true for the weak and strong forces.

5. *Field* refers to our mental image of how action at a distance takes place. How can a particle in one place "communicate" with a particle in a different place? We visualize space as being filled with fields. Everything in these quantum field theories is a field.

D. The theory entails some fancy mathematics, but in the end, the story is one that we can think about in fairly concrete terms and has been successful aesthetically, mathematically, and physically.

II. First, let's examine the aesthetics.

A. This theory has built into it essentially every symmetry of nature that we have been able to think of and that we might hope exists in the universe.

B. It is also a minimal theory. It is extraordinarily simple in the sense of having a few ingredients and a few ideas behind it. We have observed, for example, the six quarks and six leptons in the laboratory, and we don't include anything else in the theory except the Higgs particle.

    1. This theory was essentially complete in 1967, and it hasn't been tweaked in any significant way since then.

    2. In biology, chemistry, geology, and other sciences, we often start with a simple approximation and make it richer as we gather more data and become more precise. In particle physics, the situation is different. We started off with the simplest theory and found that it just kept working. We built new accelerators, discovered new particles, learned a great deal since 1967, but it all fits in with the minimal electroweak theory.

C. The theory also unifies forces of nature. What we thought were completely different forces—electricity, magnetism, light, the weak force—all are just one force viewed from different angles in this mathematical theory.

D. Some symmetries of nature are broken in the standard model, resulting in mysteries, in some cases, and deeper understanding, in others.

    1. For example, left and right are no longer an exact symmetry of nature itself. The laws of physics are different for something spinning like a left hand spins and something spinning like a right hand spins, but they're only different when you consider weak interactions.

    2. The laws are the same for electrical forces, strong forces, and gravitational forces. Only the weak force appears to violate this symmetry of nature. That's in the standard model, but it can't be explained; it is just an observed fact of nature.

3. Other broken symmetries can be explained. For example, symmetry is broken between two of the force carriers, the photon and the Z. In some ways, they seem similar. They both have spin 1, and they carry some aspect of the electroweak force, but the photon is massless, and the Z particle is massive. That's an electroweak symmetry breaking. We believe that this breakage arises from the presence of the Higgs particle.

4. The standard model, then, gives us an explanation for why these two forces, which we would think are completely symmetrical, seem, in fact, to be so different from each other in the real world.

III. Let's look at the mathematical success of this theory.

    A. The mathematics really boils down to the fact that this theory doesn't contradict itself in any obvious way. If we calculate something, we always get finite answers.

    B. There are no probabilities that can be computed in the standard model that come out greater than 1 or less than 0. Any other results would constitute a mathematical inconsistency. Earlier models had that problem, but the standard model does not.

IV. Finally, let's turn to the physical success of this theory. A theory is only good if the results it predicts match the results from the laboratory.

    A. Every year, the particle data group at Berkeley puts out a collection of all the information that has been gathered in particle physics.

        1. First, it shows a summary of the standard model, including the ingredients and the formulas. Then comes a list of particles and their properties. Every piece of data in this list includes a reference to a paper or a journal article, backed up by experiments that resulted in the numbers.

        2. In fact, this tabulation can be found published in a volume that runs to hundreds of pages. What's stunning about this mountain of information is that it all comes from the first couple of pages—the standard model and the formulas for doing these calculations.

3. To date, I know of no significant discrepancies between the theoretical calculations and the experimental observables.

B. Let's look at another success of the standard model that's a bit more qualitative but equally convincing.

1. In 1967, Weinberg worked out a theory that predicted the existence of a new particle, the Z boson. Almost twenty years later, when we finally achieved the necessary energy to produce the Z particle, we detected its presence in a bubble chamber.

2. The marvel is that a human being made a prediction about a fundamental particle that would not be observed for twenty years. That kind of prediction of a new fundamental particle is a powerful indicator that our theory does, indeed, help us understand the world.

3. Of course, the W, the tau-flavored neutrino, and the top quark were all similarly predicted before their discoveries. In fact, the physics of the neutrino may be one of the few areas of the standard model that needs to be tweaked a bit for full understanding.

V. We should also note that even if we discover something odd about, for example, quarks, we're not going to throw out the standard model, because the model does have a bit of leeway in it.

A. Imagine that we make a discovery of a fourth generation of quarks; such a discovery would modify the standard model, but it wouldn't shatter it. The framework would still exist and could be generalized to incorporate some new heavier particles.

B. We might extend and deepen the standard model, as we have Isaac Newton's theory of gravity, but the basic model would still be accurate. No matter what we discover in the future, we're still going to have atoms and quarks, and they will continue to combine in certain ways.

C. Consider also that the standard model makes both qualitative and quantitative predictions about the existence of new particles. We can predict, for example, exact numbers for the magnetic strength of an electron. As I mentioned earlier, this number is 2.00231930435.

D. Thus, the electroweak theory may not be the ultimate theory of nature, but we know that it is extraordinarily accurate. If some new laws of physics take over beyond the standard model, we know that those laws will not affect an observable until the thirteenth digit, because we've already checked the accuracy of the first twelve.

VI. In the future, you may read articles or hear news stories about discoveries that are touted as disproving the standard model.

   A. What these discoveries most likely will do is extend the standard model in an unexpected direction. We might be heading toward a deeper theory of nature, but the idea that the standard model would break down is almost inconceivable at this point.

   B. That is not to say that the standard model doesn't have some bothersome aspects.

     1. For example, there are twenty-three properties that cannot be computed from the standard model; they must be measured in the laboratory.

     2. We also have a large number of particles, including quarks, leptons, force carriers, and the Higgs.

   C. For the rest of this course, we will talk about the limitations and puzzles in the standard model, along with some even wilder speculations.

Essential Reading:

Kane, *The Particle Garden*, chapter 6.

't Hooft, *In Search of the Ultimate Building Blocks*, chapters 16 and 18.

Recommended Reading:

See recommended readings for Lecture Seventeen.

The central repository summarizing all standard model information is compiled by the Particle Data Group of Berkeley at http://pdg.lbl.gov/.

Information about the status of the standard model is usually quite technical. For example, Jens Erler and Paul Langacker at the University of Pennsylvania keep an up-to-date summary at http://dept.physics.upenn.edu/~erler/ electroweak/index.html. Some of it may be readable, but for the most part, it is designed for particle physicists.

Questions to Consider:

1. What other scientific theories can you think of that are as successful as the standard model? Are they "complete"? How well do they stack up when compared with the standard model?

2. Why do I say that the standard model can't be the "final story"? In what senses is it flawed or incomplete? (Your answer may depend on your personal philosophy about science!)

Lecture Eighteen—Transcript
The Greatest Success Story in Physics

Last time we talked about the electroweak theory; the theory of Weinberg and Salam that puts together electricity, magnetism, light, and the weak force of nature, and all the associated particles and force carrier that make a coherent mathematical framework. Today, I don't want to talk about anything new. We've learned an awful lot of particles, an awful lot of concepts, and I just want to try to consolidate everything that we've been talking about. We have now come to the stage where we really can talk about the standard model in its conceptual fullness. I want to talk about some of its successes, experimental, and a little bit more abstract successes. That's really the plan for today, just to take a step back and look at this intellectual achievement that the human race has made. You know, I view this as on a par with the collective works of Shakespeare, or something of that nature, where we really have come up with something that's very profound, and very deep, and, in principle, relatively easy to understand, although the details are some tough going.

Let me begin by reminding you of what I mean by the standard model. We have a set of quarks, six of them; and we have a set of leptons, six of them. Each one of these is considered to be a fundamental particle of nature. It has certain properties, which we just list; you can imagine tabulating these things. An electric charge, a weak charge—that's part of the electroweak theory—a mass, a spin, and not much else. That's pretty much the kinds of properties that you have to attribute to these points. Those are the fundamental building blocks of everything and anything. Think about this for a second. Think about the enormous complexity of the world around us. Everything from the hardness of a table, to the softness of human skin, to the almost the ethereal nothingness of the air around us; the colors that you see, the light that strikes your eyes, the sound that you make. All of that stuff can be understood, coming from just the rules and the players of the standard model.

The rules are these theories, quantum chromodynamics and the electroweak theory, or the Weinberg-Salam model, as it's also called. And let me throw out the, kind of, full-blown techno-babble at you; it's a renormalizable, relativistic, quantum gauge field theory. Okay? So, let's talk about those words. We can unpack those words because we really already have talked about all of them.

Renormalizable is a fancy, mathematical statement that says if you include all of the subtle quantum mechanics, you start to get, in principle, some infinities. You're adding a whole bunch of progressively smaller and smaller corrections that add up to be, not just big, but infinitely large, but renormalizable means we can sweep it all under a rug. We pay one little price, which is that there are a few things that the standard model cannot predict. We have to go out and measure them, but everything else is completely finite. We use Feynman's rules, and we can calculate anything we want. Renormalizability is a condition on any theory of nature; at least it's so far been an incredibly useful condition because it means that it's mathematically consistent.

Renormalizable, relativistic—it has to satisfy what Albert Einstein has told us about the nature of space and time, which includes the symmetries that Albert Einstein has recognized about space and time.

Relativistic quantum: it has to satisfy all of the laws of quantum mechanics which were first speculated upon in the early 1900s, and then turned rigorous by Heisenberg and Schrödinger, and ultimately Dirac and many other players—Pauli and Fermi and all those characters in the 1920s and 1930s. Quantum mechanics was quite well established by the early 1930s, and today really is unchanged. We have been testing it, studying it, and quantum mechanics hasn't continued to evolve in any way. So, a field theory, a quantum field theory like we're talking about, just has to incorporate all of those laws, such as the Heisenberg Uncertainty Principle, for example.

Quantum gauge field theory: a gauge that refers to symmetry of nature, a very abstract symmetry of nature that, apparently, all the forces, all the fundamental forces have. In the beginning, we knew that electricity and magnetism had this symmetry. That was observed from the mathematics of the 1800s, and it was such a nice symmetry. It's abstract; I can't talk about it as left-right symmetry, or sideways symmetry. It's a little bit more of a mathematical symmetry. Symmetry means you can make a change in what you call things. You can make a change, yet the answers all come out the same. There is an invariance in your theory, when you look at it from a different perspective. That's what symmetry is, in its most general sense. It's wonderful—and a little bit magical—that this gauge symmetry, which we observed to be true for electricity and magnetism, is also true for all the other forces of nature; at least the weak force, and the strong force, as well. How do I know that it's a good symmetry? Because we imposed it on the theory, and now we've been tested the consequences of that theory in the laboratory, and it keeps working. That's how it is that I can make the statement that apparently the strong force of nature also has this symmetry.

Gauge field theory means that we have this mental image of how it is that you can get action at a distance, how a particle over here can communicate with a particle over there. We visualize space as being filled with fields. Everything in these quantum field theories is a field. Normally I think of the forces as being force fields. But in fact, all of the particles are in a certain sense equally particles, the electron as much as the photon. There is an electron field in the universe, as well as a photon field. This is the theory: a renormalizable, relativistic quantum gauge field theory. It's quite a mouthful, and it's really what we've been spending a good part of all of the lectures so far trying to understand. It's fancy mathematics, but in the end, the story is really one that you can think about in fairly concrete terms. This theory has been successful on a lot of levels. I would call it successful aesthetically, mathematically, and physically; and I'd like to talk about all three of those dimensions.

First of all, I'll discuss "aesthetically." This theory has built into it, essentially, every symmetry of nature that we have been able to think of, that you might hope that the universe has; we've put it into the theory, and it makes it very compelling and very appealing. It's also a minimal theory. It may not look minimal, and it's a little bit hard, when you've been working with this for your whole career, to step back and ask if this really is simple. To me, it's extraordinarily simple, in the sense of just having a few ingredients and a few ideas behind it. And, minimal, meaning—I guess—that, for Mr. Weinberg in 1967, he had to write down a mathematical theory. In principle, you can write down a really complicated theory to describe the weak interaction, nut he chose to write the absolutely simplest one he could. Every time he had a choice, whether to make up a new particle, he chose to go with the fewest number possible. We've observed the six quarks and the six leptons in laboratory experiments, so we have to include them. We don't include anything else, except for the Higgs. The Higgs has not yet been seen, and we'll come back and talk about it. It's the sort of one mysterious piece, actually, of the story. With that one possible exception, it is a truly minimal theory.

You have to think about how amazing this is. In 1967, this theory was published, and it hasn't been tweaked in any significant way since then. You introduce a minimal theory, usually the physicists' first idea, "Let's just try the simplest one and see if it works," and if it doesn't, he can always add more. We can make it more complicated to try to match the data. That's the way biology, chemistry, geology, and so on, often work. You start with a simple approximation, then you make it richer and richer as you get more and more data, and become more and more precise. Here, we have a rather different situation. We started off with the most minimal theory, and then it just kept working, and it kept working even until today. We never had to make it more complicated. Even after we built new accelerators, we discovered new particles. We learned an awful lot after 1967, but it all fit in with the exact same minimal, electroweak theory. So that's a really lovely aesthetic idea that, I think, compels people to pay some attention to this theory, and believe in it as a statement about the scientific truth or nature of reality.

It unifies forces of nature. What we thought were completely different forces of nature: electricity, magnetism, light, if you like; the weak force, the weak neutral forces of nature, all of those are really one, in this mathematical theory. It's just one force viewed from different angles, abstract angles. And that's a really lovely idea. Again, there's an aesthetic appeal of this theory.

There are some symmetries of nature, which are broken in the standard model, and some of them are mysteries, and some of them are deeply understood now because of the theory. For example, left and right are no longer an exact symmetry of nature itself. The laws of physics are different for something spinning like a left hand spins, and for something spinning like a right hand spins. They're only different when you consider weak interactions. The laws are the same for electrical forces, strong forces, and gravitational forces; only the weak force appears to violate this symmetry of nature. That's in the standard model, and I can't explain it to you, because nobody knows why; it just is an observed fact of nature.

But there are other broken symmetries, which we can explain. For example, we have force carriers, the photon and the Z. They, in some ways, seem like similar things. I mean, they're spin one objects, and they carry some aspect of the electroweak force, but there's a broken symmetry between them. One of them is without mass, the photon; one of them is massive, the Z particle. That's an electroweak symmetry breaking. That's the fancy word for that observed fact of nature that one of these force carriers has mass and the other doesn't. We believe we understand that. It arises from the presence of the Higgs particle, which we're going to be talking about.

The standard model actually gives you an explanation of why it is that these two forces of nature, which, on the one hand seem to be completely symmetrical, but on the practical hand, in the real world, seem to be so different from one another. If you were to heat the universe, which you could do in a laboratory by smashing particles together, or by going back to the early universe like the Big Bang, you would discover that the weak and electromagnetic interactions are, in fact, identical. They merge together at super high energies because the standard model has unified them. Those are all sort of lovely mathematical, or aesthetic, arguments.

Mathematical arguments really boil down to the fact that this theory doesn't contradict itself in any obvious way. If you calculate something, you always get finite answers. There are no probabilities that can be computed in the standard model that come out bigger than one or less than zero; that would be a mathematical inconsistency. Earlier models had that problem, but the standard model doesn't. So, again, all of this stuff is very nice, and to physicists it kind of helps you to believe in the truth of the theory. But doggone it, you know, a theory is only good, in my mind, anyway, and this is a personal opinion, if you can go into the laboratory and make some measurements, calculate some numbers, and compare the numbers you predict with the numbers you get in the laboratory. That, to me, is really what it means to have a correct or successful theory of nature. I'll take quantitative over aesthetic any day, even if the theory gets a little ugly, if it's a good, predictive theory. That is certainly useful science, in any case. It may not be the most fundamental, or the end of the story, that's all.

Every year, the Particle Data Group at Berkley keeps up a table, a collection of all of the information that we've been gathering over the years. You can go on the Web and look up Particle Data Group, if you're interested, and you'll find tabulations. First, there's a summary of the standard model that tell you what the ingredients are and what the formulas are. Then there will be a list of the particles.

First the fundamental ones: the electron has this mass, and this magnetic strength, and this electric charge, and so on; just a table. Every piece of data includes a reference to a paper, a journal article, or maybe several; so you can go and see what experiments were done to give us these numbers. They go on and have tabulations, not only of the fundamental particles, but of all the built-up particles, such as the the pions, and the kaons, and the protons, and the complicated particles in the zoo, which aren't really so complicated after all. They're just three quarks put together, or a quark and an anti-quark.

If you look at this—you can get a physical publication of it, and it's a big, thick, fat book. It's the collected information that we have, and each page is incredibly dense, because they're not really telling you everything, they're just telling you where to go to find out more details about that particular number, and that particular information. It's quite stunning, when you think about it. That big, fat book and all of the thousands and thousands of pages to which it refers, all comes from the first couple of pages, the standard model; and people have been spending years doing these calculations. To date, I know of no significant discrepancies between the theoretical calculations and the experimental observables.

Everybody's looking for it. Everybody would like to find some kind of a crack in the standard model, because that's the nature of physicists. It's no fun just going out and verifying what people are telling you you're going to see. It's much more fun if you get a surprise, a curiosity, something we don't understand; and, of course, these things still happen. They're often in subtle aspects of the standard model, but at some fundamental level, we keep hunting for cracks, and we're not finding them.

Let me talk about another success of the standard model that's a little bit more qualitative, but to me, equally convincing. Mr. Weinberg, in 1967, worked out a theory, and said, "I predict the existence of a new particle, the Z boson." Almost 20 years later, we go into a laboratory, and get to the energy, finally, that he said we need to get to; and there it is, in the bubble chamber, a new particle of nature. The Z particle is real; it leaves behind a track. You have to think about that for a second. How can a human being make a prediction about a fundamental particle that won't be observed for 20 years? Can he just be kind of making wild guesses? It's not as if Weinberg wrote paper after paper making a whole bunch of guesses, and one of them came true. He wrote one paper about this and argued convincingly that it should be correct, and it was. To me, I just find that kind of prediction, of a new fundamental force, or a new fundamental particle, to be a powerful indicator that we really do understand something. We're not just approximating or curve-fitting; we're really talking about some deeper level of understanding about the world. Of course it wasn't just the Z; it was the W, tau-flavored neutrino, and the top quark. All of these things were predicted in advance of their discoveries and later found where we were looking.

The tau neutrino, found in 2000, was a huge experimental effort, and it seems to be exactly like a muon neutrino, or an electron neutrino, except that it has tau-ness, whatever that might mean. It means that when it whacks into a proton, it produces a tau particle, rather than producing an electron or a muon, and you can segregate tau-neutrino beams, mu-neutrino beams, electron-neutrino beams. We'll be coming back, in future lectures, to talk about the current effort that people are making to understand the physics of these neutrinos. It's one of the few places, in fact, where there is already a hint that maybe the standard model does need to be tweaked up a little bit. Finally, after almost 30 years of attempts to find a crack, the neutrino sector is the one place where it seems to be that maybe you don't quite understand how the world works. There may be some interesting funny business, so we have to come back and talk about that.

Now, having said that, I also want to emphasize that, if we do discover some funny business with the quarks, we're not going to toss the standard model. At least, there would be no reason to, as long as the new data isn't in radical disagreement with the fundamental premises because the standard model does have a little bit of leeway in it. We could, for example, make a discovery of fourth generation of quarks, but that wouldn't shatter the standard model. It would be a wonderful surprise; everybody would be very excited, and we'd do lots of experiments to learn about it. That's already happened once. It would fit in to our framework of understanding. A fourth generation of quarks would, how should we phrase it? It would change the standard model, it would modify it; but it wouldn't shatter it. The framework would still be there, and we can generalize that framework to incorporate some new heavier particles. If we discovered a new light particle that didn't fit in, in any way, then we might have some serious worries. But that would be kind of like saying, "Yeah, maybe some day I'll hold this pen and it'll go flying up in the air, and that would ruin Isaac Newton's theory of gravity." Well it surly would, but I don't think it's ever likely to happen unless, you know, a little black hole goes flying over the top of the room, and then I guess we could understand it. In fact, it would be something beyond Isaac Newton's theory.

Today, we look back at Isaac Newton's theory and ponder if it is right or wrong. Some people would say, "Oh, it's wrong because Albert Einstein proved that F is not quite equal to ma when things get very relativistic," and I would disagree. I would say, "Sure, F=ma—for any object moving at ordinary speeds." It's a fabulously accurate law of nature; it describes the way the world works. The fact that a super-fast particle behaves slightly differently just means we have to stretch our understanding of F=ma; we have to deepen and broaden it. I can't imagine any scenario, ever, that's going to take away F=ma and Newton's law of gravity. All I can imagine is exciting new discoveries that deepen, or extend, the realm of applicability of the laws of physics.

I think the same thing has to be true of the standard model. No matter what we discover in the future, there are still going to be atoms in the world. We've seen direct evidence of them. There are still going to be quarks in the world; we've seen direct evidence of them. They're going to combine in the ways that the standard model says, and at low energies, or even high energies, like the highest that we can produce today, at the dawn of the 21st century. I think all of the laws that we have been testing, we've tested; and they're correct. So whatever wonderful things we discover in the future are going to certainly modify, almost surely modify our understanding of the standard model. But it's hard to imagine how they could break it.

Let me give you another example. The standard model not only makes these qualitative predictions about the existence of new particles, but you can predict numbers for experiments. What kind of numbers? Some of them are very exact specific numbers. For example, the standard model tells you what the magnetic strength of an electron is. I've mentioned that number before, because it is perhaps the greatest numerical success of the standard model. I'll repeat that number because I love it so much - 2.00231930435 - twelve digits that explain a fact of nature about this little particle, the electron, and how it behaves when you put it near a magnet. The fellow who did that calculation's name is Kinoshita, and here's a little quote from Mr. Kinoshita. "Unlike previous theories, QED"— and he actually meant the electroweak theory—has no obvious limitation since no theory is likely to be absolutely true, however"— I want you to think about that statement—"since no theory is likely to be absolutely true, physicists have been trying to discover where the limitations of QED might be found." There are a lot of deep ideas in that sentence. He doesn't believe that QED, really the electroweak theory, is necessarily the ultimate theory of nature, and neither do I. What he's saying is that it's an extraordinarily accurate one; and how do we find out its limits? Where does it begin to break down? Okay? If there's some new physics, beyond the standard model, some new particle or new idea that we've never thought of so far, what we know experimentally is, it's only going to affect that observable in the 13th decimal place because we've already checked the first 12. So the first place where the standard model can break down is off there in the parts-per-billion level. So it may be that that's going to happen, and it would certainly be interesting. It would change our worldview a little bit, but it's not going to change the first 12 decimal places of our understanding of the world.

That calculation is a lovely one, and people have done others like it. The calculation for the muon works almost equally well. The calculation for the proton failed because the proton wasn't a fundamental particle. But if you try to understand properties of the underlying quarks, then you can make more quantitative predictions. The energy of hydrogen atoms, and the transitions—for instance, the Lamb shift that was first observed in 1947, that led us on this path towards quantum electrodynamics, a little splitting of two lines of hydrogen from—wasn't really one color; it was really two closely spaced colors. That number has been calculated now to accuracy that approaches the accuracy of that magnetic number, the magnetic moment for the electron. All of these quantitative successes tell us that if you're going to find a crack in the standard model, it's probably going to be a subtle one. What that might mean is that it's going to occur at some very high energy. So we're probably going to find some very heavy particle, if there's something new beyond the standard model, and that's the likely place that you could imagine where the standard model might end up breaking down.

After you've listened to this course, you're going to hear lots of articles, hear stories, read articles about science, about physics —

they appear from time to time in "The New York Times," in "Discover Magazine," and "Scientific American."—about the discoveries that are going on in particle-physics accelerators, and you'll hear all these buzzwords. I can almost guarantee you that, every time a big discovery is made, the press will make some sensational noises about, the standard model has been proven wrong, and you have to understand what they mean by that. The standard model was defined 30 years ago, and anything new, technically, could be argued to be proving the standard model wrong. If a neutrino is not without mass, we've proven the standard model wrong. If the magnetic moment of the electron disagrees in the 13th or 14th decimal place, we've proven the standard model wrong. Physicists will jump up and down because they want the press attention like anybody else; and the press is excited, because the physicists are excited. It is exciting, but bear in mind what it really means. It really means that we have extended the standard model in some unexpected way. We might be heading toward a deeper theory of nature, but the only way that I could imagine the standard model really breaking would be if gravity starts turning upside down some day. Or something—just sort of inconceivably radical—that all of a sudden, the new experiments disagree with the old ones. It's almost inconceivable at this point.

As a physicist, I of observe in my colleagues two reactions to these spectacular successes of the standard model. On the one hand, you have the physicists who are really pleased. They're a bit cocky and self-satisfied: I mean, look at it. We can write it down on a couple of pieces of paper; we can describe the world at a fundamental level— we've done it! All right? We understand the world. This has been a dream of human beings since 2,500 years ago, and probably longer. We know what Mr. Democritus's atoms are; we know what they're made of, we know the bottom line. It's a lovely thought, and maybe we are done. It's possible; it's at least conceivable. We've been peeling open this onion and we got to the nugget at the bottom. It's also quite conceivable. With the other group's reaction, I think probably the more common attitude among working physicists, is that there's still more layers to that onion. We have found a very lovely, round, smooth, elegant layer that explains everything up above it; and perhaps we can still look deeper. We can understand other aspects of the standard model. As a, sort of a cynical or aggressive physicist, you might start poking holes at it.

Nowadays, when I hear colloquia with especially young physicists, they always begin by saying well, we have the standard model, and it's very successful, but—then they start listing things that bother them about the standard model. For example, there are approximately 23 numbers, numbers that you have to go in the laboratory to measure and put into that particle data table. You can't compute them from scratch. What's that about? In fundamental physics, shouldn't we just be able to compute everything about the world? Well, maybe we can, maybe we can't. I don't know if that's the way the world works or not, but 23 is starting to be a big number. The same thing with the total number of particles: six quarks, six leptons, a whole bunch of force carriers, plus the Higgs; it's getting to be a big number. What's that about? Can't we understand the world in terms of something simpler? Even deeper still, what about these generations? Well, we've got the up, down, electron, and electron neutrino, the light generation; and they describe pretty much everything in the ordinary world. Who ordered the next generation? Why do we need them, why are they there, those heavier particles? It's a good question.

When we came to the third generation, in the 1970s, all of a sudden people are saying, "I don't know, this is starting to look like the periodic table of atoms all over again. There are rows and columns; the columns have very similar properties, the masses are increasing. Surely there's a story here." There's some underlying physics, and the standard model doesn't tell you that story. The standard model just says, this is the world, let's work from this, and now we can explain everything else. So it's certainly a popular idea nowadays that there's got to be something, and the buzzword is, beyond the standard model.

So for the rest of this course, we're going to be talking about the limitations, the present puzzles, and the curiosities in the standard model. In the very end, in the last couple of lectures, I want to really talk about some even wilder speculations. People have really started thinking about what, at the moment, are pretty radical ideas that are very elegant, they're mathematically compelling, and they really simplify the story at a conceptual level, although they complicate the math. It's very speculative and not yet tested.

What I want to leave you with, in this lecture, is the sense that the standard model really is successful, no matter if people say, "Well, it's a great theory, but..."It is a great theory. It really does describe the world, and every experiment I know of, in the atomic and subatomic realm, is described quantitatively by the standard model of particle physics.

Lecture Nineteen
The Higgs Particle

Scope:

The mysterious Higgs particle is the least understood piece of our story so far and the *one* central part not yet directly verified. In this lecture, we ask a number of questions about the Higgs: Why should we believe in its existence? How can we picture it, and what role does it play in the standard model? Why is it so important to "find" a Higgs? How would we go about looking for such a thing, and what would happen if we looked for it and it wasn't there? We conclude by discussing the rise and fall of the superconducting supercollider (SSC), the machine specifically designed to answer our questions about the Higgs.

> No one can say whether any one accelerator will let us make the last step to a final theory. I do know that these machines are necessary successors to a historical progression of great scientific instruments… Whether or not the final laws of nature are discovered in our lifetime, it is a great thing for us to carry on the tradition of holding nature up to examination, of asking again and again why it is the way it is.
>
> —Steven Weinberg (*Dreams of a Final Theory*, p. 275)

Outline

I. We have talked about all the fundamental particles that we currently know about, except for one—the Higgs boson.

    A. In the standard model, the Higgs is responsible for the defining characteristic of any particle, its mass. It also functions in distinguishing between the weak and electromagnetic forces, and it may have played a role in the evolution of the universe.

    B. The Higgs is the most poorly understood part of the standard model to date. Everything else we have talked about has been extremely well established for many years in the laboratory. The Higgs, however, has been established mathematically but not physically. We have no direct evidence of the existence of a Higgs particle.

    C. Let's recall for a moment why the Higgs was proposed.

1. In trying to understand the weak force of nature, physicists believed this force should have gauge symmetry, because the other forces in the universe had gauge symmetry.

2. If gauge symmetry is observed in the weak force, as it is in electricity and magnetism, these forces will be completely symmetrical in many ways. Specifically, the weak force carrier will be massless. That idea, however, contradicted the data.

3. Every piece of data says that the weak force has very short range. It is almost a contact force, which is why it's so weak. The force carriers—the W and Z particles—are massive. How could we reconcile gauge symmetry, which says that these carrier should be massless, with the fact that they are massive?

4. The answer was a mathematical trick, the prediction or assumption of the existence of a new particle of nature.

   a. Remember, in quantum mechanics, particles and waves are two aspects of the same thing. Similarly, if we think about physics as a quantum field theory, particles and fields are two aspects of the same thing.

   b. This idea is most obvious in thinking about force carriers. How do I visualize a photon? First, I visualize an electric field, but that's not the photon. The photon is the traveling wave that results when the electric field is jiggled. The photon is also the particle of light.

   c. Every particle of nature can be thought of in this same abstract way as the ripple in a field.

   d. Thus, Higgs proposed a new field—not an electric field or a magnetic field, but the Higgs field, which permeates space. The ripple in that field would be called the Higgs particle.

D. The unusual thing about this Higgs field is that it is finite but everywhere. The Higgs field exists inside of atoms in the empty space between the electrons and quarks. It even exists in outer space. It is a uniform background in which we all live.

   1. Usually, we would think about outer space as being close to a vacuum. We would imagine that an electric field is strong when it's near an object but that it then fades away.

   2. With the Higgs, however, to make sense of the weak interaction and to make the theory mathematically consistent, we were obligated to postulate that the Higgs field is everywhere.

   3. When I walk through the room, then, I'm walking through a sea of the Higgs field. What would be the effect on me? That depends on the interaction of the particles in my body with the Higgs field.

   4. One of the things that would happen as I'm walking, if the particles in my body are interacting with the Higgs field, would be some sort of resistance to my motion.

E. Before we talk about the search for direct evidence of the Higgs, which we have not yet found, I want to touch on one another aspect of it.

   1. In nature, the weak force and the electric force seem completely different. One of them has to do with radioactivity; the other is everyday life. The carrier of electricity is massless, which means that generating electricity and electric forces is easy. But the carrier of the weak force is massive, which means that the likelihood of weak interactions is improbable.

   2. A symmetry in the standard model says that these two forces of nature are the same. How, then, does that symmetry get broken? How does the universe change from one in which weak forces and electric forces are identical to the one we live in where the forces are so different?

3. The answer is that the Higgs is responsible for symmetry breaking. In the standard model, the W and Z bosons interact with the Higgs field very strongly and it slows them down a great deal. They become massive.

4. We call this phenomenon *electroweak symmetry breaking*. If we want to understand why the weak force and the electric force seem to be the same yet are so different, we must postulate something like the Higgs.

II. How do we look for a particle like the Higgs? With the neutrinos, a mathematical theory predicted their existence and the exact probability of their interaction. The situation is a little different with the Higgs.

   A. The standard model cannot tell us how massive the Higgs field is. The phrase *how massive* refers to how much energy we have to pour into a small region of space to create a ripple in the Higgs field.

   B. Again, imagine that we live in a sort of unusual fluid, and we want to create a wave. In water, the slightest perturbation will create a wave, but that is not true of the Higgs field. The Higgs is so massive that we need to add a lot of energy to create a ripple, which would be a particle and would leave direct evidence behind in a bubble chamber.

   C. We could find this particle through a direct or an indirect search.

      1. The indirect search would be to look for the presence of a Higgs, because any particle of nature, if it's real, can be virtually created for a very short time, then would disappear again. This is how we began to search for the top quark before we had accelerators that were energetic enough to actually make one in the laboratory.

      2. This method is called *precision physics*. We make very accurate measurements and very accurate standard-model calculations. We have only one unknown—the mass of the Higgs—therefore, we can compare the measurements and the calculations and try to deduce the mass of the Higgs.

3. Physicists have been trying this method for thirty years now and are beginning to hone in on the mass. Unfortunately, the Higgs effects on other processes tend to be extremely subtle compared to even the small effects of a top quark. The best guess for the mass of the Higgs today from precision data is somewhere between 100 times proton mass and 200 times proton mass.

4. If we know this range, why don't we make a Higgs particle? At Fermilab, we can achieve a trillion eV. In principle, that's more than enough energy to create a Higgs. What happens, though, when we add all this energy to a small region of space? We would produce the whole zoo of particles, but the probability of producing a Higgs is so small that we would not expect to have seen one yet, even given the millions and millions of other quantum particle production events that we have observed.

5. At Fermilab, the strategy to increase the likelihood of seeing an event has been to upgrade the intensity of the beam to increase the number of proton and anti-proton collisions. In Europe, at CERN, the strategy is to increase the energy. Around 2007, CERN will be able to achieve 14 trillion eV, which will certainly be enough energy to see a Higgs if they exist.

6. In the 1980s, the United States began a project to build a truly gigantic accelerator—a superconducting supercollider. The project was abandoned in the 1990s because of lack of funding.

III. I believe that the demise of the superconducting supercollider was symbolic of a shift in U.S. priorities regarding particle physics compared to other areas of physics and other sciences.

A. From World War II until the 1990s, particle physics was at the top of the list for funding and facilities. This field was viewed as the most fundamental and, therefore, the most worthy of all the sciences.

B. That idea seems to have changed now. Particle physics is still very much alive, but now, it is one player among all the branches of physics and, indeed, among all the branches of science.

C. Let's finish this lecture by asking, "What if we had built this superconducting supercollider and hadn't found the Higgs?"

    1. Mathematics tells us that we would expect to find this particle, but we could easily imagine that the Higgs might not show up the way we would expect it to. What would happen if we took the Higgs out of the standard model?

    2. The answer is that some aspects of the model would survive, but in some ways, the standard model would collapse on itself. In particular, if we try to calculate events at a couple of trillion eV, then the theory would start to yield infinities. In other words, the theory is fine at low energies, but when we reach the energies of superconducting supercolliders, the theory might break down and yield answers that don't make sense.

    3. That fact would tell us that something deeper is going on. The Higgs is a minimal theory. That is to say, it is the simplest possible mechanism we have come up with that is consistent with everything we know so far and makes the theory coherent.

    4. I might almost guarantee that something will happen at a trillion eV that we don't know about today. The symmetry of nature between electric and weak forces is going to merge or break down at those energies, but we're not quite sure exactly how.

    5. If we find something else, we would have to reconstruct the standard model to account for the Higgs sector.

D. The Higgs, then, is the last piece of the standard model and the most important in the sense of understanding mass, the fundamental property of everything, and understanding symmetry breaking, which is the key idea that unifies the weak and electromagnetic forces. And it's the one piece that we have not yet verified in the laboratory.

Essential Reading:

Kane, *The Particle Garden*, chapters 3 and 8.

Weinberg, *Dreams of a Final Theory*, chapter XII and afterward.

Barnett, Muhry, and Quinn, *The Charm of Strange Quarks*, chapter 9.2.

't Hooft, *In Search of the Ultimate Building Blocks*, chapter 11.

Recommended Reading:

Lederman, *The God Particle*, chapter 8, second half, starting from "The Standard Model is a shaky platform."

http://www.hep.ucl.ac.uk/~djm/higgsa.html. In 1993, the then-current Science Minister of the United Kingdom, William Waldegrave, issued a challenge to physicists to answer the questions "What is the Higgs boson, and why do we want to find it?" on one side of a single sheet of paper. This link is David J. Miller's prize-winning "qualitative lay-person's explanation." Other replies can be found at http://hepwww.ph.qmw.ac.uk/epp/higgs.html.

Questions to Consider:

1. Leon Lederman, former director of Fermilab and Nobel Prize winner, wrote a book about the Higgs called *The God Particle*. Few people in the physics community use that name for the Higgs. Why do you suppose he chose that title? Are you sympathetic with his choice? Why or why not?

2. If you could go back in time and cast the deciding vote in the Senate to end or continue construction of the superconducting supercollider, how would you vote? Why? What factors would influence your decision most strongly?

Lecture Nineteen—Transcript
The Higgs Particle

We've been talking about the standard model, trying to understand the conceptual framework and the players—the fundamental particles that make up the world that we live in. We've talked about all of the fundamental players that we know about today, except for one, which I've really only mentioned in passing. It's a very important player - very esoteric, but also quite relevant if you want to understand how things work, and that's the Higgs boson, the Higgs particle. The Higgs is named after a physicist named Peter Higgs, and its role in the standard model; although it's quite formal and mathematical, it really is the thing that's responsible for the defining characteristic of any particle, its mass. So the Higgs plays this key role and, also, plays a role in distinguishing between those forces that are presumably unified now: weak and electromagnetic. And it plays a role, potentially, in the evolution and development of the universe as a whole. It's quite unique in this respect: that something very, very large scale—cosmology, and the structure of the universe—may in fact depend, and be determined, by this subatomic particle.

So today I want to talk about the Higgs; what is it, why do we believe in it? It is definitely the most poorly understood part of the standard model to date. Everything else we've been talking about has been extremely well established for many, many years now in the laboratory. The Higgs has been established mathematically, but not physically. We have no direct evidence of the existence of a Higgs particle yet, and it's big business in the physics world. There are a lot of money, a lot of energy, a lot of time and a lot of effort being devoted to finding the Higgs particle. It will certainly be found. It has been in the news and will certainly be in the news again in the future. In fact, it has even played a role in U.S. politics, which I'll talk about today. So I think it makes it an interesting particle to learn about.

Let me remind you—we've mentioned it before—but let me tell you about why the Higgs was proposed, what it does. We wanted to understand the weak force of nature, and it was believed, pretty much just because the other forces had gauge symmetry, that the weak force should also have gauge symmetry. This is a very abstract idea; it's a kind of a mathematical property of a theory that says if you shift something, physics doesn't really care. The world doesn't really care what number you choose to define as zero volts in some electric circuit. So, if you believe that gauge symmetry is a symmetry of nature—and we've already had extremely good evidence that it was a symmetry of electricity and magnetism and the strong force, and maybe the weak force too; if you want that— then you discover that the electric forces and the weak forces will be completely symmetrical in a lot of ways. They will not only be unified; the weak force carrier would be without mass, and that's in direct contradiction with data. Every piece of data says that the weak force is very, very short range; it's like a contact. That's why it's so weak. A neutrino has to be right on top of another particle in order for you to have any kind of a chance of seeing a weak interaction, in a certain sense. The force carriers, the W and Z particles, are massive. So how do you reconcile gauge symmetry, which says they should be without mass, with the fact that they're massive? The answer is a mathematical trick. It's the prediction, or assumption, of the existence of this new particle of nature.

Now, when I talk about "particle"—and in quantum mechanics you can talk about particle or wave—it's kind of two aspects of the same thing. Similarly I can talk about particles or fields, now that we're thinking about physics as quantum field theory. The place where it's most obvious is when you're thinking about the force carriers. Okay, how do I visualize a photon, a particle of light? Well, first I visualize an electric field. I have a little charge, and there's this invisible, maybe even abstract or mathematical, electric field permeating space. That's not the photon; the photon is what you get if you wiggle that field. If you take the charge and make it move up and down, then the field will get a ripple in it, and the ripple will propagate through space; and it's that traveling wave, it's that ripple, that's the photon. That is the particle of light.

Every particle of nature can be thought of, in this same abstract way, as the ripple in a field, so Mr. Higgs proposes that there exists a new field of nature. It's not an electric field, and it's not a magnetic field; it's what we now call the Higgs field. If you have a ripple in that field then you would call it a Higgs particle. Now the really unusual thing about this Higgs field, the thing that makes it special, is that it asks if there is a field that permeates space. It was the sort of brainstorm of these folks like Weinberg, Salam, Glashow and Higgs all putting the story together. It's not zero; it's finite. It's everywhere

- inside of atoms, in all that empty space between the electrons and the quarks, outside; even in deep, dark, outer space. There's a Higgs field everywhere, like a uniform background that we all live in. This is a wacky idea. I mean, normally we think about dark outer space as being pretty close to a vacuum. There are a few photons that travel through dark outer space, because they're starlight, but pretty much what we imagine when we think of fields is that there's a charge, and there's an electric field that's very strong near it, then that field fades away. So as you get far away from things, you expect that fields should get very small, but the Higgs does not.

In order to make sense of the weak interaction—in order to make the theory mathematically consistent—we were obligated to postulate that there's this Higgs field everywhere. So as I walk through the room, I'm walking through a sea of Higgs field, and what would the effect on me be? Well, that depends on the interaction of the particles in my body with the Higgs field. That's another of your assumptions. Right now, all we're doing is playing a what-if game. That's how theory often begins. You just say, "Well, what if there were a field of nature everywhere, and what if most of the particles, the other fundamental particles, interacted with it? Okay?

Well, one of the things that would happen is, as I walk, if the particles in my body were interacting with that Higgs field, there's going to be some sort of resistance to my motion. What I'm trying to do here is to describe some very formal mathematics and make it concrete. You have to appreciate that I'm always doing this in this course; and here I'm really stretching the metaphor about as far as I can. If what I was saying were literally correct, then you would imagine that all objects would come to a halt, because they are walking through this goo, but that's not what happens. An object in motion remains in motion. Newton's laws are still true, even in the presence of the Higgs, but an object in motion feels more sluggish than it would if there was no Higgs field around. That's probably the best way to think about it.

So we're kind of like fish underwater, swimming through this water; and the fish are always the last to notice the water. It's there, it's important for them, but they're going to notice other fish first; and they're going to notice the effects, maybe, of the water causing, you know, waves, causing things to move around. We live in this stuff. It interacts with our bodies. It's what creates the inertia, or in effect the mass, of all the particles; and yet, it took us a long time just to recognize the possibility of its existence.

It's a very formal idea, and, when I was first introduced, in graduate school to the Higgs mechanism, the mathematical framework, I learned that there's assumption after assumption being piled on. We're assuming a new field; we're assuming that it's not zero; we're assuming that the particles interact with it in specific ways. Then, you start to draw some conclusions, and those conclusions match all the weak data. In fact, lots more than just the weak data; the masses of the particles, everything begins to tie in, in this lovely way that we've seen. The standard model is a beautiful, self-contained theory, which describes the world. So on the one hand, everything fits together, and the standard model is a spectacular quantitative success. On the other hand, this Higgs business just seems pretty ad hoc. Now, maybe it's just because it's a more recent discovery. You know, way back in the early 1930s Mr. Dirac proposed something very mathematical and formal, namely, anti-matter and could hardly believe it himself. We see the same thing with the neutrino. Many of the particles that came out of mathematics were at first sort of viewed with suspicion; it seemed so formal and abstract. The quarks themselves didn't seem like real things. What we want is evidence, direct evidence, for the existence of the Higgs.

Before I get to our search for the direct evidence—because we don't have it yet, okay, this is still a hunt—I want to say another word about why the Higgs is such an important thing in this theory. In nature, the weak force and the electric force seem completely different. They are as different as night and day. One of them has to do with radioactivity, the other with everyday life. The carrier of electricity is without mass, so it's really easy to generate electricity, and electric forces; but the carrier of the weak force is very massive, so it's highly improbable to create—to have weak interactions occur. There is, in fact, symmetry in the standard model that says that these two forces of nature are one and the same, viewed from a different perspective. So how does that symmetry get broken? How do you go from a universe where weak forces and electric forces are identical— that has some sort of mathematical or high-energy universe—to the one we live in, where the forces are so different? And the answer is the Higgs. It's the Higgs that's responsible for symmetry breaking.

In the standard model, the W and Z bosons interact with this Higgs field that's everywhere. As they're traveling along they, in fact, interact very strongly with it, and so it slows them down a lot. They become very massive. So it's the Higgs field that breaks the symmetry. We call this electroweak symmetry breaking; that's the fancy expression for it in the world of physics. And, if you want to understand that phenomenon of nature—why does the weak force and the electric force seem both to be the same, and to be so different—you have to understand the Higgs. There either has to be one, or there has to be something else. If it's not the Higgs, if we're wrong in our guess, it has to be something. At least, we believe there should be some reason why this symmetry gets broken.

I think we should be glad that the Higgs exists, if it does, because symmetry breaking is not a bad thing. It's a good thing. The world is much more boring when everything is completely symmetrical. Artists know this. When they create paintings, it's very rare that they'll draw perfect geometrical symmetry. It's the breaking of the symmetry that gets your interest. Imagine that we lived in a sphere, a very symmetrical universe, and it was filled with some gas, some water vapor. Okay? It would be a beautifully symmetrical universe. There's water vapor in all directions, the pressure's the same everywhere, and nothing interesting is going on. Life would get more interesting if you cooled down that sphere, cooled it down to a certain critical temperature where the water vapor begins to condense into liquid water. Okay, at that lower temperature, you have some physics going on. You've got a little pool of liquid water here, and some vapor over there, and you can swim in the water and jump out of the water and, there are boundaries; that means there are physics phenomena going on. Life gets interesting, and that's sort of what's happening in our universe. We could imagine a universe. In fact, in an accelerator at ultra-high energies—higher energies than we've reached so far—or, in the early universe, very close to the Big Bang; when the universe is, in effect, very hot, the electric force and the weak force become like this uniform water vapor. It's all the same. The two forces are identical, and indistinguishable, and it's lovely and symmetric, but not so interesting and not so much fun to live there. In our universe, which has cooled off, the two forces separated, and so we get the two different, distinct phenomena. So this is all kind of motivation for why we believe in it, and why it might be important to our understanding of the world. So let me talk now about how you go hunting for a particle like this.

It's, in a certain sense, like looking for neutrinos. You believe in them because there's a mathematical theory that predicts their existence. With the neutrinos, it's pretty clear from the theory how you should go looking for them, because the theory itself tells you exactly what the probability of interaction is, so you can figure out how to design a big detector. It's a little tougher with the Higgs because, unfortunately, the one thing that the standard model cannot tell us is how massive this Higgs field itself is. When I say how massive I mean, how much energy has to pour into a small region of space to create a ripple in that Higgs field. So, I'm sort of imagining an unusual fluid, right? We're walking through this universe that's filled with, not water, but Higgs; and what we want to do is create a wave. It's not like water, where just the slightest little perturbation will create a wave; that's a particle without mass that's easy to make. The Higgs is massive, so you need to pour a lot of energy in to create a ripple, which would—once you've created it, it's a real particle, the Higgs particle—leave a track in a bubble chamber; it would decay into other particles. It would be as obvious as any of the fundamental particles, if we could create one.

There are a couple of ways you could imagine doing this, either a direct search or an indirect search. The indirect search would be to look for the presence of a Higgs because any particle of nature if it's real, can be virtually created, and then disappear again, for a very short amount of time. Any particle, including the Higgs, can do that. This is how we begin to search for the top quark before we had accelerators that were energetic enough to actually make one in the laboratory. It's called precision physics. You make a very, very accurate measurement of something. You make a very, very accurate standard-model calculation, and there's only one unknown—the mass of the Higgs—and so you can compare the two, and try to deduce the mass of the Higgs.

We've been trying this for 30 years now, ever since the Higgs mechanism was proposed, and we're beginning to hone in on it. Unfortunately, the Higgs effects on other processes tend to be rather wimpy compared to, say even the small effects of a top quark. The effects are very, very subtle effects, so they're hard to pin down exactly. We had predicted the mass of the top quark to within ten per cent before we actually found one. The Higgs is, right now I think a mass somewhere between 100 times a proton mass and 200 times a proton mass, so that's the best guess today from this precision data. We continue to collect precision data, so presumably those limits are going to get narrower and narrower.

Why not just make one? Between 100 and 200 proton masses is how much energy you have to put into a small region of space, so we ought to be able to do that. At Fermilab we have a TeV, or a trillion electron-volts which is plenty enough energy, in principle, to create a Higgs. The problem is, if you pour all this energy into a small region of space, something happens. Most of the time you get protons and anti-protons, electrons and anti-electrons, pions, and kaons or all the zoo of particles, including top quarks and anti-top quarks. Everything you can produce, you will produce. All right? That's sort of the way quantum mechanics works. Everything is probabilistic. The more probable an event is, the more you will see coming out in your detector, and we worked out the probability of creating a Higgs particle in the standard model. The one unknown is its mass, so you just sort of take a guess. Suppose it's 200 times the mass of a proton, what would the probability be? The answer is, very small. So we're going to Fermilab and looking for these things, but the probability is so small, in fact, that it's so far not even expected that we would have seen even one such event, compared to the millions upon millions of other quantum-particle-production events. So you're truly looking a needle in a haystack. If we make one, it'll be pretty clear. The signature of a Higgs particle in a bubble chamber, or a modern version of a bubble chamber, is going to be quite distinctive. We believe that once we make one we'll know, but we just haven't made one yet.

The American strategy at Fermilab has been to upgrade the intensity of the beam. It's very difficult for us to increase the energy. We've already done the upgrade to a trillion electron-volts; it was a big expensive project, and upping it even more would require stronger magnets, bigger accelerator. We just don't have the funding at the moment for that kind of a project, so we're just trying to make more and more and more protons and anti-protons collide together. If you have a low-probability event, it's like rolling the dice—or, more appropriately, buying lottery tickets. If you have only got a one-in-a-million chance, that's all you've have. You might as well buy more and more and more tickets; actually, that's a very bad strategy with the lottery, because you have to pay money for each of those tickets. Well, with the Higgs, that's really the idea at Fermilab. Increase the luminosity, or intensity, and hope that we get enough events that one or two of them will be a Higgs.

The Europeans decided to take the brute-force approach. There was an accelerator in Europe called CERN (the European Center for Nuclear Research), which they have just recently shut down. They're revamping the energy, the magnets, and the whole system, so they can go up to much higher energy. I believe their new energy, in 2007 if all goes well, will be 17 trillion electron-volts, compared to our one. They're going to go for high energies, which also increases, it turns out, the probability of producing the Higgs, and they will certainly be able to see them if they're there, if they're where we're expecting them to be.

The United States made a big effort to find the Higgs a long time ago. In the 1980s, a bunch of physicists got together. The standard model was in existence, and we knew almost all the pieces that we know today, except for the Higgs. So in the early 1980s it was proposed that we build a truly gigantic accelerator. It was going to be called the Superconducting Supercollider. It's a little ridiculous; there are a lot of supers. Physicists need some new adjectives, I think. The term "superconducting" was considered because, if you really want ultra-high-energy protons to go in a circle, and not fly away, you have to have a big magnet to make them curve around in a circle. This machine was of mammoth proportions. It was going to be something like, boy, 53 miles around; that is, fifty-three miles around this ring. Magnets were to be used; if they just used a conventional magnet, it would not have been strong enough. If they had used a very powerful electromagnet, it would not have been strong enough. They needed superconducting metal, which can withstand enormously high electric currents, to create the magnet. That's why it was superconducting, and supercollider because it was to be of extraordinarily high energy. We're talking 20 TeV in each particle beam that was going to smash into each other, so that means forty-trillion-electron-volt collisions. That would have been plenty. Had this gone as was planned at the time, it would already be running today. In fact, by the late 1990s this machine would have turned on.

It was proposed in the 1980s and went through a lot of reviews and then—first in the physics community and in the United States political community—Congress approved the project. The original estimates were eight billion dollars, and it was funded. This was big science, biggest particle-physics experiment since the Manhattan Project - which really doesn't belong in the field of particle-physics research; that was a U.S. military project. That eight-billion-dollar figure started climbing, and they started building the tunnels. They started designing and building the magnets. Everything was going, and every year, of course, Congress would revisit and engage in more debates. Finally, in the early 1990s, times were tougher, and the project was canned. It was pretty much, I think, a political decision.

In fact, it was completely a political decision, not a scientific decision. They had already spent, by that time, two billion dollars digging part of the tunnel and designing some of the system. There were many tragic aspects of this Superconducting Supercollider's demise. You know, was very sad, in a certain sense, for the physics community, that we lost this opportunity to find a new particle of nature; but, it's also tragic when the U.S. government essentially threw away two billion dollars. You can argue about whether it's worth the money to design such a facility; it's an interesting and important argument, and physicists were also arguing this just as much as the politicians were. Nobody wants to start a project and throw it away, so I think there were many lessons learned; and one of them is, if you're going to do a project like this, we really are going to have to make it an international collaboration. We're going to have to make sure that the funding gets spread out in some way that it's not going to disappear in the middle.

Just to set the stage, I guess it's worth looking at the financial scale of some other big science projects. We have a space station in orbit right now, and that project, I mean, it's hard to estimate costs of these things, but it's roughly a twenty-five-billion-dollar project. I think most scientists, even astronomers and physicists, agree that the science coming out of the space station is probably less obvious and less exciting then the physics that was aimed for in the Superconducting Supercollider. The motivations for the space station are somewhat different, I think. The Human Genome Project is a biology experiment that was cost three billion dollars, somewhat cheaper than the Superconducting Supercollidert, and it was a great success. Its interesting to compare these projects. Another useful number to look at is what fraction of the U.S. federal budget would the Superconducting Supercollider have been? The answer is one one-hundredth of one percent of the U.S. federal budget. So, on the one hand, it's a huge amount of money; on the other hand, it's small compared to all the other monies that we're spending. You can imagine the political and social debates about where we should be spending our money. Even within the physics community, some people are nervous that if you put too much money into one pot, it's going to get taken away from another, but others say, "No, it's really just federal funding that's adding to our scientific effort." In any case, I believe that the demise of the Superconducting Supercollider was symbolic of a shift in U.S. priorities regarding particle physics, compared to the rest of physics and the rest of science.

I think from World War II until the Superconducting Supercollider, particle physics was kind of at the top of the heap. They were getting the big money, the big facilities, and there was a certain sense in which it was viewed as the most fundamental, therefore, the most worthy of all the fields. I think that idea has changed now. Particle physics is alive, very much alive, even though this big project disappeared. In future lectures we're going to be talking about all the exciting stuff that's still going on in other accelerators and in other types of particle-physics experiments. But I think, now, particle physics is one player among many, among all the branches of physics, and indeed among all the branches of science. That's probably a healthy thing as well.

I'd like to finish with this question: "What if we had built this multi-billion-dollar machine but didn't find the Higgs? I mean, this is a mathematician effectively telling you that we expect this particle of nature to exist. It's quite compelling, but it's not proof. You have to see it in the laboratory. This is science. You could always imagine— in fact you could easily imagine—that the Higgs wouldn't show up the way we'd expect it. I think the argument at the time was that that would have been really interesting, too.

Okay, we have this extraordinarily successful model. You may ask yourself what would happen if you took the Higgs out of the model. The answer is that some aspects of the model survive, but the standard model begins to collapse in on itself. In particular, if you try to calculate what goes on at a couple of trillion electron-volts of energy, then the theory would start to give infinities. In other words, the theory is fine; still, at low energies. But, when you reach these Superconducting Supercollider kind of energies, or the European (I believe their acronym is LHC, Large Hadron Collider.), which is what they're building at CERN, because they're going to smash big hadrons – really big, strongly interacting particles - together. The theory would break down and give you some crazy answers, which would tell you that something is going on. It might be the Higgs. The Higgs is called a minimal theory. That is to say, it is the simplest possible mechanism we've been able to come up with, which is consistent with everything we know so far, and it makes the theory coherent. It's minimal. It doesn't mean it's true.

What I can almost guarantee you is that something has to happen at a trillion electron-volts that we don't know about today. It's either the Higgs, or something else. The symmetry of nature between electric and weak forces is going to merge, or break down, at those energies. We're not quite sure exactly how. We have a theory that makes a prediction, and we'd like to verify it; that's sort of the beauty of finding the Higgs, but if you find something else, well that's great, too. Then we go back to the drawing boards, and we reconstruct our standard model to fix it up in the Higgs sector. That would be the way we would express that.

So, the Higgs is the last piece of the standard model. It's he most important in the sense of understanding mass, the fundamental property of everything. Understanding symmetry breaking, is sort of the key idea, the unification of weak and electromagnetic forces. It's the one piece we've never really verified in the laboratory. We haven't seen one. We don't have any direct evidence yet. There was actually a hint at CERN just before they shut down for their upgrade. There were one or two events that were consistent, not gold plated, but they were consistent with being Higgs. There was a big hoop-de-doo at that laboratory, because the physicists said, "Gosh, let's keep running, let's keep running, and, you know, keep rolling those dice. If we have one or two, we ought to find some more." Then the laboratory director had a terrible decision to make: to continue running at this lower energy, with a low probability or to shut down for eight years, build the brand new machine, spend all that money, and be guaranteed of finding the thing and learning all about it. It was an agonizing decision, but in the end they decided to shut down to do the upgrade, and that's what they're doing.

Meanwhile we, in the United States, are continuing to look at Fermilab. So if they were correct—actually, that evidence has since been essentially retracted—there may have been other explanations for those events. It would be great if we could find evidence for the Higgs, with our existing facility; but most likely, we're going to have to go to a higher-energy machine in order to do it.

We really won't be able to say with confidence that the standard model is complete until we've either found the Higgs or found what else there is that plays the role of a Higgs. At that point, I think we will be able to argue that the standard model is truly a complete theory of nature. So this is, as you can understand, a pretty big deal in the world of particle physics. It's one of the reasons why so much money and effort is being spent. I could almost guarantee you that, in the next few years—certainly in the next dozen years—you will be seeing newspaper articles about either the discovery, which would be spectacular, or the non-discovery, which would be equally spectacular, of the Higgs particle, either in the United States or at this new facility in Europe.

Lecture Twenty
The Solar Neutrino Puzzle

Scope:

Neutrinos are among the most mysterious and intriguing particles in the standard model. There remains a great deal that we do not know about them. We have always assumed that they are massless, but is that really the case? What would happen if they did have mass? We might also ask about solar neutrinos. Evidence suggests that far fewer neutrinos are coming from the sun than we would expect. Is there a way to make sense of that? Could the answer be something novel about the way neutrinos behave? In this lecture, we discuss physics deep in mine shafts, an alternative to accelerator physics. We also talk about neutrinos changing "flavor." What does that term mean, and how could we ever tell? We already have a small but growing body of evidence for "neutrino physics beyond the standard model." If we establish this science, why won't it "shatter" the standard model?

> You could argue that all the experiments are simply wrong, but this is highly unlikely.
>
> —Sudbury Neutrino Observatory Web page

Outline

I. The neutrino is an intriguing particle and still not fully understood. Just recently, some data have hinted at the possibility that the standard model may not be completely correct concerning neutrinos.

   A. Remember that the neutrino is a lepton. It has no mass, no charge, and no color. The only force of nature it feels is the weak force.

   B. The massless aspect of the neutrino is part of its mystery. If a particle is massless, it is incredibly easy to produce.

   1. The other massless particle with which we're familiar is the photon. A photon is a traveling electromagnetic energy bundle, but it has no rest mass. It is always moving at the speed of light.

2. A neutrino is quite different. It is not a force carrier. It is itself one of the fundamental constituents. Yet, relativity tells us that if it is massless, it will always be moving at the speed of light.

3. We might ask: Why is it massless? The photon is massless because of gauge symmetry, but there is no such principle associated with the neutrino.

4. Suppose that we measured the mass of the neutrino and it turned out to be .00001 in some unit system, a tiny but non-zero number. Would that break the standard model? The answer is no. We would have to adjust the standard model in some places, but finding mass in a neutrino would not break the model. In fact, we now have some hints that the neutrino may have mass.

C. Another important aspect of neutrinos is that they seem to exist in three flavors: the electron flavor, the muon flavor, and the tau flavor.

1. We talk about electron number as a property of particles. An electron or an electron-neutrino both have electron number 1. Apparently, electron number is a conserved quantum number.

2. As particles move and interact, an electron could just bounce, preserving electron number, or it might undergo a weak interaction. A W boson might be exchanged, and the particles would transform. The electron will transform but only into an electron-type neutrino to conserve total electron number.

3. Again, until recently, it was believed that electron number, as well as muon number and tau number, were absolute exact conserved numbers. We have not discovered any symmetry of nature that would correspond to conserving electron number; it seems to be an accidental conservation.

II. Let's leave the world of neutrinos for a moment and talk about the sun. The two subjects seem disconnected, but they are closely tied together.

A. For many years, physicists and astronomers have been trying to understand what the sun is and how it works. These scientists have constructed what we might call a standard model of the sun.

1. This truly is a model, not a fundamental theory of nature. It is a collection of many branches of physics—heat, thermodynamics, light, sound, vibration, and materials—put together to describe the sun. This model is very successful and, to a certain extent, gives us a good understanding of the sun.

2. One aspect of that understanding involves the nuclear reactions at the core that power the sun. We know how many such nuclear reactions are occurring, and we know that they involve protons smashing together with other protons at very high temperature and energy to form nuclei.

3. When protons bind to protons, in order to stabilize, one of the protons must turn into a neutron; that is a weak decay that releases a neutrino. According to the laws of nuclear physics, if we know how many nuclear reactions are going on, we know exactly how many neutrinos are coming out of the sun.

4. The standard solar model makes a definite prediction about how many neutrinos flow out of the sun every second, which is 60 billion neutrinos per square centimeter per second everywhere in the orbit of earth.

B. In the 1960s, a physicist named Ray Davis thought that with a big enough detector, we should be able to see neutrinos from the sun.

1. Davis looked at nuclear reactions in which a neutrino hits a nucleus and makes a transformation occur. One such reaction was in a chlorine atom. If a chlorine atom is hit by a neutrino, the neutrino will convert into an electron because it's a weak interaction, and the chlorine nucleus will convert into an argon nucleus, which forms a radioactive gas and should be easy to detect.

2. Davis filled a railroad car with carbon tetrachloride, a cleaning fluid, then buried it in a mine. He buried the material, because otherwise, he would get too many other interactions from cosmic rays.

3. The idea was that a couple of times a day, one or two atoms in the railroad car would transform from chlorine

into argon. The argon would bubble up to the top of the tanker and be collected, then the radioactivity would be detected by a Geiger counter.

    4. Davis's experiment worked, but he collected only about a third of the neutrinos that the standard model predicted he would. This was the first direct evidence that neutrinos come from the sun, but the fact of the missing two-thirds of the neutrinos was bothersome.

C. Davis and others worked to solve the solar neutrino puzzle.

    1. Davis placed a highly radioactive source next to his tank and collected the number of neutrinos he expected. This result points to the idea that there really is something special about the neutrinos coming from the sun.

    2. In the 1980s, the United States, the Soviet Union, and the Europeans conducted similar experiments using tanks of gallium, which is liquid metal and transforms into germanium. These results showed that the number of neutrinos coming from the sun was less than predicted by a factor of two.

    3. Japan entered the story with a giant water detector, a tank of very pure water, called Kamiokande, deep in a mine in Japan. This experiment found something extra.

        a. When a neutrino hits the nucleus or the electrons in the water tank, the transformation occurs. Some energy is released, and the outgoing particles carry the momentum of the neutrino. If the neutrino comes in from a certain direction, we see a spray of particles going out in that direction.

        b. Using light detectors, scientists at Kamiokande saw for the first time that the neutrinos really were coming directly from the sun. In fact, Kamiokande and its second-generation upgrade, Super Kamiokande, have produced images of the sun.

    4. Despite all these efforts, we were still left with the solar neutrino puzzle: too few neutrinos arrive from the sun.

D. In working on the puzzle, scientists saw two obvious points at which our understanding might be incorrect.

    1. First, the standard solar model may be wrong; the sun may produce fewer neutrinos than we thought.

2. The other problem could be with the standard model of particle physics. Suppose that an electron-flavored neutrino, which is produced in the nuclear reaction in the sun, travels the long path from the sun to the earth, and as it's moving along, imagine that it could oscillate in flavor from an electron-type neutrino to a muon-type neutrino.

3. The laws of quantum mechanics say that if neutrinos are not truly massless particles, then this can happen. In fact, we've seen exactly the same thing happen before with quarks. (A down quark can oscillate into a strange quark.)

4. How do we visualize this phenomenon? Imagine that a number of neutrinos leave the sun; they are all electron types because that's what the nuclear reactions in the sun produce. As they travel, they oscillate and, by the time they reach earth, half might be electron-flavored and half, muon-flavored. Unfortunately, our detectors have been designed to look only for electron-type neutrinos.

E. What experiment would verify that the total number of neutrinos predicted is coming out of the sun, but they are changing flavor before they reach earth?

1. The Canadians built an underground neutrino detector called the Sudbury Neutrino Observatory (SNO). SNO is a water detector and can see transformations, the same as all the other detectors. SNO also has the possibility of measuring a weak neutral current.

2. Remember that the weak force can manifest itself in two ways according to the standard model. First, the weak force can be seen when a neutrino changes into an electron and, at the same time, transforms whatever it is hitting from one nucleus into another. That's the usual beta decay weak interaction.

3. The weak force can also be mediated by the exchange of Z bosons. This interaction is neutral; there is no transformation. A neutrino comes in, exchanges a virtual Z boson, and hits the nucleus, but no transformation occurs. In detecting the neutrino in this weak interaction, all that can be observed is a recoil of the nucleus.

4. SNO is capable of detecting any flavor of neutrino and is beginning to publish results. Scientists there are seeing the full solar neutrino flux when they look in this weak neutral sector. Thus, the sun is behaving just as we thought it should.

III. We seem to now have evidence that neutrinos can change flavor and, therefore, according to quantum mechanics, neutrinos are massive. What is the significance of this discovery?

A. The most important theoretical argument for the significance of this finding would be that it is a break in the standard model. Such a break would mean that our understanding of the world is incomplete, which is exciting. The discovery that the neutrino is not massless would also enhance the standard model by making it more symmetrical.

B. The practical aspect of this discovery lies in an astrophysical use that no one would have dreamed of even twenty years ago. We have now formed images of the core of the sun using neutrinos that other scientists may be able to use as tools for gathering information.

C. The third consequence of this discovery relates to cosmology, the study of the universe.

1. If we consider that astronomically huge numbers of neutrinos exist in the galaxy and that they have mass, we must ask whether they will have a gravitational effect on the universe.

2. As the universe is expanding, all these neutrinos are pulling it back, and they may produce enough gravity to help halt the expansion and cause the opposite of the Big Bang, the Big Crunch. The fate of the universe may rest in this exotic particle.

Essential Reading:

Kane, *The Particle Garden*, chapter 5, pp. 86–90.

Barnett, Muhry, and Quinn, *The Charm of Strange Quarks*, pp. 143–145.

't Hooft, *In Search of the Ultimate Building Blocks*, chapter 19.

Recommended Reading:

See John Bahcall's Web site, http://www.sns.ias.edu/~jnb/ (check the link on the left for "popular accounts").

The SNO collaboration's Web site, http://www.sno.phy.queensu.ca/, is a good place to find its latest news and summaries of other experimental efforts.

Questions to Consider:

1. Until SNO, all the solar neutrino experiments agreed that there was a *deficit* in the number of electron neutrinos from the sun. What did SNO do that was new and helped resolve whether the deficit comes from the *solar* physics (e.g., lower temperature in the sun's center than we thought) as opposed to *neutrino* physics (e.g., flavor oscillations)?

2. Most physicists have speculated that the electron neutrinos from the sun might oscillate into mu or tau neutrinos. Others have claimed that the electron neutrinos might oscillate into yet another kind of neutrino, a *sterile* type that would not interact in any way with ordinary detectors. What would be the *difference* in what SNO would see in these two scenarios?

Lecture Twenty—Transcript
The Solar Neutrino Puzzle

Despite the mystery and the importance of the Higgs particle to the standard model, my favorite is still the neutrino. Far and away, it's the most intriguing and appealing of all the fundamental particles to me. I'm not quite sure why; it's partly that it's such a mysterious little object, and even today, there are still lots of aspects of neutrinos that we don't really understand fully.

The standard model is a minimal theory. That is to say, we take what data we have, we write down the simplest possible model that's consistent with it, and then we go out and test and see how well we've done. So far it's worked very well, but just recently there have been some hints that perhaps we haven't quite got the story completely correct with the neutrinos. So today I want to talk about where we're at, and what we're learning about neutrinos.

Remember what these particles are. This is a particle which is fundamental, it's one of the leptons; it has no mass, no charge, no color, and no strong force. The only force of nature that it can feel, really, is the electroweak, truly the weak force of nature - not the electric part, just the weak part. This massless business is part of the mystery of the neutrino. What does it mean for a particle to be without mass, "massless?" It's incredibly easy to produce. The other massless particle we're most familiar with is the photon. If you take a photon, it's a traveling electromagnetic energy bundle, but it has no rest mass. You can't take a photon and make it sit still. It's always running at the speed of light. A neutrino is quite different from a photon. It is not a force carrier; it is itself one of the fundamental constituents, yet, what we're saying is you can't take a neutrino and hold it still. If it's massless, relativity says it's always going to travel at the speed of light.

Now, a deep question that you could ask is why is it massless? See, that's a little bit of a funny question. In the standard model, don't we just collect the masses and write them down? We fill out tables by looking at the data. So the answer is, it's massless because it appears in experiments to be massless, but sometimes, in the standard model, there is a reason. For example, there is a deep, theoretical reason why the photon is massless; namely, gauge symmetry. Gauge symmetry is a principle. It's symmetry of the universe. It has to do with the nature of electricity and magnetism; and if gauge symmetry is correct, then the photon must be massless. It works out from the mathematics. It shouldn't necessarily be obvious to the casual viewer, but it is a definite consequence, and there is no such principle associated with the neutrino. There is no fundamental or deep mathematical reason why it needs to be massless. We have just said that it is because, so far, there's no experimental evidence for sluggishness, or inertia, associated with the neutrino.

Suppose we made a very delicate little experiment and measured the mass of the neutrino, and it turned out not to be zero after all. Maybe it's .00001 in some unit system, a tiny but non-zero number. Would that break the standard model? The answer is definitely not. You could just scratch-out the zero in the table and replace it with .00001. Actually you'd have to do a little bit more than that. The standard model, as it's constructed, really makes the neutrino special. There are certain characteristics of the neutrino; for example, the fact that every neutrino in the universe, as it's running away from you, has a spin that points counterclockwise. It's a left-handed particle. That would also have to be modified. That statement about the world would get fixed up, if we discovered that the neutrino has mass.

People have been looking for many, many years, making very delicate measurements of the production and detection of neutrinos, trying to see if they have some mass. We have no direct evidence yet, so whatever it is, it's a very, very small number. But we do have some hints now that maybe it isn't zero.

There's another aspect of neutrinos that's very important in our present understanding of them. There seem to be three different kinds—we call them flavors—of neutrinos. It's just a kind of a whimsical name. There are the electron flavor, the muon flavor, and the tau flavor, that seem to be distinct particles. In fact, now we talk about electron number as a property of particles. An electron, or an electron neutrino, each has electron number one. So, electron number apparently is a conserved, quantum number in nature. As particles move and interact, an electron could just bounce, preserving electron number; or it might undergo a weak interaction, so a little W boson might be exchanged, and particles transform. The electron will transform, but only into an electron-type neutrino, in order to conserve total electron number.

Again, until recently it was believed that electron number—and separately, muon number, and separately, tau number—were absolute, exact, conserved numbers. You know, Emmy Noether, a mathematician in the early 1900s, said that when you have symmetry of nature, it's associated with a conservation law. We don't have any symmetry of nature, that we've discovered, that would correspond to conserving electron number, so, it's sort of an accidentally conserved thing. When that happens in nature you're sort of looking and asking if we can find an experiment where we see lepton number changing. Again, this is something we're hunting for, and I'm going to tell you about the way that we hunt for these things shortly.

Let me leave the world of neutrinos for a moment, and tell you about the sun. It seems disconnected, but we'll see there's a very close connection. For many, many years, physicists and astronomers have been trying to understand what the sun is, and how it works. It is obviously very important for an astronomer to know what the sun is; because, after all, all the other stars are suns as well, and this is the closest one. We can study it very easily, so people have constructed what you might call the standard model of the sun. I use the word "standard" now in completely the generic English sense; just as an ordinary, everyday model of the sun that people can accept and believe that describes how it behaves. How bright it is, the color, what it's made of and all of the things that you associate with the sun. This truly is a model. It's not a fundamental theory of nature. We just have a big ball of gas, and we're trying to describe it as accurately as we can. There are certain things about the sun that are very difficult to measure, such as how hot it is in the middle. We can't get in there with a thermometer, so we have to make deductions. Based on what you see on the outside, and based on the laws of physics and nuclear physics, as we know them, what should the temperature be in the middle?

So the standard model is a kind of a collection of all the branches of physics—heat, and thermodynamics, and light, and sound, and vibration, and materials—all put together to describe this object, and it's a very successful model. It can predict all of the features of the sun down to details such as sunspots and solar flares. To a certain extent, we have a good understanding of the sun.

One of the aspects of that understanding is nuclear reaction at the core, which powers it. We know how bright it is, so we know how many such nuclear reactions are occurring very, very precisely. We know what they are; it involves protons smashing together with other protons at very, very high temperature and energy, forming nuclei. It's a strong interaction of nature that binds protons and neutrons together. Here you've got protons binding to protons, and in order to stabilize, one of the protons has to turn into a neutron, effectively; and that is a transformation that's a weak decay, and so a neutrino is released. According to the laws of nuclear physics, if you know how many nuclear reactions are going on, you know exactly how many neutrinos are coming out of the sun. So the standard solar model makes a very definite prediction for how many neutrinos flow out of the sun every second, and—since we know how far away we are— how many are passing through us, our bodies, our detectors.

A long time ago, in the 1960s, a physicist named Ray Davis decided this is a big number. It is, to be exact, 60 billion neutrinos per square centimeter, per second, everywhere, and here at the orbit of planet Earth, almost 100 billion. That's a big number. Even though these neutrinos are very low energy—they're coming from low-energy nuclear reactions in the sun—and even though neutrinos are very wimpy particles, if we built a big enough detector, thought Ray Davis, we should be able to find evidence that there really are these neutrinos coming from the sun.

After all, any individual neutrino has a tiny probability of interaction, but you've got an awful lot of them. So you're buying a lot of lottery tickets, and if you could build a big detector, you would just be increasing the number of nuclei available for those little neutrinos to bump into. So what are you going to do? Ray Davis looks at all the various nuclear reactions where a neutrino comes in, hits a nucleus and makes a transformation occur. And his favorite was to take a chlorine atom, and if a neutrino hits it, the neutrino will convert into an electron—because it's a weak interaction—and the chlorine nucleus will convert into an argon nucleus. That's what was known from nuclear physics. Argon is a gas, but it's not only a gas. This argon that you produce is a radioactive gas, so it should be fairly easy to detect. A little Geiger counter would click if an argon atom was nearby and decayed. So what we need is a big tank filled with chlorine.

What he used was cleaning fluid. A very clever idea because it was carbon tetrachloride, so it had lots of chlorine atoms in it. It's also quite innocuous stuff, not a big biohazard. He took a railroad car, a tanker, and filled it with carbon tetrachloride then buried it deep in a mine, the Homestake Mine in South Dakota.

It was buried in a mine because we're looking for a very, very tiny signal. Only once or twice a day is such an event likely to happen, according to the laws of particle physics, which he knew about in the 1960s when he built this device. If we put this detector here in this room—remember there are cosmic rays raining down on us all the time, and cosmic rays can also make nuclear reactions happen, and at a much higher rate because the cosmic rays interact electrically as well as weakly, and strongly as well as weakly—we would just be completely swamped out with other stuff going on. It's as if you're looking for a really dim light, you're not going to go into a bright room and look for the light; you're going to go into the darkest room you can possibly find.

So they went deep down into the Homestake Mine in South Dakota and just started waiting. The idea was that every now and again, a couple of events a day, a single atom (I mean you have to realize the spectacular scale of this experiment.) or one or two atoms, in this railroad car is going to transform from chlorine into argon. Argon is a gas, so it will bubble up to the top; you have some collectors up at the top, and then you hold them in front of a Geiger counter for a while to see if a radioactive argon atom will appear. He would sweep through the tank with some other gas to collect the individual argons, and it worked. It was an amazing experiment, and indeed, every month he would collect a couple of dozen atoms.

Now, remember, Ray Davis knows what the prediction is for the total number of neutrinos; and he knows all of the nuclear and particle physics of the day, which is pretty much the same as what we know today, almost, so he could make a quantitative prediction. The standard solar model, combined with the standard model of particle physics, says you should get so many neutrino events per month. What he got was about a third of that.

At first people were just very proud of him. He did a great job, which was, in a certain sense, the first direct proof that neutrinos come from the sun. You might even argue it's the first direct proof that the sun is really undergoing nuclear reactions. This was very cool, good stuff. But after a while this factor of three started to bug some people. They wanted to know why they were seeing fewer neutrinos, by a big factor, coming from the sun than were predicted.

At first, it was known in the literature and began to sort of grow and be called the solar neutrino puzzle. So, where are these solar neutrinos? I think that even when I was a graduate student, I remember reading about the solar neutrino puzzle, and most people said, "Ah, come on. Maybe he's, well, missing a couple. I mean, these are atoms in a giant tank! Maybe he doesn't collect them all." But he was a great physicist—actually still is, he's continuing work on this experiment—and he did a lot of careful checks. For example, he would take a highly radioactive source, and put it right next to his tank. He had a source, and he knew how many neutrinos were coming out of it; and then he *did* collect what he expected. So there really did seem to be something special about the neutrinos from the sun; he really seemed to understand his tank.

This kept going. He was collecting more and more data and improving the accuracy. Finally other people began to get interested. There were several new experiments in the years after this. In the 1980s, the United States got together with the Soviets and built something kind of like it down deep in a mine, but instead of using chlorine we used gallium, which is a big tank of liquid metal. The gallium would transform; the neutrinos would turn into electrons, and the gallium would turn into germanium, then we could count and collect the germanium. There was a European experiment, also, that was done with the same idea, with gallium; both of those independent experiments agreed that the number of neutrinos coming from the sun is fewer, by a factor of two in their case, or three in the chlorine case, than what we expected. So the solar neutrino puzzle is just getting bigger. It's not going away.

The Japanese entered the story with a giant water detector, a giant tank of very, very pure water. It was called Kamiokanda, deep in a mine in Japan; and again, it was a neutrino coming in, whacking into the water and making a transformation. But this time you have something extra. When the neutrino whacked into the nucleus, or the electrons, in the water tank and the transformation occurred, some energy was dumped; and that energy carried the momentum of the neutrino. If the neutrino came in from a certain direction, you had a little spray of particles going out in that direction. If the tanks are lined with detectors—actually just light detectors, big photo-multiplier tubes is the name for a big light detector—it was possible, actually, to see which direction the neutrino was coming from. So, for the first time ever, not only did we have evidence that there were neutrinos, but there was direct evidence that they really were coming from the sun.

In fact, Kamiokanda, and its second-generation upgrade, Super Kamiokanda, which is even bigger—this is gigantic, okay? It is many, many stories tall. It's like a ten-story building filled with water, and they have produced images of the sun. The images were beautiful, beautiful images, because you actually seeing the neutrinos that were coming right from the center of the sun. Then, instead of seeing the sun in light, they were seeing the sun in neutrinos. So we started to do some astrophysics. But again, they saw fewer neutrino events than they had expected, by about a factor of two or so. So everybody agreed that there was a solar neutrino puzzle. By the way, this is a little footnote. There was a tragic accident at the Super Kamiokanda facility just a year or so ago. As they were filling it back up again with water after a routine cleaning, one of the photo-multiplier tubes imploded, and the shock wave traveled through the water, created a chain reaction, and they lost thousands of these photo-multiplier tubes. It costs millions of dollars of damage, and so this wonderful detector has been shut down. Hopefully it will be rebuilt because it was a great facility, doing all sorts of good neutrino physics.

How are we going to understand this puzzle? I think that by the time all of these experiments have been put together, and they all agree with one another, no longer will they be dismissed any one as being just experimental uncertainty. There are two obvious places where we might not understand the world correctly. Maybe we don't understand the sun; maybe the standard solar model is just wrong, and there are fewer neutrinos produced in the sun than we thought.

There are various reasons why you would believe the standard solar model; it's a good, robust model. And of course, those folks were paying careful attention to these experiments. As the years went by they refined their model and came up with new tests. In recent years they came up with a lovely test. If you understand the sun, including the detailed structure of temperature as a function of distance in the sun, you can predict the resulting vibrations of the surface of the sun. It's called "helioseismography," and it's like measuring seismic vibrations on planet Earth, but we're actually watching the sun vibrate. The pattern of vibrations is very sensitively dependent on the solar model. If you change the temperature in the middle of the sun a little bit, you change the pattern of vibrations a lot, and it's working very, very well. It really seems as though we understand the sun, and we certainly know the total number of neutrinos, because we know the total brightness of the sun. So I think the standard-solar-model folks defended themselves very well, and we're almost obligated to believe what they're telling us because the data is very robust.

So what else could be wrong? It could be particle physics. Here's the wild idea that people came up with, actually, fairly early on in the story. Suppose that what I said in the beginning of this lecture, that what the minimal standard model says is wrong. Suppose that an electron-flavored neutrino, which is produced in the nuclear reaction in the sun, is traveling the long travel path from sun to earth, and as it's moving along, imagine if it could oscillate in flavor, from an electron-type neutrino to a muon-type neutrino.

Now, why would this happen? Turns out the laws of quantum mechanics say that, if you have massive neutrinos—if they're not truly massless particles—this can happen. It's one of those weird quantum things that is really hard to understand, but it comes out of the math. In fact, we've seen exactly the same thing happen before with quarks. A down quark can oscillate in flavor, if you like, into a strange quark. We have observed this phenomena. It's a fascinating phenomena in the quark world, which we haven't had time to talk about. It works in the quark world because quarks have mass.

The neutrinos need to be massive for this story to explain what's going on, and if they're massive, it's allowed to happen. The rules of quantum mechanics allow an electron-flavored neutrino to turn, spontaneously, into a muon type. In fact, it'll turn into a muon type, or a tau type, and then back again. It's a kind of a cyclic oscillation.

How am I visualizing this? You have a bunch of neutrinos leaving the sun, and they're all electron types because that's what the nuclear reactions in the sun produce. It's beta decay; beta decays produce electrons, and therefore electron neutrinos. Now they might oscillate on their way, and by the time they get to Earth half of them might be electron-flavored, and half might be muon-flavored. Every detector that I've described so far was specifically designed to look for the transformation where an electron-type neutrino produced an electron, and some other transformation. If you had a muon-type neutrino coming in, it wouldn't do a darn thing in your detector, because it doesn't have enough energy to produce the muon that it needs to produce. Muons are very, very heavy particles. So muon neutrinos would just go cruising right through your detector and the electron neutrino are the ones you would detect. That might explain why you're seeing fewer than you expected, because you're only measuring one flavor.

Okay, it's as if you go to the store and buy a pint of vanilla ice cream. As you're walking home, quantum mechanics takes over, and some of your vanilla ice cream transforms into chocolate and some into strawberry, so by the time you get home you have Neapolitan—I think it's Neapolitan—and if you only like vanilla ice cream. You say, "Hey, I bought a pint, but now I only have a third of a pint because I don't want to eat that chocolate and strawberry." It's a slightly weak analogy, but that's the basic idea here. If that's true, how could we find out? What experiment can you think of that would verify that there really are the total number of neutrinos coming out of the sun, but they're simply changing flavor?

The Canadians came up with a great idea, and they built another one of these underground neutrino detectors. It's in a little town called Sudbury; it's the Sudbury Neutrino Observatory and has the wonderful Canadian acronym SNO. SNO is designed to make the following detection. First of all, it does the same thing as all the other detectors did, it can see transformations; it's a water detector. But they also have the possibility of measuring a weak neutral current. Remember that the weak force can manifest itself in two different ways, according to the standard model. The obvious way, the way that it's been seen since the 1930s, is where a neutrino changes, transforms, into an electron; and at the same time transforms whatever it's hitting from one nucleus into another. That's the usual beta decay, weak interaction.

But Weinberg and company discovered a new force of nature. It's the weak neutral force mediated by the exchange of Z bosons. It's neutral, so there's no transformation. A neutrino just comes in, exchanges a little virtual Z boson, and whacks the nucleus. No transformation happens, just neutrino in and neutrino out. So what do you see in the laboratory? You see a nucleus just happily sitting there. Then, all of a sudden, boom! It was knocked into, by something invisible. You can detect the presence of the neutrino by this weak interaction, and all you see is just a little recoiling nucleus, which will show up as a little light signal in your detector.

So they built this thing capable of detecting, and it doesn't care what flavor neutrino you have. An electron neutrino can bump into you, a muon, or a tau-type neutrino, it doesn't matter; they will bump equally as strong. It's a low-probability event, so you have to be patient. They've been running for over a year; and, indeed, they have begun to publish their results. They're seeing the full solar neutrino flux when they look in this weak neutral sector. They're seeing them all. So the sun is, after all, behaving just as we thought. There is the full, total number of neutrinos. And, it really does look as though some of them are transforming into other types because when they only look at the electron type, they're seeing the usual reduction; but when they look at them all, with this neutral current, they see everything.

So that's big news. Okay, we seem to now have evidence that neutrinos can change flavor and therefore, according to quantum mechanics, neutrinos are massive. So now, it's a big experimental effort. There are lots of new facilities being designed, coming online, to try to pin the story down. I'm sure that in the near and distant future, you will be reading newspaper articles about neutrinos, as we discover what kinds there are, and what's the likelihood that one will transform into the other, and what's their mass. It's fun stuff, and it's also pretty esoteric stuff. I mean, I know that a perfectly legitimate reaction to all this is to say, well, it's interesting, but do we really care? I mean, why does it matter if the neutrino has mass, or doesn't have mass? So let me sort of finish up here with a discussion of a number of reasons why you might care, ranging from the, kind of, theoretical to the more applied.

The most important theoretical reason that I can argue for why you care is we have this standard model of particle physics, a framework for understanding the world. It's been around for, basically, thirty-plus years now. It says the neutrino is massless, and, once an electron neutrino, always an electron neutrino. This would be the first time—in my professional career, and in many physicists' lifetimes nowadays—that we would have a breaking of the standard model. That's a pretty big deal. If you break the standard model, then it means that our understanding of the world is really not complete, and we expect that it's not complete. So that's, you know, that's exciting. It's a shift in our worldview. It's not a complete destruction of the standard model, by any means. The whole picture still holds together. After all, in the quark sector we had up and down quarks; they were both massive. Then, in the lepton sector we had the electron and the electron neutrino, and one of them was massive. Shoot, why isn't the other one massive? It almost seems as though it should be. It seems desirable that neutrinos should have mass. It's lovely and symmetrical and would make the standard model nicer. It was a slight artifice of the physicists of the 1960s to say, "Well, the neutrino is massless." They were trying to keep the theory as simple as they possibly could do, and by making it simple, they had to make the neutrino this oddball, the massless particle. So now, what we're suggesting is maybe the neutrino isn't such an oddball; it just happens to be quite light, and it took a while for us to figure that out. So there's this breaking-of-the-standard-model aspect that makes it interesting to physicists.

Then there's the practical aspect and it's not practical in the sense of American consumers, at least, not yet. I'm not talking about neutrino TV. I am talking about an astrophysical use of neutrinos that nobody had ever even dreamed of even 20 or 30 years ago. We have now formed images of the core of the sun using neutrinos. That's a wonderful tool. It's a tool for other scientists. Now, you can start to think of all the possibilities. We can measure the inside of the sun; there's no other way to get information directly from the inside of the sun. The only reason this works is, neutrinos are formed in the middle of the sun, and then they have a tiny probability of interacting, even though the sun is hot and dense. Most of them just make it right to our detectors without hitting anything along the way. In fact, most of them go right through our detectors; that's why we need such big neutrino detectors. Light is produced in the center of the sun, and it immediately bounces around and gets absorbed by other atoms. It takes a million years for light to reach from the center of the sun to the outside. And by then, it's undergone so many interactions that we're not seeing the middle of the sun; we're seeing the edge of the sun.

You could imagine looking at a supernova, and the core of the supernova—something that's unimaginable by regular astronomy—or the center of our galaxy. So it's a tool, neutrino astrophysics. This is just now beginning. If you want to do neutrino astrophysics, though, you really better understand neutrinos. You can't do neutrino astrophysics and say, "Well, we're not sure if it has mass, or if it oscillates, because you're going to be off in your predictions about the center of some galactic phenomenon by factors of two or three, unless we figure out what the story is with the neutrinos." So this is a motivation for the particle physicists to get their story straight and figure out what's going on.

The third consequence—kind of a very large-scale consequence is cosmological. Cosmology is the study of the universe as a whole. How did it begin, the Big Bang; how did it evolve to where it is today, and where is it headed in the future? It's the big question, in a certain sense, where is the universe headed?

Remember the sun is producing these, just gigantic numbers of neutrinos every second, and it always has been; they're all flying out. Most of them just continue to fly along their merry way in straight-line path essentially forever; and every star in the universe is doing that. So the universe is just filled with neutrinos. There are an astronomically huge number of neutrinos passing through us, and there are neutrinos other than the ones coming from the sun. There are neutrinos coming all the way back from the Big Bang itself.

Now imagine, for a moment, that these neutrinos have mass. Okay? That's a new idea that we're just beginning to wrestle with. If all of those neutrinos have a tiny mass; add up a whole lot of tiny numbers, and you get a big number. Think about the effects on, say, a galaxy. It there are a whole bunch of massive neutrinos floating around, they're going to gravitationally attract. All right? Mass creates gravity. As the universe is expanding—and we are observing that it's expanding—all these massive neutrinos are pulling it back again. So if they're massive enough—we don't know yet, but if they're massive enough—they may produce enough gravity to turn around that expansion, halt it; and then we might end up with a big crunch, the opposite of the Big Bang. So the fate of the universe may rest in the hands of this exotic little wisp of a particle.

Lecture Twenty-One
Back to the Future I—Experiments to Come

Scope:

This lecture highlights some of the current issues and directions in experimental particle physics. Many physicists continue to look for small deviations in the standard model, but we are also looking farther afield, for physics beyond the expected. One of the big efforts today is a search for violations of matter/antimatter symmetry. Some such searches take place at "bottom factories," high-energy accelerator facilities redesigned to produce heavy quarks. Novel neutrino beams that travel vast distances through the earth are also under construction, as are new high-energy machines, including RHIC, designed to study the conditions of extreme density and temperature that existed a fraction of a second after the Big Bang. Plans are underway for next-generation accelerators. We'll close with the increasing role of non-accelerator physics, including the giant arrays of detectors built in the desert, tundra, and under the Antarctic ice sheet to look for ultra-high-energy cosmic rays.

> It is a capital mistake to theorize before one has data. Insensibly one begins to twist facts to suit theories instead of theories to suit facts.
>
> —Sherlock Holmes (*Scandal in Bohemia*)

Outline

I. In the last couple of lectures, we've talked about puzzles that physicists are investigating today, such as the puzzle of the Higgs boson or the mass of neutrinos. This lecture looks at some of the other directions that particle physics is taking by focusing on current programs led by experimentalists.

II. The first project we'll look at is called *CP violation*, which might be thought of as the difference between matter and antimatter.

    A. *CP violation* refers to a breaking of a symmetry that for years, many scientists believed should be present. This symmetry is between particles and anti-particles.

B. We've talked about how the weak interaction violates the symmetry of handedness. If you have a particle that's spinning in a left-handed sense and it interacts weakly, it will have a completely different interaction than a particle that is spinning in a right-handed sense. Only the weak interaction violates parity or mirror symmetry.

C. Even after the discovery of parity violation, physicists thought that matter/antimatter symmetry was an elegant symmetry of nature.

   1. Imagine that you have some heavy particle that can decay, according to quantum mechanics, in various ways. If you're working with high energy, there might be various pathways or possibilities for how the particle might fall apart.

   2. We would expect that if matter and antimatter are symmetrical, the way a particle would decay would match with the way its anti-partner would decay. Of course, the particle will decay into certain particles and the anti-particle might decay into the anti-particles, but the relative probabilities should be the same.

D. In 1964, Cronin and Fitch performed an experiment in which they looked at the decay of one of the heavy mesons now called a *kaon*.

   1. The kaon is a strange particle. Microscopically, it consists of a strange quark and an anti-down quark.

   2. Remember that a strange particle has charge $-1/3$, and a down quark has charge $-1/3$. An anti-down is $+1/3$. This kaon, then, is a neutral particle.

   3. The kaon also has various decay possibilities. A kaon decay might result in an electron and a pion. The electron would be negative and the pion would be positive so that total electric charge is conserved. The decay must also result in some electron-type neutrino to cancel the electron number that is lost. We will see the electron and the pi+, or we might see an anti-electron and a pi −, the anti-particles.

   4. We might also expect, given that we started with a neutral object, that these two results would be equally likely: matter and antimatter are symmetrical.

E. Cronin and Fitch discovered, however, a violation of symmetry. For every 1,000 times the kaon might decay in one path, it would decay 1,003 times in the other path. A great deal of data had to be collected before this tiny break in matter/antimatter symmetry was recognized.

F. How was this break built into the standard model?

    1. The answer is rather subtle and mathematical, but the general idea is as follows: The standard model includes an experimental number that must be measured, and this experiment did that measurement. You might think of this number that belongs in the standard model as telling us how much CP violation, or matter/antimatter discrepancy, there is.

    2. The number can range from 0 to 1. Zero would mean no breaking, perfect symmetry. One would mean a 100 percent breaking, absolutely no symmetry. In principle, the number could have been anything, but in practice, it's .003.

G. Physicists were amazed by this breaking of symmetry and the expansion it offered in our understanding of antimatter.

    1. We might use this knowledge to ask very basic questions, such as why the world is made of matter. Why isn't it made of antimatter or, at least, why isn't it half antimatter?

    2. If matter and antimatter are completely mirror images, then every time an event created a particle, it would be equally likely to create an anti-particle. Go back all the way to the Big Bang when all matter was originally produced from a hot bundle of energy. We should have equal numbers of electrons and anti-electrons, protons and anti-protons, and so on.

    3. Most of these would have been annihilated, and the universe today would basically just be energy. Yet the universe that we live in appears to have matter everywhere and almost no antimatter.

    4. How do we know that the sun isn't made of antimatter and we're made of matter and we're just lucky that we haven't yet touched the sun? The sun spews out particles constantly—mostly protons—in the solar wind. If they were anti-protons, there would be antimatter explosions all the time, but we don't see that. We know the sun is not made of antimatter.

5. How about other stars in our galaxy? Not only our galaxy, but even the space between galaxies, is filled with a gas, mostly hydrogen, a little helium and lithium, and other light elements. Astronomers can see light being absorbed and emitted by this gas. It also appears to be matter because cosmic rays pass through it and we don't see matter/antimatter explosions.

6. We return to the original question: Why are we here? Apparently, there's something special about matter in relation to antimatter. This is really the motivation for studying fundamental physics. An understanding of the difference between particles and anti-particles can help explain the cosmic fact that we are here.

H. Scientists have made measurements in these kaon systems starting in the 1960s and ever since and found that there is an asymmetry in the universe between matter and antimatter. That finding goes in the right direction to explaining why there is a little bit more matter than antimatter, but it doesn't go far enough. The numbers don't work out.

I. If we work out how much matter and antimatter should be left over today from the Big Bang, based on the standard model, we cannot account for the amount of matter that exists so it's still something of a puzzle. Physicists are setting up accelerator experiments to look at modern versions of this kaon decay.

III. Let's look at some other experiments that are going on today that give a sense of the kinds of topics physicists are interested in.

A. I've talked a lot about the solar neutrino puzzle and the desire of particle physicists to understand whether neutrinos have mass and whether they oscillate.

1. The accelerator at Fermilab is used in experiments that are different from those involving big tanks buried in mines. In this research, protons are smashed into a target and the resulting spray of particles is examined. Many of these particles are pions and kaons and particle/anti-particle pairs.

2. Next, magnets are set up to sweep most of the particles out of the way and leave behind a beam of, for example, positively charged pions. The energy of that beam can be controlled by tweaking the energy of the accelerator and the strength of the magnet.

3. Pions decay, and one of the results of that decay is neutrinos. The pion beam creates a beam of neutrinos, as well as electrons, muons, and other particles. If you smash these particles into a target—a wall that is 200 feet thick of steel and concrete—they are absorbed, and they come to a halt. Nothing comes out the other side of the wall except a beam of neutrinos.

4. The direction and energy of this beam can also be controlled, as can the flavor of the neutrinos. Instead of waiting for low-energy neutrinos from the sun to come and hit our detectors, we are actually able to produce many neutrino events.

B. Another topic of interest in particle physics is the ability to build higher energy machines. This has been a quest since the origins of quantum mechanics, because the higher the energy that can be achieved, the finer the microscope that results.

1. Some scientists are beginning to do research on the "next linear collider." The idea is to accelerate electrons and anti-electrons or muons and anti-muons in a giant linear machine.

2. Brookhaven has also recently built a machine, the *relativistic heavy ion collider* (RHIC), used to study both nuclear and particle physics. The idea of RHIC is to accelerate large particles, such as lead nuclei, into each other. The result is something like a pancake filled with quarks and gluons. The prediction of the standard model is that we may actually form a new state of matter, a quark-gluon plasma with certain fairly simple properties.

C. We also see developments in physics that do not involve accelerators. Some researchers are returning to the physics of the 1920s and looking at cosmic rays.

1. Cosmic rays come from a variety of sources, not just the sun. In fact, we're not even sure where all the cosmic rays come from. They might be from supernovas; they

might be from some very energetic, exotic phenomena at the center of galaxies.

2. We do know that cosmic rays are high-energy particles, mostly protons, that strike the earth's upper atmosphere, producing some kind of nuclear reaction. A proton strikes against a nucleus and produces some particles, which in turn, strike other nuclei in the atmosphere, which in turn, strike others, resulting in a shower of particles.

3. We've observed that the higher the energy you go to in looking for cosmic rays, the fewer events you get. If we wait long enough, however, we occasionally see a cosmic ray event of stupendous energy, along the lines of 10^{20} eV—billions of times more energy than we can produce.

4. Nature gives us this particle accelerator, but the bad news is that we have to wait for it and we don't know when or where it will occur. Detectors for these occurrences are built in out of the way places, such as in the desert or under the Antarctic ice sheet.

5. These ultra-high-energy cosmic rays are interesting both to cosmologists, who want to learn about the astrophysical phenomenon that produces them, and to particle physicists, who want to know what will happen in a particle physics event with 10^{20} eV of energy.

IV. We could go on about particle physics and astrophysics and experiments being performed today that boil down to looking for high-energy physics, trying to solve the puzzles in the standard model. Your job in the future will be to connect the exotic experiments and results you hear about with the elements of the standard model that we've constructed in this course.

Essential Reading:

Kane, *The Particle Garden*, Appendix C.

Barnett, Muhry, and Quinn, *The Charm of Strange Quarks*, chapter 2.11.

Recommended Reading:

Riordan, *The Hunting of the Quark*, chapter 16.

Lederman, *The God Particle*, chapter 7, section on "Slightly broken symmetry."

Wilczek and Devine, *Longing for the Harmonies*, chapter 27.

Questions to Consider:

1. If an astronomer looks at distant star, is there any way she can tell whether the star is made of matter as opposed to *entirely* of antimatter? (If not, how could we conclude that the universe is mostly matter and very little antimatter?)

2. If a physicist is interested in learning about neutrino oscillations, what are the primary advantages of using an accelerator-generated neutrino beam, rather than just looking at the naturally produced (and enormously abundant) solar neutrinos?

Lecture Twenty-One—Transcript
Back to the Future I—Experiments to Come

In the last couple of lectures, we've been talking about puzzles and phenomena that people are investigating today concerning the standard model; for example, the puzzle of the Higgs boson, or trying to understand the mass of neutrinos. These are hot topics, and the physics community, the particle-physics community, is actively investigating, both in the laboratory and in theory calculations. It is by no means the end of the story. There are an awful lot of topics that are very hot right now, in the sense of either puzzles, or curiosities, or something that's connected with this world of particle physics that we're trying to understand. In today's lecture I want to try to just give you a sense for some of these other directions that particle physicists are heading in, and I'm going to focus this lecture on the experiments and the experimental-led programs. The theorists are kind of off now on their own, looking at more exotic theories, theories beyond or beneath the standard model. And in the next lecture we'll come back and talk about where the theorists are thinking about, and where the action is. There are a whole bunch of projects going on, and I can't possibly explain all of them. What I'd like to do is begin with one that's a pretty big research program. There isn't just one group, there are many, many groups at many different accelerator facilities studying this phenomena. I'll tell you about it, and then we'll go on and talk just a little bit about a wider number of other experiments of different types.

The experiment that I want to first tell you about, or the project, goes by a really dry name. It's called, CP violation. It's a shame because physicists are usually pretty savvy about coming up with amusing or interesting names for things, part of which, I suppose, is that it makes it better when you're trying to talk to the general public. People can get more interested in a gluon than they can in CP violation. I believe that CP violation could just be called the difference between matter and anti-matter, although that's not quite technically right, and physicists shy away because it's not exactly right. CP violation refers to a breaking of symmetry that many people, for many years, believed should be present. It's symmetry we haven't talked much about, but it comes down basically to the symmetry between particles and anti-particles.

We've talked about how the weak interaction violates the symmetry of handedness. If you have a particle that's spinning in a left-handed sense, and it interacts weakly, it will have a completely different interaction than a particle that's spinning in a right-handed sense, as a right-handed, threaded, screw is different from a left-hand threaded screw. One of them will fit in the hole and the other one won't. Only the weak interaction violates parity, or mirror, symmetry. For a long time, even after the discovery of parity violation, people thought that matter-antimatter symmetry was a beautiful, elegant symmetry of nature, and there were a variety of experiments done to test this. I think it's one of those things where you ask physicists and they say, "Oh sure, it's obvious that there's no difference between matter and anti-matter". Yet, it's so obvious, but if it's not tested you really should go and look, and see whether nature does the obvious thing. Nature often has big surprises up its sleeves for us.

Let me try to get a little bit more specific about what I'm saying. Imagine that you have some particle, one of the members of the zoo, some heavy particle that can decay, and it has various, different possible decays because it's quantum mechanics. So if you have lots of energy, there might be various, different pathways or possibilities for how you might fall apart. Now what you would imagine, if matter and anti-matter were completely symmetrical, is that they way a particle decays would match the way its anti-partner decays. Of course, the particle will decay into certain particles, and the anti-particle might decay into anti-particles, but the relative probabilities should be exactly the same. There should be a deep natural symmetry between matter and anti-matter. There was an experiment done in 1964, by Cronin and Fitch, in which one looked at the decay of one of those mesons, one of those heavy mesons, called the kaon. They received the Nobel Prize for this experiment.

The kaon is a strange particle. In fact, microscopically it consists of a strange quark and an anti-down quark inside of it. Now let's just think about that for a second. Strange particle has charge minus one-third; down has minus one-third, so anti-down is plus one-third. This is a neutral particle. The kaon has total charge zero, and it has various different decay possibilities. Let me just look them up, because you never remember these things. You might see an electron and a pion come out. The electron would be negative, and the pion would be positive, so that total electric charge is conserved. There must also be some electron-type neutrino coming out, to cancel the electron number that's running away, but you won't see that in the laboratory because it's a neutrino, so it has very low probability of interacting. You see the electron and the pi plus; or, you might see an anti-electron and a pi minus, the anti-particles. You might expect, since you started with a neutral object, that it would be equally likely to go to either. Matter and anti-matter should be symmetrical. You might expect it, as everybody did, but when they did the experiment they discovered there was a violation of symmetry. It was a little bit different. It wasn't like parity, where the symmetry was broken completely. In parity we saw 100 percent left-handed neutrinos and no right-handed neutrinos. It was as broken as could be. Here, it was more like, for every thousand times it chose to decay in one path, it would decay a thousand and three times in the other path. As you can imagine, it took a long time, and a lot of statistics, before they could convince themselves that there was really a difference. Because it's quantum mechanics, you're always tossing a coin. One thing might happen or another thing might happen. You have really have to collect a lot of data before you can see such a tiny breaking of matter-anti-matter symmetry. CP, the term, comes from C, which is charge reversal and P for parity. It's a technical word, and it really doesn't matter why we call it CP, but it amounts to something that's very closely related to matter-anti-matter symmetry.

You might ask, if this phenomenon, which was observed in 1964 already, was consistent with the standard model as we know it today. The answer is yes, it's a little bit of a cheat to say that because the standard model didn't exist yet in 1964, and as we built the standard model, we made sure that it was consistent with all the data known at the time. How do you get this matter-antimatter symmetry to be broken in the standard model? The answer is rather subtle and mathematical, so let me not try to go into the details; but the point is, there is a number, an experimental number, in the standard model— it's a parameter—and you simply have to go and measure it. This experiment did that measurement, so we didn't know in advance that the standard model didn't predict this phenomenon; we simply observed it, and we wrote it down and tabulated it. You might think of this number, that belongs in the standard model, which tells you how much CP violation, or matter-anti-matter discrepancy, symmetry breaking, there is. It's a number that could range from zero to one. Zero would mean no breaking, perfect symmetry. One would mean 100 percent breaking, absolutely no symmetry between matter and anti-matter. In principle it could have been anything. In practice it's .003, a really, really tiny number, but not quite zero. It's a funny story.

You know, most people don't really come into this business with any expectations. If I told you that there's matter-anti-matter symmetry, you would have accepted it; and if I said there's not matter-anti-matter symmetry, you would have accepted. To a physicist, though, matter and anti-matter—going all the way back to the 1920s—really seemed to be mirror images. Until the breaking of mirror symmetry, it surely seemed that matter and antimatter really should be identical. To the physics community it really was kind of a shock. Maybe not quite as much of a shock as the breaking of parity, but still one that made people shake their heads and say, "This is quite amazing." We use anti-matter all the time. I don't want you to think that this is completely esoteric stuff. We make anti-matter in the laboratory; we use it in medical technology. PET scans involve the use of interaction of anti-matter with human beings, and I can easily imagine a future where our technological society will make even more use of anti-matter, so I think it is useful to understand what anti-matter is and how it works. It may even become practically useful. There's a story that 150 years ago the prime minister of England was visiting a laboratory where they were studying electricity and asked—I believe it was Michael Faraday—"Of what use is this electricity stuff?" and Michael Faraday said, "I'm not sure, sir, but someday you may tax it." That was an interesting response, kind of a techno-response that seems more contemporary than from back in the 1800s. He was quite farsighted.

We want to understand CP violation. Let me also motivate it with an even deeper question. Suppose I ask you why we are here. I'm not a religion professor, so when I ask why are we here, I'm not asking some moral or ethical question or some metaphysical question. I mean literally, why are we here? Okay? Think about it for a second. What I'm proposing to you, throughout this course, is that we have a world made of matter, particles, but why isn't it made of anti-matter? Or at least, why isn't it fifty-fifty? If matter and anti-matter are complete mirror images, if there were a perfect symmetry in nature, then every time an event created a particle, it would be equally likely to create an anti-particle. Go back all the way to the Big Bang, when all the matter was originally produced from this hot bundle of energy. You should have equal numbers of electrons and anti-electrons, protons and anti-protons, hydrogen atoms and anti-hydrogen atoms. Most of them would have then annihilated with one another, and so the universe today would basically just be a bunch of energy, a bunch of photons running around. Maybe, here and there would be a few smatterings of atoms, and a few smatterings of anti-atoms that haven't yet met. It doesn't appear to be the universe that we live in. The universe that we live in looks as though there is matter everywhere, but there's almost no anti-matter. You really have to struggle to find a few rare bits of it in cosmic rays, or in our accelerators. It would be a fair question to ask how we know that. Maybe the sun is made of anti-matter, and we're made of matter, and we just are lucky that we haven't yet touched the sun. But we have touched the sun; we do it all the time, because the sun is spewing out particles. It's called the solar wind. It consists mostly of protons, some neutrons, and some electrons, and they're all flying out and they hit our atmosphere. If they were anti-protons, there would be little anti-matter explosions going on all the time, but we don't see that. So we know the sun is not made of anti-matter, and when you look at the star, it's glowing. You can't tell, *a priori*, whether it's matter that's glowing or anti-matter; because, if matter and anti-matter are symmetrical, they glow the same.

We have this direct physical evidence that the sun is made of matter. How about other stars in our galaxy? Well, it turns out that not only our galaxy is filled with a gas, even the space between galaxies is filled with a gas. It's mostly hydrogen, a little helium and lithium and other light elements. It's tenuous, but it spreads out throughout the entire observed universe; the astronomers can see light being absorbed and emitted by this gas. It also appears to be matter because cosmic rays pass through it, and we aren't seeing little matter-anti-matter explosions anywhere. There are no boundaries anywhere in the universe, so if some stars were matter and some stars were anti-matter, there should be places in between them where you see these little explosions. Matter-anti-matter explosions are very easy to detect. If an electron and an anti-electron annihilate, they produce radiation of a very definite energy. So we would know, and it surely looks as though the universe really is made of matter. So now I ask the question again, why are we here? Why isn't it fifty-fifty? Apparently, there's something special, or better, about matter than about anti-matter. I think this is really the motivation for studying the fundamental physics. Let's look in our laboratories and understand why, and what, is the difference between particles and anti-particles so that we can explain this cosmic fact that we are here.

People have made the measurements in these kaon systems, starting in the 1960s and working their way forward, and they had this very small number. Here is the puzzle. If you work it out, there is a difference between the decays of particle and the decays—and therefore, working backwards—the production of particles and anti-particles. So there is a difference; there is asymmetry in the universe between matter and anti-matter. That goes in the right direction toward explaining why there is a little bit more matter than anti-matter, but it doesn't go far enough. The numbers don't work out. If you do the calculation, you think you understand the basic physics of the Big Bang. We think we understand the standard model, and we work out how much matter should there be today, and how much anti-matter should there be left over today from the Big Bang, based on just the standard model. What we would discover is, it should be more matter than antimatter, but not the overwhelming amount of matter that we have today. It's not a qualitative problem, but it is a quantitative problem with the standard model. People are busy setting up accelerator experiments to look at modern versions of this kaon decay. For example, instead of having a strange quark and an anti-up quark, how about if we use a bottom quark? Use bottom particles in order to study CP violation, matter-anti-matter violation, at higher energies, which begins to take us a little bit closer to the conditions of the Big Bang, so I can't tell you the answer; we don't know. We're working on it. There are lots of accelerators and lots of groups of physicists who are studying this. I imagine that when they make their discoveries, especially if it's something that disagrees with the standard model, you will hear about it. This will be one of those things that the popular press will surely pick up.

Let me leave CP violation and just spend some time telling you about a bunch of other experiments, not quite in so much detail, that are going on today, to give you a sense about the kinds of new stuff that folks are curious about and are thinking about. I've talked a lot about the solar-neutrino puzzle and the desire of particle physicists to understand whether neutrinos have mass and whether they oscillate. It's not the case that the only experiments that we've been doing involve building a big tank, of water or cleaning fluid, burying it in a mine, and sitting and waiting patiently. We have also decided to take a more proactive approach. If you have a particle accelerator, such as

Fermilab, and you take that proton beam, normally you smash the protons and anti-protons together. You have a lot of energy, and you produce a whole bunch of particles. Typically, you analyze all those particles to learn some particle physics with them. Another thing you might do is just to take those protons and smack them into a wall. You're going to put a lot of energy into the wall; you're going to produce a whole spray of particles. Many of them will be pions, kaons, and particle/antiparticle pairs, and you could start setting up some magnets. With magnets, different particles follow different paths, so you can sweep most of the particles out of the way and leave behind one little beam of, let's say, positively charged pions. Now you have a beam of positively charged pions, and you can control the energy of that beam by tweaking the energy of your accelerator and of the magnet. Pions decay, and one of the things that they decay into is neutrinos.

So imagine that you run this pion beam for a while; it's creating a beam of neutrinos as well as other stuff, electrons, for example; muons. Then you put another wall in front of them and this time it's thick - maybe 100 or 200 feet of steel and concrete. The particles smash into the wall become absorbed and dump their energy. They heat the wall up just a little bit, and they come to a halt, you still have another couple hundred feet of concrete to go. What's going to come out the back? Absolutely nothing; this is the biggest, most secure radiation-prevention system that you could imagine, except the neutrinos will make it through. Now you have a beam of neutrinos, and you can control the direction of the beam of neutrinos by controlling the direction of your original pion beam. You can aim those neutrinos at something, and you can change their energy. You can even, if you're clever, decide whether you want a beam that's all electron-flavored neutrinos or all muon-flavored neutrinos, by controlling the original particles that you started with. So this is great stuff. Instead of just kind of waiting for these low-energy neutrinos from the sun to come and hit our detector—first of all, these are very high-energy neutrinos, and the higher the energy, the stronger the weak force of nature appears; it interacts with more probability— these neutrino detectors are now getting many, many, many events. So, it's actually getting easier to detect neutrinos in this way because they have higher energy and, therefore, higher probability.

This program is just starting; we have some preliminary data. There are a whole bunch of accelerators around the world that are trying to do this. If you want to learn about the properties of neutrinos, if you want to learn whether they change from one flavor to another, you have this very beautifully controlled experiment now. You can start to figure out exactly how it's all working, and what the energy dependence is, and all that good stuff. In fact, there's an experiment that they're working on, where they take that beam of neutrinos and they just beam it right down into the earth. There's a beam at the end of Fermilab, in Chicago, that's just pointing down into the earth at an angle, and so everything gets absorbed except the neutrinos, which are now traveling into the earth at an angle. They're cutting a chord through planet Earth, and they're aimed carefully so that they come out in Minnesota where they've set up a big detector. You have got this huge distance, right? One of the things we would like to mock up is the huge distance between the sun and the earth, to explain the solar-neutrino puzzle. That's a really long distance. If we can get that one to work, we might even be able to beam them all the way through to Japan. It's kind of wild stuff; and this is now physics of the future.

Another possibility, of course, in the world of particle physics which people are very interested in is the ability to build higher energy machines. It's always been a quest, ever since the first origins of quantum mechanics. The higher the energy you go to, the finer microscope you have. You're learning about new particles; you're learning about the substructure of the existing particles. People always want to go to higher energies. In the United States, Fermilab is the biggest, highest-energy machine we have, and there are no immediate plans for a higher-energy-still machine. We are starting to do research on what some people are calling the "next linear collider." That would be the next-generation experiment or facility. It's—nobody's working on the Superconducting Supercollider anymore, because Congress definitely ended that one. So one of the key ingredients is not to make it quite so expensive. The next linear collider; the word linear refers to a straight line instead of a big circle, such as Stanford. Stanford was such a successful machine, the idea here was to accelerate either electrons or anti-electrons in some giant linear machine, or maybe even muons and anti-muons, which would give you even more wallop. This would be a great way to produce ultra-high energies in a very small region of space.

This is a very international collaboration; I think there's a lot more political savvy, now, about what it takes to get a big, high-energy facility constructed all the way through to completion; we will see. I'm sure that as this makes progress beyond the research and development stage, and people are actually seeking funding in the hundreds-of-millions to billions-of-dollars range in Congress, there will probably be articles, and you'll have to decide if you want your local senator to vote for or against this machine. So it's nice to have some sense of what's coming up.

We have just recently built a new machine. It's not quite a particle physics machine; it's kind of a machine that studies both nuclear and particle physics, so it's not trying to go to ultra-high-energies, exactly. It's called RHIC, the Relativistic Heavy Ion Collider. It's in Brookhaven, Long Island, in the existing Brookhaven National Lab facility. The idea of RHIC was, instead of accelerating an electron, or a proton, in a big accelerator to take the biggest thing possible, such as the lead nucleus then accelerate two lead nuclei and smash them one into another. It's an extraordinarily high-energy machine, but the real big deal is not to go to higher energies, but to go to high density. It's another regime in physics that we really haven't explored. It's walking away from simplicity and heading more in the direction of complexity. Lots of physicists are interested in what happens when complicated systems interact and how they behave. In fact, the purpose of most of physics, and most of science is to understand complicated things. One of the lucky and beautiful things about particle physics, in general, is that we get to study the absolutely simplest things. We can all be simpletons about our science. At RHIC, they're going to take, basically, a highly relativistic lead nucleus, and another highly relativistic lead nucleus, or gold on gold; a variety of things can be accelerated then smack them together; you'll get a little pancake. It will be a pancake filled with quarks and gluons. The prediction of the standard model is that we may actually form a new state of matter. You have solid, liquid, and gas. This is a quark-gluon plasma, which would have properties that the standard model says are actually fairly simple. When you have that much stuff that close together—remember, the strong force gets weaker when particles are close together—it should actually be almost like a free-particle gas. We think that we have some ideas of what to expect, but there will surely be many surprises. That's another direction of high-energy physics in the near future. They're just online now. They've been collecting data for a year or so, and I expect to see news coming out of these facilities.

There's also physics going on that you might call non-accelerator. The accelerator is a wonderful laboratory, a tool for studying high-energy physics. We migrated towards the accelerator starting in the 1930s, all the way up through today, because of the control and the high energy that it gives us. It's like a giant magnifying glass that magnifies; the higher the energy, the finer the magnification, but you can also just go back to the old physics of the 1920s, and look at cosmic rays. In a certain sense, that's what those neutrino folks are doing. They build a detector deep in a mine, and they just wait for the solar neutrinos to come through them.

People are also thinking about just good old cosmic rays, the stuff that rains down on us all the time. Cosmic rays come from a variety of sources, not just from the sun. In fact, we're not even sure where all the cosmic rays are coming from. It might be from supernovas; it might be from some very energetic, exotic phenomena at the center of galaxies. What we know is that there are high-energy particles, mostly protons, which strike the earth's upper atmosphere, and when they hit the upper atmosphere, there's some kind of nuclear reaction; it's called a shower. The proton strikes against a nucleus and produces some particles, which in turn strike other nuclei up in the atmosphere. They, in turn strike, others and others, and you get a shower of many, many particles. The higher energy you start with, the more particles you will end up with here on planet Earth. That's the origin of the cosmic rays that were discovered and understood way back in the 1930s.

In those days, they would send up an emulsion in a balloon. They would go up to a certain height and see some small event. Typically the energies associated with those events were rather small: MeVs, millions of electron-volts, small by modern standards of accelerators. But cosmic rays are random, and we've been looking ever since. We haven't completely abandoned cosmic-ray research, and what we've observed are a whole bunch of cosmic rays at low energy. There are some cosmic rays at higher energy, and a few at even higher energy. The higher energy you have, the fewer events result. We haven't found a cutoff yet, so if you're patient, and you wait long enough, every now and again you can see a cosmic-ray event of stupendous energy. We're talking you know, 10^{20} electron-volts; billions upon billions of times greater energy than the energy that we can produce at Fermilab, or even with the Superconducting Supercollider. It's as if nature had produced this particle accelerator for us, and that's the good news; it's free, but you have to wait; and that's the bad news. At Fermilab you get millions per second, and in the cosmic accelerator you may have to wait for a year, and then you don't know where it's going to be. Where are you going to build your detector? The trick is, just to pick some out-of-the-way place, where land is cheap. You go out to the desert, or the tundra, or under the ocean, or under the Antarctic ice sheet, and you build a big detector, and you just wait.

This has been going on for some time and there are lots of new projects being constructed. Frequently these projects are collaborative with Third World countries; sometimes that's where the facilities are actually being built. It's a nice opportunity for a country that doesn't have the financial resources to build a giant accelerator or detector, to nonetheless develop really contemporary high-energy physics research. These ultra-high-energy cosmic rays are interesting both to the cosmologists, who want to know where the heck these things are coming from—"What kind of astrophysical phenomenon is producing these high-energy rays?"—and to the particle physicists who say, "Hey, what's going to happen if you have a particle physics event with 10^{20} electron-volts of energy? One of the experiments being designed is under the Antarctic ice sheet. You just basically put detectors down there, and it's as though the ice sheet itself were a giant bubble chamber. If the particles strike the ice sheet and they produce a shower, they will produce a little bit of light; and you can spread this thing out over hundreds of square miles. It turns out that beneath the snow pack, the ice itself is very optically transparent, so once you create a photon, it will travel a long distance. That's really what you want. If you want to see a high-energy event, it's going to spread out over very large distances. So, kind of wild stuff is going on there, too.

I could just keep going. I could go for entire lectures about all the particle physics, and astrophysics, and connection experiments that are going on today, that boil down to looking for high-energy physics, trying to pin down the details and the puzzles that still exist in the standard model. I wish I could tell you about all of them. I think what I have to leave you with is the sense that, when you go out, you will certainly see these things and it may be something I've never mentioned. Something such as a magnetic monopole search, or a dark-matter search, or a search for gravity waves or a search for large extra dimensions. These are exotic names. I guess what I would like for you to walk away from this course with is the understanding that we do have this framework, the standard model, that you can hang this exotic new physics on. Whatever we find is going to fit into this picture that we've developed, most likely. It's a very robust picture, the standard model. It's extremely successful, quantitatively. And so, no matter what kind of cool, exotic, new stuff we find, your job, then, is to hook it in and say, "Ah yes, this connects with the Higgs, or the neutrino mass, or the zoo of fundamental particles. I think that's part of the fun because there are going to be all sorts of new experiments coming out that I can't even dream of today.

Lecture Twenty-Two
Back to the Future II—Puzzles and Progress

Scope:

If the standard model is such a great success, why are many physicists looking beyond it for some deeper and more fundamental theory of nature? Their reasons fall into the categories of practicality, aesthetics, and mathematics. None of these is, by itself, convincing proof that such a deeper theory exists, but taken together, they make it hard to believe that we're at the end of the line. Where are we headed next? We must begin with the missing link of gravity. We'll talk about issues of simplicity, unification, and grand unification. Then, we'll look at two conceptual developments that, to many physicists, seem to be the best candidates for new physics. We'll look at both supersymmetry and the new and highly promising theory of strings.

> I know that this defies the law of gravity, but, you see, I never studied law.
>
> —Bugs Bunny

Outline

I. In the last lecture, we talked about the directions that particle physics is taking in the world of experiments. In this lecture, we'll see that theorists are also looking to go beyond or beneath the standard model. We have several theoretical hints that the standard model, beautiful and successful as it is, is not the final story. In fact, for a number of reasons, it can't be.

   A. You may have noticed that I have left one topic—gravity— out of this story almost throughout the course. Gravity is a fundamental force of nature and the one that is most obvious to us.

      1. Newton's description of the force of gravity was fairly simple and, over the years, quite successful. In 1915, Newton's theory was deepened by Einstein with the general theory of relativity.

2. Newton's theory left open the question of why the force of gravity is present between two massive objects, but Einstein gave us a geometrical picture of space-time that allowed us to understand this attraction.

B. You might think that we could merge these two theories—the standard model of particle physics, which explains all the forces of nature except gravity, and the general theory of relativity, which includes gravity. The result would be a complete description of the world.

C. The problem, though, is that Einstein's general theory of relativity is inconsistent with quantum mechanics. It is not a quantum field theory; it's a classical theory of nature.

    1. Gravity does obey relativity, which is necessary for any correct theory of nature as far as we know today, but it doesn't, for example, satisfy the Heisenberg uncertainty principle. There is some mathematical contradiction between general relativity and quantum physics.

    2. Gravity hasn't played a significant role in our study, because it affects only big objects. In fact, despite the attraction that we feel on earth, gravity is the weakest force. The attraction of individual atoms is miniscule, but it adds up so that we feel the force.

    3. Think of a hydrogen atom. It has a proton and an orbiting electron. The electron is held in orbit by an electrical attraction. Electricity is not a particularly strong force of nature, but if we compare the electrical attraction of the electron to the proton with the gravitational attraction, the ratio is 10^{36}.

    4. That tiny effect is almost unnoticeable, and it's also why physicists have not really addressed the idea that gravity is inconsistent with quantum mechanics.

    5. Some particle physics theorists, however, have begun to wonder if a fundamental theory of nature can be found that would be consistent with both quantum mechanics and general relativity.

6. The study of black holes, for example, requires such a connection. Black holes are particle-like, involving quantum mechanics, but they're also heavy, which brings in gravity. The same is true for the study of cosmology. Once again, the distance scales are incredibly small, but the energy density is very high.

II. Let's turn to another topic, called *supersymmetry*, that theorists are exploring to try to come up with a deeper theory of nature.

    A. We have found and worked out all the possible geometrical symmetries that are available in space-time, such as translational symmetry, parity, and matter/antimatter symmetry. They are all either realized or broken in some way, but they're all relevant in the theory of gravity or particle physics, except for one, supersymmetry.

    B. We can think of supersymmetry as analogous to matter/antimatter symmetry, that is, as a "pretty good" symmetry of nature.

        1. Imagine a symmetry between fermions and bosons. Remember the difference between these two: Fermions—electrons, protons, and quarks—are like particles; they don't sit on top of each other. Bosons, such as photons and the other force carriers, will sit on top of each other.

        2. What if these two kinds of particles were completely symmetrical? What if there was some intimate connection between them, just as there is an intimate connection between protons and anti-protons?

        3. This is the question of supersymmetry: Does every particle have a partner that has a different spin but is otherwise almost the same? We know that a top quark has an anti-partner, the anti-top quark, but does it have a supersymmetric partner? We currently have no evidence for super partners for any of the existing particles.

        4. The names for these partner particles, if they're discovered, will be whimsical. For the fermions, the partner of a quark will be a *squark* and the partner of a top quark will be a *stop squark*. For the bosons, the partner of a photon will be a *photino*, and so on.

C. Theorists have begun working out the mathematical consequences of supersymmetry and made some interesting discoveries.

    1. They've discovered, for example, that if supersymmetry exists, we can add it to the standard model. In fact, the model tells us a little bit about the behavior and properties of these particles.

    2. For example, we would expect to produce these particles at an energy of around a trillion eV. Our next generation of particle accelerators at Fermilab and the large hydron collider in Europe should be able to produce supersymmetric particles if they exist.

III. Probably the most exciting explorations in the world of theoretical particle physics are in the complex field of *string theory*.

    A. Let me try to give you an idea about string theory by asking: What is the single most fundamental idea of particle physics? Your answer might be that the world is made of particles.

    B. That's what particle physics is based on. QCD and the electroweak theory postulate a world filled with point-like objects. We can't visualize a point because it is a mathematical entity, but we can attribute certain properties to it, such as charge, mass, and spin. We can then make calculations about these particles according to the rules of quantum field theory.

    C. String theory asserts that perhaps the world is not made of points. Maybe the fundamental constituents, the building blocks, are actually little lines or strings. A constituent might be a little line with two ends, or a closed loop, like a doughnut.

    D. The most significant aspect of this theory is that it would allow the whole universe to be understood in terms of just one string. In string theory, we don't have many different kinds of fundamental particles. There is only the string, and all objects are made of string. The theory is as unified as it could possibly be.

1. An up quark might be thought of as a string that vibrates in a particular pattern. A different, more energetic pattern might be a charm quark.
2. The forces, too, would be understood to come from the string.

E. String theory also addresses the problem of renormalizability in the standard model.
1. Remember that some calculations in particle physics result in mathematical infinities that must be renormalized. In string theory, there are no such infinities.
2. The infinities in the standard model spring from the assumed existence of physically point-like particles. Points can get arbitrarily close to each other, and the closer they get, the stronger the fields become. If the particles are infinitely close, the calculations can go all the way to the limit of infinite fields. Strings, however, spread out over some distance, which can never get any smaller than the size of the string itself.

F. What is a string made of? String theorists postulate the existence of a string, but it's not made of anything. It is not, for example, made of "string atoms," which would be fundamental particles.

G. How do strings interact?
1. In the current standard model, we can imagine two particles interacting as they move along and creating, spontaneously, a virtual photon that travels between them.
2. In string theory, two strings move along and, at a certain point, they come together. Perhaps they sort of fold together to form one larger string for a brief moment, then that one string might split apart again into two strings. That might be the interaction of two fundamental particles.
3. In our contemporary language, the intermediate state describes particles and virtual particles, but in string theory, there was never anything but strings interacting. Further, there are never any infinities because the size of the string is limiting.

H. What is the size of a string? String theorists can actually put a number on it, a number that comes from another idea that is bothersome in particle physics.

   1. Remember that the electric and weak forces are unified at a high energy scale—trillions of eV. But also recall that we have not yet determined whether the strong force is unified with electricity and the weak force. Right now, we assert that the forces are different, but might they, in fact, merge together at some ultra-high energy?

   2. Once scientists thought about this *grand unification*, they also wondered about the inclusion of gravity. We can even estimate the energy at which all these forces might come together, which is about 10^{19} GeV.

   3. Quantum mechanics says that an ultra-high-energy scale corresponds to a tiny distance, and that's the size of the string.

IV. String theory offers the possibility of an ultimate unified theory in which all physical observables can be computed from a mathematical framework.

   A. In working with the mathematics, we have found that supersymmetry is a consequence of string theory. The theorists are, in a sense, making a prediction about the existence of supersymmetric particles, which begins to place the theory in the realm of physics.

   B. String theory also predicts the theory of general relativity as a low-energy effective theory. That is to say that the mathematics of strings predicts Einstein's general theory of relativity.

   C. Finally, string theory has some strange aspects. For example, in order to make the theory mathematically consistent, it has to be true that strings live in more than three spatial dimensions. That would mean that other dimensions exist that we haven't noticed yet.

   D. String theory has the potential to be the greatest revolution in physics since the discovery of relativity and quantum mechanics. It is not yet fully developed, but it is definitely a topic to take note of.

Essential Reading:

Kane, *The Particle Garden*, chapters 9–11.

Weinberg, *Dreams of a Final Theory*, chapter IX.

Barnett, Muhry, and Quinn, *The Charm of Strange Quarks*, chapters 9.3–9.5.

't Hooft, *In Search of the Ultimate Building Blocks*, from chapter 22 on.

Recommended Reading:

Greene, *The Elegant Universe*, Part III. (A great book—take your time and read the whole thing!)

Lederman, *The God Particle*, first half of chapter 9, through the section on superstrings.

Calle, *Superstrings and Other Things*, chapter 25, sections on "GUTS" and "Superstrings."

Krauss, *Fear of Physics*, chapter 6.

Wilczek and Devine, *Longing for the Harmonies*, Tenth Theme.

Questions to Consider:

1. Given the successes of the standard model and the arguments that something may exist "beyond" the standard model, what are your feelings about looking for such new and exotic physics, requiring significant commitments of taxpayer-supported funding and physicists' time?

2. Look up the size (length) of a superstring. How many times smaller than a proton is that? Can you make up some kind of analogy in the form "String size is to a proton as proton size is to _____"?

3. What would you call the supersymmetric partner of each of the quarks? (Remember the top's partner is the *stop*) Can you pronounce them all?

Lecture Twenty-Two—Transcript
Back to the Future II: Puzzles and Progress

In the last lecture, we talked about the direction in which particle physics is going in the world of experiments, and about the exotic experiments that are trying to probe the puzzles and corners of the standard model. Theorists are also very busy, and the big question here is, what's beyond, or beneath, the standard model? There are lots of hints—no direct evidence whatsoever, but lots of theoretical hints—that perhaps the standard model, beautiful and successful as it is, is not the final story. It's not the last chapter in our understanding of the world. So today I want to talk about some of these, both the motivations and the wild ideas, the speculative ideas of the particle physicists today.

There is one, perhaps the most, compelling reason for me to argue to you that the standard model not only is not the final story, but it can't be. Okay. It cannot be the ultimate theory of nature, and, you may have actually noticed that there's one thing I've left off this whole story, almost throughout the entire course, and that is gravity. Where's gravity in this story? It's a force of nature that's very fundamental; we live with it every day. In fact, of all the forces of nature, everything I've been talking about, the one that's the most obvious to all of us, the one that we live with, is gravity. I haven't said word one about it. I use it as a metaphor, when I talk about the old physics of planetary systems, and Isaac Newton. Well, Isaac Newton did figure out gravity to a certain extent. He wrote down a formula, which explained it—I shouldn't say explained—described how gravity works, in a fairly simple way. Over the years it was actually very successful. It was successful in explaining planetary motion, and it was successful enough for us to get people to land on the moon, and for probes to land on Mars and Venus. The theory of gravity developed by Newton is a great and successful theory; and in 1915, it was modified, deepened, incredibly and radically, by Albert Einstein. This post-special theory of relativity is called the General Theory of Relativity, so Albert Einstein, you could argue, fixed up the theory of gravity. Not that there was really anything wrong with it, until you pushed the theory of gravity off to some sort of extreme, as near a black hole or in the early universe.

Albert Einstein's theory didn't just push the extremes; it also went a level deeper. You could always ask the question, why? Why is the force of gravity present between two massive objects? Isaac Newton doesn't tell you why; he just tells you how it is. He describes the world. Albert Einstein went much further in explaining why. He gave us a geometrical picture of space-time, in which we could really understand why massive objects attract one another. They warp the geometry of space-time then follow the path of least resistance, in a certain sense. You can always ask, but why? You can always think that there might be another layer deeper. Nobody found anything beyond Albert Einstein's General Theory of Relativity, at least until some of the modern speculations that I'm going to discuss.

So, what's the situation here? We've got the standard model of particle physics I've been telling you all about, on the one hand, which explains all forces of nature, except gravity; then, on the other hand, there's Albert Einstein's General Theory of Relativity, which explains gravity. Now, you might say, "Well, that's fine. We have these two theories, and when we put them together and we call that the standard model. Now we've described everything because after all, the standard model tells you what all the particles are. Einstein doesn't change that; there are still quarks and leptons. We have a theory of all the other forces; we have a theory of gravity, and everything is successful. The theory of gravity describes our solar system; Isaac Newton's laws are the correct approximation for Albert Einstein's laws of gravity in the regime of ordinary masses. You can also test general relativity by going to some super extremes, or by going to very, very high precision. You discover that Newton's laws just begin to break down in the nth decimal place, then you need general relativity.

There's a deep problem still. You can't just tack the two theories together and say, "That's our model of the world because Albert Einstein's General Theory of Relativity is inconsistent with quantum mechanics." It is not a quantum field theory; it's a classical theory of nature. It does obey relativity, which is important and necessary for any correct theory of nature, as far as we know today; but it doesn't, for example, satisfy the Heisenberg Uncertainty Principle, which is experimentally verified. There's something contradictory, mathematically contradictory, between general relativity and quantum physics, so it cannot be the case that we completely understand the world.

So far it hasn't mattered a hoot, because when do you worry about gravity? You worry about gravity when you're looking at big things. I mean, the theory of gravity describes the weakest force of all. Gravity is truly a weak, weak, weak force. You're probably thinking, I don't understand: gravity's a pain in the neck. Right? Gravity is the strongest force I can think of, and the only reason you think that is because you just happen to be born right next to a really big planet. Okay? The only reason you think gravity is strong, is because, just by coincidence, we all live next to this gigantic ball of rock. Every atom in the planet Earth attracts us. And, that attraction is really miniscule. It is almost immeasurably miniscule. It's only because there are so many of them, and they all add up, that we've ever even noticed gravity. If we had been born and raised on some starship floating around in outer space, we wouldn't, maybe, even know about gravity unless we'd started looking at planets going in orbit. Certainly, in particle physics experiments, there is no way we would have ever noticed gravity.

Think of a hydrogen atom, a proton and an electron, and the electron's going around in orbit. Why? Why doesn't it fly away? It doesn't fly away because of an electrical attraction. Now, electricity is not a particularly strong force of nature; the strong nuclear force is much stronger. But, compare the electrical attraction of the electron to the proton with the gravitational attraction, and the difference is 10^{36}. Now, I can't even think of that number. It's a billion, billion, billion, billion times less gravitational force than electrical force. There's such a tiny effect that nobody would ever even think of worrying about it, or noticing it. There's not even a conceivable particle-physics experiment, to date, that comes anywhere close to caring about gravity. This is why physicists have not really worried about the fact that gravity is inconsistent with quantum mechanics. You see, quantum mechanics is only important when you're looking at little things; when you look at little things you don't care about gravity. They have been disconnected in the laboratory, so the fact that they're mathematically inconsistent hasn't worried people. Well, it hasn't worried too many people, but the particle theorists have begun to wonder whether there is, in fact, a fundamental theory of nature that would be consistent with both.

It's partly just mathematical, or aesthetic, argument compelling us to look for a truly unified theory. It's also the case that if, for instance, you're interested in black holes, very exotic, but real—at least we believe they're real, there is some astronomical evidence that these things are real objects—black holes really require that you know both quantum mechanics and general relativity, or gravity and the other forces. Everything is put together. They're tiny, they're particle like; you need to worry about quantum mechanics, but they're heavy, so you also have to worry about gravity. It's the same thing if you're interested in cosmology, the study of the universe as a whole, and in particular its origin, the Big Bang because once again, there is this incredibly small distance scale, with very high energy density. Putting those two things together means you need gravity and quantum physics.

These are motivations for looking beyond the standard model. The standard model cannot be consistent in this way, so we need some new theory of nature. It's also true, just forgetting about gravity, as I've already talked about some of the reasons why you might be curious. For instance, there are so many unknowns, 23 numbers that you have to go out into the laboratory and measure, before you can start making predictions. There are so many particles, six quarks and six leptons; and they even start to form these little lovely patterns of increasing mass, and are duplicating generation two and generation three of the particles, which are like photocopies of the lighter ones. What's all that about? Okay? All of these things lead us to try to come up with some other, deeper theory of nature. Let me tell you about some of the ideas - two, in particular, that are being bandied about right now. I say it loosely; actually these are intense fields of theoretical research and lots of particle physicists are spending their careers trying to think about what this new physics might look like.

The first new idea—and it's not really a complete idea, it's a part of the second idea I want to tell you about—goes by the name of supersymmetry. I have to laugh a little bit, because as I said, physicists are over using this word "super", but, when we were studying the nature of space-time and particle physics, we were discovering all these symmetries of nature. Some of them were geometrical, like translational symmetry, which says the laws of physics are the same in different places; and there is time-translation symmetry, which says that the laws of physics are symmetric when you look at different times. Then there were these more abstract symmetries, such as mirror or parity symmetry, or matter-anti-matter symmetry. The mathematicians have been able to actually work out all the possible geometrical symmetries that are available in space-time and found them all. They are all either realized or broken in some way, but they're all relevant in the theory of gravity and/or particle physics—except for one. One symmetry remained that had never played any role in the theory; and it's now called "supersymmetry."

The easiest way—it's very mathematical, I can't, sort of, give you a geometrical explanation of supersymmetry—the way I think about it is an analogy to matter-anti-matter, just as that's a pretty good symmetry of nature. Imagine, imagine if there was symmetry between particles that we call fermions and particles we call bosons. That is to say, spin one-half, the fermions, and an integer such as zero, or one, or two, the bosons. Remember the difference between fermions and bosons. Fermions are kind of particle-y. They are the particle-y particles. They are the ones that don't like to sit on top of each other. Electrons, and protons, and quarks - pretty much anything you think of as a particle is a fermion. The bosons are the ones that do like to sit on top of each other. For example, light is perfectly happy—you can have two photons sitting in the same place at the same time. In fact, all of the force-carrying particles are bosons. The gluons, the photons, even the W and Z particles. Whether they're massive or not.

You have these two kinds of particles in the world. The particles and the force carriers, and what if they were completely symmetrical? What if there was some intimate connection, just as there's an intimate connection between a proton and an anti-proton? That's supersymmetry. It's an idea, just an idea. Is it real? Is there really a partner, of every particle out there that has a different spin, but is otherwise almost the same? Let's go look. Suppose that you took a quark, like a top quark, and asked, does it have a supersymmetric partner? It has an anti-partner, the anti-top quark, but does it have something with a different spin that is otherwise almost the same? The answer is no, there's no evidence for super-partners of any of the existing particles.

I have to tell you about the naming convention, because it's kind of whimsical, and you may be hearing about super-particles in the future, if these things are real, if we do discover them; so here's the convention. If you have a particle of spin one-half, and you're talking about its super-partner—which would have an integer spin, like spin zero—then you get the name by just adding an S on the front. It's the super-partner, so you add an S on the front. So the partner of a quark is a squark. The partner of a top quark is a stop squark. It's embarrassing, and when you start thinking about all of them, some of them are pretty goofy. The partner of a neutrino would be a sneutrino, but that's the convention for all the existing fermions. If you have a boson, there's a different naming convention; we add an "ino" at the end. I kind of like that because I become a Steverino, assuming I'm a boson. A photon becomes a photino. A gluon's partner would be a gluino. So what am I saying? It's like having a proton and an anti-proton. They're not the same thing, but they're connected, they're partners, they're symmetrical. Now we're saying a photon would have a partner in the universe, a photino, which has a different spin. It's a different particle, but they're somehow connected. So people are looking for super-particles.

The theorists have begun working out the mathematical consequences. What if supersymmetry really is symmetry of nature? They've discovered some very interesting things. First of all, they've discovered that, if this is true, we can fix up the standard model. We don't toss it. Instead, we just add the super-partners, and in fact, the model almost already tells you how they're going to behave, and what their properties are. Not completely, so the theorists are still struggling, and working to try to understand, what would a photino be like? One of the things that they have concluded is, in order for the mathematics to all be consistent, these super-partners can't be super-duper heavy, to use the technical word, but they can't be as light as the existing particles, because otherwise we would have already seen them. So it's a kind of a Goldilocks thing, they can't be too heavy and they can't be too light; and in fact the region of energy where we expect them is around a trillion electron-volts. So our next generation of particle accelerators: Fermilab, and in particular the laboratory being built in Europe, the LHC, the Large Hadron Collider, will be able to produce supersymmetric particles if they exist. So that's, you know, another one of those things that you can expect to see in the newspaper. It'll be a big deal. It would be a whole new family of particles. If we found them, it would be a radical, radical revision, but still not a scrapping of the standard model.

Now, this is all kind of fun and interesting stuff for particle physics, but that's not really where the action is right now. The big action, in the world of theoretical particle physics, is in a field which is called string theory. I think string theory has actually reached the popular media. There have been some nice books that try to present string theory in terms like in this course that are intuitive. It's a pretty difficult mathematical theory. In fact, compared to relativistic quantum field theory, that's kindergarten stuff compared to string theory. The mathematics is really horrendous. It would take me—I would have to dedicate many years of my life, just to learn the math that's required to become a string theorist. So I haven't done that; so what I'm telling you about is what I know from reading colloquia, but not from actually doing the calculations myself, unlike many of the topics in particle physics, which I have studied myself.

So what is the idea of string theory? Let me ask you, what is the basic, single, most fundamental idea of particle physics? I would say, it's that the world is made of particles. Okay? That's what particle physics says; everything else is detail. The world is made of particles. It goes all the way back to Mr. Democritus's idea of how the world is built. That's what particle physics is based on. Quantum chromodynamics and the electroweak theory postulate a world filled with little point-like objects. You can't visualize a point, it's a mathematical entity. You attribute properties to the points: charge, mass, spin; and then you start calculating according to the rules of quantum field theory, which is a theory of points. So that's the basic idea of particle physics as I have been describing it to you.

String theory says, maybe the world is not made of little points. Maybe the fundamental constituents, the building blocks, are actually somehow little lines, little strings. They might be a little line with two N's, or they might actually be a little loop, like a little doughnut of some kind. It's a, kind of a wild idea, but if you can believe that the world is made of points, I suppose you can also believe that the world is made of little strings, running around interacting with one another. Now why is this such a great idea? First of all, it's generalizable. Once you start thinking about little strings, you can start asking about little sheets, or little balls, in higher and higher dimensions. And in fact, string theorists are heading in that direction, and that generalization is called M theory. That's the buzzword. I don't want to go into any of those details. Let's just talk about the basic idea here.

The beautiful thing, the amazing thing about string theory is, there is just one string. That's it. The whole universe can be understood in terms of the string. Okay? It's not like you have an up quark particle, and a down quark particle, and an electron particle, and each one of those is a completely distinct kind of point—so that's why we're a little bit unhappy with the standard model, there's so many different kinds of fundamental particles. Now we have this theory, which is as unified as it could possibly be. There is only the string, and all objects are made of string. So, for example, what's an up quark? Imagine a little string that vibrates in one particular pattern; one pattern might be an up quark. A different, more energetic pattern might be a charm quark. A different pattern might be an electron, or even a W boson. Everything, not just the particles, but the forces, are all understood in string theory to come from the string. It's just, you know, as a mathematician, or from an aesthetic point of view, you can see the appeal of this idea. And now the question is, is it physics? Can you really make mathematical equations? Can you work it out, and decide whether this is in fact a correct, accurate, quantitative description of nature?

At the moment, string theory really is a mathematical theory. It is not, yet, in my personal opinion, physics; in the sense that there are very few direct physical predictions that string theory can make. People are still working on the basic structure of the theory. It's kind of, to my mind, a little bit like Niels Bohr in 19—early 1910s, who is trying to piece together a theory of quantum physics, but he doesn't know quantum mechanics yet. He's trying to create quantum mechanics, but he doesn't have all the tools, he doesn't have all the ideas, he doesn't have all the data yet. And, so he's just forming a tentative theory, the beginnings of quantum mechanics. And I see string theory, now, as a formative science, and it may pan out, or it may not. It—we're going to have to check it out, and see whether it does. But let me tell you some of the great things about string theory, because there's been a lot of effort.

It's quite recent business. Okay? People started thinking about strings, I don't know, in the '70s and '80s; and there wasn't really a whole lot of activity until really the 1990s. So this is really a very recent theoretical phenomenon. Let me tell you about a few of the amazing things. First of all, one of the problems that we all have with the standard model, one of the things we don't really like about the standard model, is this renormalizability thing. Remember what renormalizability meant. If you have a theory of point particles, and you work out, what is the effect of virtual particle-antiparticle creation, which is a part of quantum mechanics, you discover that you get infinite contributions to your theory, mathematical infinities which you have to sweep under the rug. It's not quite a cheat, but it's almost a cheat. There are few things that you cannot compute in the standard model, like the mass of an electron. There's just no way, in the model, to compute that physical quantity. You've just got to go out and measure it.

In string theory, there are no such infinities. It turns out that the origin of the infinities, the reason why you have to worry about renormalizability, is because you've got points, and points can get arbitrarily close to one another. And the closer they get, the stronger the fields get; and you can go all the way to the limit of infinite fields, if the particles are infinitely close. That's the kind of physical explanation for that mathematical infinity. But strings are different. They spread out over some distance, and you can never get smaller distances than the size of the string itself. Okay? Let me say some more words about this string, because you might be asking well, what is the string made of? And that's not a question that you can, or should, ask a string theorist. They are postulating the existence of a string. It's not made of anything. It's not made of little string atoms, otherwise those would be your fundamental particles. So that's a little bit hard for me to wrap my head around, but it's just one of the mathematical inputs to this theory.

Imagine the interaction of two electrons. Okay? In the present model, I imagine two particles cruising along, and then they create—spontaneously out of nowhere—say a virtual photon, which travels between them; and that's how they interact with one another. How would I picture this with string theory? I would imagine two little strings moving along and at a certain point those strings come together. They might even sort of fold together to form one big string for a brief moment, and then that one big string might split back apart again and turn into two little strings. That might be the interaction of two fundamental particles. And the intermediate state would be describing particles plus virtual particles in our contemporary language. But in the string-theory language, there was never anything but strings interacting. There were never any infinities because there's this limiting size.

Now what is that size? The string theorists can actually put a number on it. And that number comes from another idea, which is something that we've been worrying about in particle physics. I've talked about how the electric and the weak forces are unified. And they unify at a rather high-energy scale, trillions of electron-volts; and in fact, in some sense, even higher still. We haven't really reached the true electroweak unification in experiments yet. The question that many physicists have today, which the standard model does not answer, is, how about the strong force? Is it unified with electricity and the weak force? Right now we just say no, we've got the strong force, and we've got the electroweak force, and they're different. The question is, might they, in fact, at some ultra-high-energy, merge together and truly unify? After all, as you go to higher and higher energies, remember that the strong force gets weaker, but the electroweak force gets stronger. So it's possible that they merge together at a certain very high energy, and in fact, we can even estimate that energy. By looking at how they depend on energy, we can estimate how high up you would have to go. And it's astronomically high; we've come nowhere close to even being able to dream of a particle accelerator that could reach this grand unification scale.

Once people thought about grand unification, then they started thinking about—I don't even know what to call it—a complete unification, which would include gravity as well. Gravity is ultra-weak down in our ordinary world, but as we go to higher and higher energies, it gets stronger. And again, you can make a crude estimate; and the energy at which all the forces of nature seem to come together is about 10^{19} GeV. Remember, the highest energy accelerator we have right now is 10^3 GeV. This is 16 orders of magnitude higher energy than any machine we can imagine building right now. It's really the realm of theorists that we're talking about, not the realm of experiment; but at least in principle you could imagine that everything unifies at that ultra-high-energy scale. Quantum mechanics say an ultra-high-energy scale corresponds to a very tiny distance, and that's the size of the string, basically.

So we've got these strings, and if this is the theory of nature, one of the nice things about it is, no infinities pop up. So that means that you have at least the hope that you can compute everything. Okay? There are no quantities that you say sorry, the theory isn't going to tell you about that. We should be able to compute the masses, and the charges, and all the forces, and everything. And it's the ultimate unified theory where all physical quantities, all physical observables and phenomena, can be computed just from this mathematical framework. Very, very elegant.

Here's another amazing thing about string theory. If you suppose that the world is made of strings, and you start working out the mathematics, and you insist that you have a coherent theory—that is to say, you insist that you can't have any infinities cropping up—that actually puts some limitations on how you write down the mathematics. And you discover that supersymmetry is present; that is to say, supersymmetry is a consequence of string theory. So the string theorists are, in a sense, making an experimental prediction that they believe there should be supersymmetric particles out there. So that begins to make it physics, if you make a prediction that we can test. Although I imagine, if we didn't find them, they would be able to sort of change their theory a little bit, because it's still in a pretty nebulous state, and say, well no, they're a little bit too heavy, and that's why you haven't seen them yet.

Not only does the theory of strings predict supersymmetry, it also predicts the theory of general relativity as a low-energy-effective theory. That is to say, the mathematics of strings predicts Einstein's General Theory of Relativity. Okay? That to me is the most mind-blowing single aspect of string theory of them all. And I think that has sold many physicists enough on the theory to spend their careers studying it some more. And think of that. We have the mathematics to describe fundamental particles, and out pops the theory of gravity as a mathematical consequence. A theory of gravity, that has been with us since 1915 and that is extremely well verified and tested. Okay? So this is—not proof, but it's certainly a compelling argument that this is a theory of nature. So it's wonderful! It includes gravity correctly, and it includes quantum mechanics correctly, and it includes the standard model. It's all there; it's all buried in this one lovely little idea of the string.

There are also some very weird aspects of string theory, almost scary weird. For example, in order to make the theory coherent, mathematically consistent, it has to be the case that strings live in more than three spatial dimensions. Okay, what does that mean? I have three dimensions that I live in, and so do you. I can go forwards and backwards, I can go left and right or I can go up and down. And that's it. Three different, perpendicular directions are available to me. Any other motion is a combination of those. I can go a little forward, and a little left, and a little up; but those are the three independent dimensions that we live in. It's the degrees of freedom of an object in quantum field theory.

In string theory, to make everything work out, we live not in three spatial dimensions, but, maybe, ten dimensions or even 26 dimensions. It depends on the details of the string theory. Okay, what does that mean? How do we picture that? This is one of the wild parts of string theory; and they even have an explanation for why we haven't noticed it so far. And that stuff is just so wild that I would need a whole other course, just on string theory, to start to convey all of these ideas about the theory. And it's well worth learning about, I think.

Let me finish off with my own personal opinion about string theory. Fascinating stuff: it has the potential to be the greatest revolution in physics since the discovery of relativity and quantum mechanics 100 years ago. It's very mathematical. It's not quite a theory yet so we kind of have to just sit and wait for these theorists to tell us whether they can come up with some quantitative predictions, whether they can really conclude that the standard model is the low-energy-effective theory of their string ideas. Okay? It may turn out to be the correct theory of nature—and it may just be completely wrong. It may just be a bunch of mathematics. So I don't think we know yet, but it's certainly something to be paying attention to. Very wild stuff.

Lecture Twenty-Three
Really Big Stuff—The Origin of the Universe

Scope:

Cosmology, the study of the universe as a whole, relates to particle physics, because matter at the very largest scales requires understanding of matter at the very tiniest. In this lecture, we examine the Big Bang scenario and see how it fits into the standard model. We also explore the relationship of *inflation* to the cosmos and define the latest buzzwords in physics, *dark matter* and *dark energy*. We'll talk about data from the COBE satellite mission and more recent astrophysical observations that teach us about the early universe and the connections between cosmic structure and the microscopic world.

> The statement that the Universe arose from inflation, if it is true, is not the end of the study of cosmic origins—it is, in fact, closer to the beginning. The details of inflation depend upon the details of the underlying particle physics, so cosmology and particle physics become intimately linked together.
>
> —Alan Guth

Outline

I. This lecture looks at cosmology, the study of the structure of the universe.

    A. Cosmology may seem unrelated to particle physics; one is the study of the largest possible system and the other, the study of the tiniest. Surprisingly, these two branches of physics are intimately connected.

    B. The Big Bang that may have begun the universe was a high-energy, high-temperature event. Because high energies correspond in quantum mechanics to small distances, the universe was in some sense tiny at the moment of the Big Bang. We need to understand the rules and constituents at the particle level to learn where the universe began and where it is going.

II. Let's begin with the Big Bang, a theory that has been around for a long time. Why do we believe in this theory for the origin of the universe?

A. First of all, imagine that you're an astronomer looking at stars. If we lived in a static universe—a universe that's very large, possibly even infinite, and has been here forever—then you would expect to see many stars, all of them moving in different directions. You should be able to determine the speed of stars, which we can using the Doppler effect, and find some sort of distribution of velocities among the stars.

B. If we start looking at distant objects, such as stars in galaxies, they all appear to be moving away from us, and the greater their distance, the faster they seem to be moving away.

C. A simple explanation exists for this effect, but it requires an abstract conception of the universe.

   1. Let's think of the universe as two dimensional. Imagine that we live on the surface of a giant ball, like a big balloon, and we are ants crawling on the surface. This conception reduces our universe to two dimensions, which curve around in the shape of a ball.

   2. If our balloon is being blown up and expanding, then all the spots on it are moving apart. Every individual ant is moving away from every other individual ant on the surface of the balloon.

   3. If you could put yourself in the worldview of one of those ants, in every direction, you would see other ants moving away from you, and the farther away they are, the faster they move.

D. We know that our universe is expanding and that the stars are moving away from us. If we run the clock backward and plug in some numbers, such as the speed and distance of these stars, we can calculate how long ago it was when that far-off galaxy we're looking at was right next to us. The answer is about 15 billion years ago.

E. We can do similar calculations for other galaxies, and we arrive at the same answer. Every galaxy, every star that is distant from us now, appears to have been very close to us about 15 billion years ago.

F. We know, then, that 15 billion years ago, the universe was in a highly compressed state. Further, all the energy of the universe was there from the beginning. Energy is conserved, which means that the universe had its origins in a very tiny, very energetic situation that resulted in the Big Bang.

G. How might we demonstrate that this theory is true?

    1. If the Big Bang occurred, we should be able to see the aftereffects, such as light and radiation. Using the laws of thermodynamics, we should also be able to predict the temperature of the residue of this explosion now, 15 billion years later.

    2. The first such observations were made in the 1960s by Pensius and Wilson, who detected radiation coming toward us from all directions in deep outer space. This *cosmic microwave background* is no longer very hot. The universe has cooled down so much that the radiation is very long wavelength.

H. Another piece of evidence for why we might believe in the Big Bang theory can be found in the dust between the stars and the galaxies.

    1. The early universe was, essentially, an accelerator experiment with very high energy and very high densities. We should be able to calculate what was produced in this accelerator, including the particles and the heavier elements.

    2. The amounts of heavy elements produced should be relatively small, because the explosion was very brief. In looking at the dust in the universe, astronomers have determined that the material is precisely what we would calculate from the Big Bang scenario.

III. Let's take a moment to discuss what's going on today in cosmology as a result of data received from satellites.

A. Cosmic background radiation is turning out to be a wonderful tool to learn about the Big Bang. The Cosmic Background Explorer (COBE) was the first satellite to collect information on this phenomenon.

    1. COBE went up in the late 1980s and made measurements that fit beautifully with theoretical expectations.

2. For example, radiation in different parts of the sky was observed to be almost identical. Remember that we're looking back in time; this identical radiation was emitted 15 billion years ago and is now traveling toward us from all directions.

B. Let's also think about variations in density in the universe.

1. The universe is divided up into "clumps," with a galaxy here and a galaxy there and nothing in between. Where do these galaxies come from? Presumably, a galaxy is some region of dust and gas that coalesced by gravity and began to form stars.

2. The differences in density are explained by similar differences in the early universe. Regions that were a little more dense at that time began to attract material and, thus, became even denser.

3. The data reveal that this model of galactic formation is consistent with what must have taken place in the early universe to have a later universe that is clumped into galaxies, as ours is.

C. Other research in cosmology is looking at *dark matter*, a substance in outer space that doesn't glow.

1. Every galaxy has some outlying stars that are almost always in some kind of orbit. By making careful measurements, we can deduce the speed and orbital path of those stars, as well as the mass in the middle that is causing the orbit.

2. If we calculate that mass, we conclude that something else exists inside the galaxy that is not glowing but is gravitating.

3. We don't quite know what this *dark matter* is. It may be yet-undiscovered particles, such as supersymmetric particles.

D. Another phenomenon that has been observed recently and is even more mysterious than dark matter is *inflation*. This phenomenon is related to what must have been occurring at the start of the Big Bang.

1. The Big Bang would have required a supply of energy that inflates the universe rapidly for a short amount of time. This inflationary scenario explains a number of

©2003 The Teaching Company Limited Partnership

other observations, including the fact that the universe looks so much the same in all directions.

2. Where would that energy come from? Possibly, from the Higgs (or a Higgs-like) field. If this field exists everywhere in the universe, it may have come from a kind of condensation after the Big Bang.

3. We imagine that the early universe, at the start of the Big Bang, was very symmetrical. All the theories were unified. The electric and the weak forces were the same in nature, and the Higgs particle had not yet condensed out. Then, as the universe expanded and cooled, the Higgs field condensed out.

4. When a gas condenses into a liquid, it emits heat. As the Higgs field condensed, it would release some form of latent heat, which is a supply of energy. That release of heat would pour energy into all the particles, which would then expand rapidly.

5. This scenario is consistent with particle physics and would explain cosmological inflation. Further, new data suggest that we are now undergoing another period of inflation; the rate of expansion is picking up as though some cosmic field is condensing and adding energy, which is called *dark energy*.

IV. We have evidence for a Big Bang about 15 billion years ago that involved an inflationary period and high temperatures. The goal of current research is to tie all these ideas together—string theory, standard model physics, and Big Bang cosmology—to form a coherent picture of the cosmos.

Essential Reading:

Kane, *The Particle Garden*, chapter 12.

Barnett, Muhry, and Quinn, *The Charm of Strange Quarks*, chapter 8.

Recommended Reading:

Lederman, *The God Particle*, second half of chapter 9, starting with the section on "Flatness and dark matter."

Weinberg, *The First Three Minutes*. (The whole book is good!)

Calle, *Superstrings and Other Things*, chapter 25, last two sections.

Wilczek and Devine, *Longing for the Harmonies*, chapters 4–6; Ninth Theme.

Questions to Consider:

1. Can you think of a method for estimating the age of the universe? How on earth can we know that it is (roughly) 15 billion years old?

2. Cosmic background radiation is the oldest light we can see. It was emitted when the universe was a few hundred thousand years old. (Any light emitted *earlier* than that existed in a universe dense enough that the light was reabsorbed.) If we cannot *see* anything from before that time, how can we *know* anything about the universe from before that time?

3. Does it make physical sense to ask, "What happened before the Big Bang"?

Lecture Twenty-Three—Transcript
Really Big Stuff—The Origin of the Universe

Today we're going to talk about some really big stuff: cosmology. It's the study of the structure of the universe. What are its origins? What does it look like today? Where is it headed? What's the fate of the cosmos as a whole? Now, it might seem, at first glance, like talking about cosmology is completely disconnected from particle physics. In fact, as disconnected as you could imagine—we've gone from the tiniest of the tiny to the largest of all possible things we could study, and one of the beautiful things It's very elegant, and very surprising—these two branches of physics are very intimately connected. It has been this way for a long time; and more so today than ever before, you need to understand particle physics to talk about the structure of the universe, and vice versa. What the cosmologists are learning about the structure of the universe is teaching us about limits of the standard model.

One way of thinking about it is, if the universe begins in some cataclysmic big bang, that's an extremely high-energy, high-temperature event. And, high energies correspond, in quantum mechanics, to small distances. Everything was really close together. In a sense, the universe was tiny at the moment of the Big Bang; so, particle physics becomes extremely important if you want to understand where everything begins, how the universe starts. You really need to understand the rules, and the constituents, so that you have a sense of what's going to happen next. So, I want to begin today by saying a little bit about the Big Bang, because it's a pretty wild theory. It's been around for a long time, and I want to discuss it as a scientific question. Not as an issue of a creation myth, but rather as a creation scenario that can be tested: a logical consequence, a mathematical structure, data to confirm this hypothesis.

Why do we believe in the Big Bang? There are many reasons. And, let me begin by giving you what I consider to be the three best arguments for this idea of the origin of the universe.

First of all, imagine that you're an astronomer looking at stars. Now, if we lived in a, kind of a static universe, a universe that's very, very large, possibly even infinite, and has been here forever, then you would expect to see a bunch of stars out there. Some of them running towards us, some of them running away from us. Moving every which way. It should be some sort of a distribution of velocities out there. Now, can we figure out the speed of a star? It's not, at first glance, obvious how you would do that. You use a simple physics effect called the Doppler effect, which you may have noticed if you're standing on a street corner, and a police car or an ambulance goes by, and you listen to the siren. It makes that characteristic—first a high pitch, when it's coming towards you, and then a low pitch as it runs away—Wheee-eeeen, as it goes by. And that effect, the Doppler effect, is completely understood; it's just a simple wave phenomenon. If the source of a wave is coming towards you, it shifts up in frequency. If it's running away from you, it shifts down in frequency. And light is also a wave phenomenon. Everything is both particle and wave. And in particular, light has many, many properties that are just completely understandable in terms of waves. If an object is glowing and it runs away from you, the color is just shifted a little bit. If it's running away from you, it's shifted a little bit more towards the red. If it's running towards you, it is shifted just a little bit more towards the blue in the spectrum.

So, if you look at stars carefully, and you measure their color, you can deduce their relative motion towards you, or away from you. And what was noticed a long time ago was that if you start looking at far-away objects, stars in galaxies, they all appear to be running away from us. And that's true in any portion of the sky: Northern hemisphere, Southern hemisphere, all directions; all the galaxies that we can see appear to be running away from us. And the farther away they are, the faster they seem to be running away from us. Think about that for a second. It's a weird concept. And, you can imagine the reaction of astronomers and physicists when they first started collecting this data. Edwin Hubble is famous for making the first experimental measurements of this effect; we've named the Hubble telescope after him in honor of this discovery.

You might first think, wow, we're really special. We must be at the center of the universe. Everything is rushing away from us. That's a possible explanation, but it really doesn't seem all that likely. And it doesn't really explain why things that are farther away from us are running away even faster still. There is actually a simpler explanation, and it requires an abstract conception of the universe as a whole. So let me simplify the universe for a moment. Instead of thinking of it as three-dimensional, think of it as two-dimensional.

Imagine that we live on the surface of some giant ball, like a big balloon. You paint little galaxies on the balloon, and we are little ants crawling around on the surface of this balloon. I've reduced our universe to two dimensions, and those two dimensions curve around in the shape of a ball. If that balloon is expanding, if somebody is blowing it up, then all the little spots on it are moving apart from one another. Every individual ant is moving away from every other little individual ant on the surface of that balloon. And, if you could put yourself in the worldview of one of those ants, what would you see? You would look around you, and in every direction you would see other ants, and they're all moving away from you; and the farther away they are, the faster they move. If they're twice as far away, they move away from you twice as rapidly. So every ant has a worldview that's the same as the one that we are presently observing. This makes us <u>not</u> special. It makes the universe quite symmetrical, and it also explains this fact that double the distance corresponds to double the speed. So this is really the origin, I think, of this idea of a Big Bang. The universe is expanding.

So run the clock backwards. If stars are running away from us now, where were they a week ago? Well, they must have been a little bit closer to us. And keep running the clock backwards, and now plug in some numbers. Look at how far away they are, and how fast they're moving, and ask how long ago was it when that faraway galaxy was right next to us, if it's been doing this motion for a long time? And the answer, nowadays, is about 15 billion years ago. About 15 billion years is the amount of time it takes for a galaxy which is presently at its observed distance, and observed velocity, to have started off right next to us.

Now, you look at another galaxy, at a different distance, and you do that calculation. You get the same number. Okay? That's again a very interesting and compelling observation. Every galaxy, every star that's far away, appears to have been very close to us about 15 billion years ago. So, what does that mean? It means 15 billion years ago, the whole universe was in some highly compressed, very small state. This is the idea of the Big Bang. We begin with everything really close together. All of the energy of the universe was there from the beginning; energy is conserved. So, if you think about that, it means that in the beginning you have this very tiny, very energetic situation, which is the Big Bang. Now, we don't yet have any of the details of the Big Bang, but this is the origin of the idea.

So, let's play the science game of what-if. Okay? What if there was a Big Bang? How could you demonstrate that this is really true? Well, the idea would be, draw some conclusions, and then check to see if those conclusions are satisfied in the world. For example, if the universe begins very hot, hot things glow, always. This is a law of physics; they emit radiation. So this early Big Bang, it's a big explosion, there should be light—among other things, there should be light—which was emitted from that explosion. And, if this Big Bang scenario says the universe is symmetrical, then that radiation should be emitted in all directions. So, any direction that you look, you should be able to see the afterglow. All right? You've got a big explosion, and then it begins to cool down; and if it's just an expanding object, the laws of thermodynamics tell you how rapidly it will cool down. So, you should be able to predict how hot is the residual of this explosion, now, 15 billion years later. You come to a conclusion and it's a quantitative conclusion. If we begin with an explosion, 15 billion years ago, then the temperature today should be—and you can express it as an energy, or what's better, as a temperature—the universe should be at a certain temperature. And so, we've gone out and looked.

In fact, the first observation of this was not intentional it was accidental. Penzias and Wilson, in the early '60s, observed this afterglow, just some radiation coming towards us from all directions from deep outer space. In fact, this radiation is coming, essentially, from the farthest you can possibly look; and it appears as though we are inside of a giant box, if you wish, that's got a certain uniform temperature. This is very compelling evidence that this scenario fits. And that background radiation is called the cosmic background radiation—sometimes called the cosmic microwave background— it's really not very hot anymore. The universe has cooled down so much that the radiation is very long wavelength, very low-energy radiation. It's not visible to the eye. You don't see a glow anymore. It's like an old fire; it starts off white-hot, and then it's red-hot, and as it cools, you can't see it with your eyes anymore, but you can still put your hands over it and feel that there is radiation coming out. And now we've waited for 15 billion years; and, of course, it's just a steady process of getting colder and colder. But, it's never going to be at zero. It's just approaching zero.

The old data of Penzias and Wilson was very crude, just a couple of data points indicating that there seemed to be this microwave radiation. We're living in a very giant, fairly cold, microwave oven, in a certain sense. Nowadays, there's much improved data. I will tell you about some of that shortly. We have sent satellites up into orbit—to get away from the noise and heat of planet Earth—and taken very, very careful measurements. And so far, it works like a champ. This idea—that you're looking at a black, dark, but warm object—is consistent with the data, at very high levels of accuracy.

The third piece of evidence that I want to mention for why we might believe that the universe begins in this cataclysm, this Big Bang, is the following. Let's now apply the laws of particle physics, the standard model, to that early universe. What we have is a big particle-physics accelerator experiment, very high energy, very high density. We should be able to calculate, if our model is correct, what was produced. You produce electrons and positrons, and protons and anti-protons. And, some of those protons will smash together, because it's very hot, just like they do today in the core of the sun, and form heavier elements. And so, you should be able to calculate all of the nucleosynthesis, the creation of elements, in those early minutes of the universe. So you sit down and work out the details. How much hydrogen do you expect, compared to how much helium, compared to how much lithium, and so on. And, the predictions are, that you shouldn't have very many heavy elements, because the cataclysm was very rapid. It's not like the sun that has been running for billions of years, cooking if you like. Here you just have a very brief explosion and then everything spreads apart. So, you only have a short amount of time to create some heavier elements. And again, we have gone out, astronomers have looked and—typically what you do is, you look not towards stars, but out into the dark spaces between the stars, and between the galaxies; and there's evidence for dust. The light that comes through that dust gets absorbed, and indicates what is the dust made of. And it appears to be made in precisely—that material is precisely what we expect from this Big Bang scenario.

These are quantitative predictions that are verified by the data. So, I think today the Big Bang scenario is accepted. It is not quite as rigorously accepted as the standard model of particle physics itself, because the amount of data that's consistent with particle physics is enormous. The amount of data associated with the Big Bang is smaller in number and more difficult; the astronomical observations are more challenging. So, I think it's a good theory, very well believed, but more subject to modification and new ideas than the standard model of particle physics itself.

Let me tell you a little bit more about what's going on today, because we have been sending up satellites, and we continue to do so. In particular, this cosmic background radiation is turning out to be just a wonderful tool to learn about this early event, this Big Bang. The first great satellite to do this was called COBE—the Cosmic Background Explorer is the acronym. COBE went up in the late '80s and made measurements for a couple of years. And, if you look at the data, it's just so beautiful. There's a theoretical expectation—it's called the blackbody curve—and the data just lies on that curve so well that you can't even see the uncertainties. They're so small on a graph that they just fit right into the line that you draw through the data points. What they observed was some interesting facts.

For example, the radiation that you see from one part of the sky is pretty much exactly identical to the radiation you see from another part of the sky. Now realize, you're looking back in time—15 billion years. This is radiation that was emitted 15 billion years ago in the Big Bang and has traveled towards us ever since. And something that comes from one side of the universe, and that comes from the other side of the universe, and reaches us, is identical. Now that's very interesting, thought provoking—it implies that the universe began all together in one spot, because that's the only way you could imagine that stuff over there, and stuff elsewhere, would know what the temperature is supposed to be. They agree, spectacularly.

And how about variations? When you look in light, you see galaxies here, and then no galaxy, and then galaxy, and then no galaxy. The universe is clumpy, and we would like to understand the clumpiness. Right? This is part of cosmology, understanding the structure of the universe that we live in. Where do galaxies come from? Well, presumably there was some region of dust and gas that coalesced by gravity, and began to form stars. And now you ask, well, why are some parts of the galaxies more dense and other parts less dense? And so, you kind of work your way backward. You say, well, in the early universe there must have been some fluctuations. Some parts were a little bit more dense and some parts were a little bit less dense, and the parts that were more dense attracted, and so they got even more and more; and so you have a kind of a feedback which forms galaxies. So this is a model of galactic formation, and you have to ask yourself, is this consistent with the Big Bang scenario? If the Big Bang is really completely uniform, then you'd have this explosion of dust and gas that's completely uniform, and then you wouldn't have any mechanism for galaxy formation. So people have been continuing to look at this data, and have noticed that there are, in fact, tiny variations. Although it's almost completely uniform, there is a little bit more density here and there, and a little bit less density in other places. It is quite consistent with what you would need, in the early universe, to have a later universe that clumped into galaxies the way ours has; so even more quantitative data indicating that this Big Bang scenario is correct.

This is a very hot field of research. There are balloons that have been sent up with observers; there are satellites that are being launched, and will be launched in the near future. They all have acronyms: BOOMERANG is one of the balloon experiments, and PLANCK and MAP are some of the satellite experiments. You'll probably be hearing about these things, because they are taking very precise data. And now, we can start to compare with the standard model, or perhaps something deeper than the standard model, because, where do those fluctuations come from?

In the standard model you have some—you can't have perfect uniformity. The Heisenberg Uncertainty Principle says there will always be fluctuations. Little particle-anti-particle pair will appear here, but not there; and there are calculations you can do, statistical calculations. What is the probability of getting a high-density region here, and a smaller-density region there? One can actually connect this physics of the cosmos to the standard model. Make numerical, quantitative predictions of what is expected for those little tiny quantum fluctuations that happened during the Big Bang and then get magnified by gravity over the years—first, turning into the observable fluctuations in the cosmic background radiation, and ultimately into the fluctuations that we see. Here's a galaxy, and there's empty space.

As we collect this data, there are many puzzles remaining. Our picture of cosmology is still, I would say, at a more primitive state than our picture of the standard model of particle physics itself. There's a lot of mysterious stuff out there that we would love to understand and we don't yet. For example, the dark matter. Let me tell you about what dark matter is, because it's cosmological in origin, but may be particle physics in action. Another connection between the very large, and the very small.

There are many evidences, scientific data points, that point to the existence of something out there, in outer space, that doesn't glow. We can't see it directly. We only infer its existence. Let me give you a simple example, although there are many of these. If you look at a galaxy, there are always some outlying stars. And, those outlying stars are all, almost always, in some kind of orbit. By making careful measurements, we can deduce the speed and the orbital path of those stars. Now, we have a theory of gravity. In fact, you can use Newton's law of gravity, and usually that's good enough; Albert Einstein's theory of gravity pretty much isn't even necessary. You could use it, but it's going to give you essentially the same results as good old Isaac Newton. If you watch an object in orbit, you can conclude, by making measurements of its orbit, what is the mass in the middle that's making it go in that orbit? We can figure out the mass of the sun, without actually going and putting it on a scale, by looking at planet Earth, or any of the planets, and seeing what our orbital motion is. It's just the laws of physics that tell you. So you look at these stars, and you calculate how much mass is there inside of their orbit, that's attracting them, preventing them from running off in a straight line. And you get a big number. And now you look with your telescopes, and you count all the stars in the galaxy, and you add up the mass of all those stars, and it doesn't even come close to what you expected. It's like one percent of what you expected. It's really radically far away. It's not, you know, as if astronomers have a difficult time; you can't really count all the stars individually. You could imagine factors-of-two mistakes, but not a factor of 100. So, apparently there's something else inside the galaxy, which is massive, which is gravitating, and yet it's not glowing.

Now, you might say, well, there's dust. And there is dust. But we know that there's dust. We can measure how much dust there is because dust absorbs light. So if you emit light, or if you absorb light, we will be able to detect it, and we wouldn't call it dark matter. So this is something else. It's something very exotic. What is it? Well, we don't know. Right? This is one of the big puzzles of cosmology, and everybody's busy, trying to figure out what is the dark matter. There are lots of ideas. It might be just a bunch of, I don't know, protons and neutrons, maybe even forming little clumps of matter, some little charcoal blocks out there, which are somehow not absorbing the sunlight. Dust is visible because it absorbs light, but allows some to pass through. If it was really black, we might not really be able to notice it, if it was also really small.

Well, that's a possibility, but now you start doing some calculations, and this Big Bang scenario doesn't predict that. I told you that we think we understand how much matter was formed in the Big Bang, and the matter that was formed, the ordinary quarks and electrons, leptons and all the ordinary stuff, adds up to about one percent of what seems to be out there. So what else could it be? Could it be anything else? Well, we already have some candidates. What about neutrinos? The universe is filled with neutrinos. Every star makes them. The Big Bang made them. There's a big, large density of neutrinos everywhere. Imagine for a moment that those neutrinos are massive. This is a possibility in particle physics; it's something that we're investigating actively today in the laboratory. If the neutrino is massive, you add up all these tiny numbers and you get a big number. And, that would be something that gravitates. There might be more neutrinos in the region of galaxies, because there's lots of gravity there. And, if they're massive, they might actually be attracted. It's an idea. And again, you have to ask yourself, well, can we verify this idea?

It turns out that the neutrinos cannot explain all the dark matter that we believe is out there. They might explain a tiny fraction of it; however, we've already put limits: the neutrino can't weigh a pound, it's a tiny object. In fact, we have very, very stringent limits. It's an extraordinary light object. So, there is just not enough mass sitting in the neutrinos to explain all the dark matter that we've hypothesized is there in order to explain other phenomena which we really can see; like the rotation of stars, the expansion of the galaxies, galaxies as a whole. All sorts of data point to dark matter. And, it points to the same amount of dark matter.

So what else could it be? Well, maybe there are other undiscovered particles, like supersymmetric particles. We've talked about those briefly. It's a very speculative idea. It's a new form of matter. The squarks, and the sleptons, and these crazy particles that are predicted by string theory. And people have been looking for them very actively, at particle-physics accelerators. If it's real, we hope to find evidence of it in future, upcoming generations of particle-physics accelerators. And if there really are supersymmetric particles, they too would exist in the universe. They would have been created in the Big Bang, which was a giant accelerator experiment 15 billion years ago; and some of them might still be sitting around, gravitating. So all of this kind of speculation is very tentative, and it hooks together astronomy, cosmology and particle physics. Everybody's working together to try to understand what this stuff is. I think that there's going to be lots of progress. I can't imagine that, over the next 10 or 15 years, there's not going to be some great discoveries that will teach us more about what this dark matter is. And so, that's something to keep your eyes open for.

The mysteries don't end here with the dark matter. There is another phenomenon going on, which is quite recently observed, and it's even more mysterious than the dark matter. I think we can imagine some new undiscovered particles out there, and we can go look for them. There's another phenomenon that happened in the early universe, and it's happening again now, and it's got the cute name "inflation". So think of the Big Bang. The naïve image of a big bang is just an explosion. And it turns out, if you work out the details, consistent with all the data that I've been talking about—in particular, this cosmic-background-radiation data—it looks now like what you really need in the beginnings of the Big Bang is a very rapid explosion. You need some supply of energy that inflates the universe very rapidly, for a very short amount of time. This inflationary scenario explains a lot of things, including the fact that the universe looks so much the same in all directions.

And where would that energy come from? Well, I can propose a mechanism consistent with the standard model of particle physics. I'm not suggesting that this is the right explanation; there are some detailed problems with it. But it might be the right conceptual explanation. Remember the Higgs particle, this bizarre part of the standard model? It is conventional physics right now. Although we don't have direct evidence for the existence of the Higgs, there's a lot of indirect evidence, and we're looking for one. The main thing, the weirdest thing, about the Higgs is that it's everywhere. It's a—we call it a condensed-out field. There is actually a non-zero value of the Higgs field everywhere. We're swimming through this stuff. And, that's why particles have mass, is because they're swimming through this Higgs field. It's not a bunch of Higgs particles; particles would be excitations, or waves, in that field. It's just the field itself.

Now, if this field exists everywhere in the universe, where did it come from? The idea in the standard model is that it condensed out. It's like water vapor that you cool. And as you cool it, it undergoes a phase change, and all of a sudden you've got liquid water. So you ask, where did the water come from? Well, it originated in this beautiful, symmetrical gas; and then, as it cooled, it condensed out. It's the same with the Higgs. We imagine that, in the early universe, at the start of the Big Bang, it was very symmetrical. All the theories unified. The electric and the weak forces are the same in nature, and the Higgs particle was not yet condensed out. And then, as the universe expands and cools, the Higgs field condenses out. And what happens when a gas condenses into a liquid? It emits some heat, some thermal energy. Farmers know about this—if they've got a crop of orange trees in Florida, and they're worried about a freak cold snap, they'll put buckets of water underneath the trees, so that if the water freezes, the emitted heat will prevent the oranges from all freezing and dying. It's a standard and understood physical phenomenon. You are releasing some latent heat. And, as the Higgs field condenses, it too would release some form of latent heat—a supply of energy. It's not creating energy out of nothing; it was there as potential and it's become manifest, but that release of heat would pour energy into all the particles, which would then expand very rapidly. This is a scenario that is consistent with particle physics. That would explain this cosmological inflation that the cosmologists independently postulated, for other reasons, and believe they have evidence really happened.

In fact, the new data, from some of these balloon observatories, is that it's happening again. The universe—you might expect—we had a Big Bang, everything is expanding, but the expansion should be slowing down, because everything's gravitating; and so you imagine that all the galaxies are kind of being pulled back in. And the question of whether the pulling back in is enough to halt the expansion, turn it around, and lead us to an ultimate crunch is an open question. But at the very least, you would expect that the expansion should be slowing down. It might be slowing down, but won't ever stop. We might continue to expand forever. But it appears, now, that we're undergoing a period of inflation again. That the rate of expansion is actually picking up, as though some cosmic field is condensing and adding energy. Well, we don't really know what's going on. It's not the Higgs; the mathematics of the Higgs doesn't explain this new expansion, this new inflation; the buzzword on the street, in particle physics and cosmology, is dark energy. It acts as though there's a new supply of energy in the universe, and since we really don't know what that dark energy is, dark energy is even more mysterious than dark matter. You could imagine some sort of particle-physics explanation, but we don't have one today. Again, an active field of research.

So let me, let me summarize with the state of the world today in cosmology. We have compelling evidence for a Big Bang, about 15 billion years ago, which involved an inflationary period, very high temperatures, particle physics in action; and, then, everything just proceeds according to the known laws of physics. The universe cools, the Higgs field is present in the universe today, the galaxies form; we see the remnants of all this stuff. It's a nice picture; it's not complete, and there are probably some holes and gaps and maybe even some fundamental ideas still missing.

If you go back early enough, the temperature gets high enough that you expect really complete unification. In fact, you expect, at some ultra-early stage of this Big Bang, that we get beyond what the standard model can tell us. Once you get up to energies which I called the plank energy, extraordinarily high temperatures, the standard-model physics begins to break down, and we really need something more fundamental—like string theory—to really tell us how this story begins. And so I think the goal, the hope, is that all of this stuff is going to tie together in a neat bundle: string theory, standard-model physics, and Big Bang cosmology, to form a coherent picture of the cosmos as a whole.

Lecture Twenty-Four
Looking Back and Looking Forward

Scope:

What have we learned after more than 100 years of intense study of fundamental particles, and what puzzles still remain? What influence does particle physics have on our lives, on science, and on our philosophical worldview? We'll conclude this course with thoughts on what you might take away from this experience—a sense of physical order and an understanding of the constituents of the world. Remember that progress in science does not generally overthrow the old, but modifies and extends it, which means that you can use your understanding of the standard model as a framework in which to fit new knowledge and understanding.

> The quality of a society is indicated by the questions it asks. One of the questions is, what is man made of? The answer is matter, and it is the nature of matter that is the domain of High Energy Physics. The society that doesn't ask this question is a suffering society.
>
> —Sid Drell

> Scientific understanding has inherent cultural value. It has great beauty. It adds to the satisfaction of our lives.
>
> —Robert Wilson (to the Joint Committee on Atomic Energy quoted in *The World Treasury of Physics, Astronomy, and Mathematics*, p. 697)

Outline

I. In this final lecture, we will look back at everything we've been talking about and try to put it into a framework.

   A. First, let's ask, "What is the standard model of particle physics?" The idea of the standard model is that we can understand all the complexity and diversity of physical phenomena in terms of the point-like elementary particles from which all objects are made.

   B. These particles interact with one another through some fairly simple and well-understood forces—the electroweak force, the strong nuclear force, and gravity.

C. Speaking generically, there are only two kinds of particles, quarks and leptons. The quarks are the strongly interacting particles that form protons and neutrons and a few more exotic particles that are found only in accelerator experiments or cosmological or astrophysical phenomenon. The leptons are the lighter ones, such as the electrons or the neutrinos that come out of the sun.

D. This theory is as quantitatively successful as any scientific theory in any branch of science. Despite its success, however, the standard model is not the end of the story. Many puzzles and questions remain, even in the framework of the standard model itself.

E. Sometimes, physicists talk about discovering a *theory of everything* (TOE), which would describe the true fundamental constituents and forces. From that basis, this theory would explain the quarks and the leptons and their interactions, and so on. In other words, this theory would explain the standard model.

   1. The standard model explains how atoms are formed. An atom is quarks forming into protons and neutrons that bind together to form a nucleus, along with electrons, which are electrically attracted. The atom can be explained by the theories of QCD, to describe the nucleus, and QED, or the electroweak theory, to describe the attraction of electrons to the nucleus.

   2. This theory explains how two hydrogen atoms can bind together and form a stable hydrogen molecule and how hydrogens and oxygens can combine to form stable water molecules. In principle, you start from this fundamental theory and work your way up to a deep understanding of chemistry, biology, and other sciences.

F. Ultimately, what particle physicists are studying is the five conceptual ideas that tie together the physical world: force and energy, matter, and space and time. Those five ingredients are the ultimate components of particle physics.

II. We began this course by asking why people care about particle physics.

   A. As we said, we can speak of spinoffs of particle physics. This branch of physics may be the one that is least related to our lives, but it has resulted in some of the most sophisticated, complex machinery ever designed, including equipment for medical diagnosis and treatment. Further, in a sense, the Web is a spinoff of particle physics.

B. Other spinoffs from particle physics are not technological, but intellectual, including the field theory itself. Quantum field theory is a general mathematical framework that forms the basis for doing calculations. It can be extended to describe interactions in a number of complicated systems, including those in biology and even economics.

C. Finally, we might note the reductionistic pleasure we find in studying particle physics and the idea that this study satisfies basic childlike curiosity.

III. What should you take away from this course?

A. The guiding idea here is that the world is orderly, made, at its core, of simple "ingredients" governed by simple laws.

B. To the best of all the data and observations we've made for the past 100 years, we've learned that the world is made of protons and neutrons, which form nuclei, with electrons around them. That picture will be deepened and broadened in the future, but it will not go away.

C. Your job in the future is to question the sensational scientific discoveries you hear about and tie them into the standard model.

1. If a supersymmetric particle is discovered, you'll ask, "How are these particles related to ordinary particles? What have they done to the standard model? How have they deepened it? What do we understand now?"

2. You should also maintain your skepticism if you hear about discoveries that fly in the face of 100 years of data.

D. A new issue in physics research today is outreach. Physicists are being asked to make a greater effort to communicate their knowledge to the public. As you hear about these exotic ideas—string theory, dark matter, dark energy, extra dimensions—you are now equipped to make some sense of them for yourself.

Essential Reading:

Weinberg, *Dreams of a Final Theory*, chapter X.

Kane, *The Particle Garden*, chapter 7.

Schwarz, *A Tour of the Subatomic Zoo*, chapter 9.

Barnett, Muhry, and Quinn, *The Charm of Strange Quarks*, pp. 204–207.

Recommended Reading:

The bibliography contains some great selections; I encourage you to look there for interesting reading. (If you haven't read anything by Feynman yet, I'd certainly recommend you pick up one of his.)

Questions to Consider:

1. What aspect of the standard model do you find most appealing, and what (if any) are you most certain will be replaced or improved upon?

2. As a final assignment, look for an article in a current magazine or on the Web that covers a development in particle physics that is *newer* than this course! How does it connect to what you have learned here? Does it change your perceptions of what you have learned?

Lecture Twenty-Four—Transcript
Looking Back and Looking Forward

In this final lecture, I want to look back at everything we've been talking about, and try to put it into a whole framework. What have we learned? Why are we interested in this stuff? Where are we headed? So, no new topics today. No new particles or new concepts of physics.

I just want to think, first of all, about what *is* the standard model of particle physics? Okay, physicists want to understand how the world works, and that means everything, from complicated things to simple things. The idea of particle physics, this branch of all of physics, is that we can understand all the complexity and diversity of physical phenomena—anything that's measurable. Everything that can be observed is understandable in terms of this framework, the standard model of particle physics, that says the world is made of little particles. Everything. Everything physical is made of little point-like elementary objects, and they interact with one another. They interact through some fairly simple and well-understood forces. In fact, there's not very many of them: the electroweak force, the strong nuclear force, and gravity. That's it. And what kind of particles are there? Well, there are really only two kinds of particles, generically: quarks and leptons. The quarks are the strongly interacting ones that ultimately form protons and neutrons, and a few more exotic particles that are found only in accelerator experiments or in cosmological or astrophysical phenomena. The leptons are the lighter ones, like the electrons that buzz around, or the neutrinos that come out of the sun. And that's the story that forms the basis.

One can imagine creating a little periodic table, kind of an analogy to the old periodic table, the one that appears in all the chemistry books, that describes the fundamental atoms of the world, like hydrogen, and helium, and carbon, and so on. Our new periodic table, of the fundamental particles, has a few entries. There's an up and a down quark, a strange and a charm, a top and a bottom. Similarly, there are six leptons. That periodic table fits on a T-shirt, so that's nice, an indication that we do have a fundamental theory of nature. On the other hand, you can't fit, on that same T-shirt, the particles or the rules. That requires a couple of pages of writing down the actual mathematical formulas which define the standard model of particle physics. If you go to the particle data tables, which is a collection of the information that we have today about particle physics, you can find precisely such a short summary of this conceptual framework for understanding the world.

It is a very, very successful theory. In fact, I would argue that there has never been, to date, any scientific theory, in any branch of science, which is so quantitatively successful. This is not hundreds, but thousands—tens of thousands of experiments over 100 years—and they are all consistent. You can do calculations, you can make pre-dictions and post-dictions; that is to say you can calculate what you expect, and compare with what has been seen, or what you will see in a future generation of accelerator—and it works. Sometimes the calculations are tough, and in those cases we can sort of calculate to maybe ten percent, and it agrees with the data. In other cases, the calculation is easier. Sometimes we can calculate with uncertainties of one percent, or a tenth of a percent, or even, in some remarkable cases, parts per billion. Twelve digits of accuracy. And again, to date, every experiment that I'm familiar with, in any branch of particle physics—that includes accelerators, it also includes radiation experiments, small-scale tabletop experiments, experiments in balloons, looking at cosmic rays, deep underground in mines—they all agree with the standard model.

It's fairly mind-boggling, the success of this theory, and makes us feel very confident that we do have a deep understanding of how the world works. The world really is made of little particles, the quarks and the leptons, and they fit together, they interact with these forces. It's nice. It's like having a worldview that we live in a solar system with the sun in the middle, and planets orbiting around it. And that, too, is a very successful picture that we have that describes nature quite quantitatively. We can use that model to send rocket ships to Mars, and beyond; and so far, except when our technology blows up, it's been successful.

Despite its wonderful successes, the standard model is not the end of the story. Physicists aren't done. There are many puzzles and many questions. Even in the framework of the standard model itself, there are some puzzles and questions. We've been talking about many of those, and, of course, there remain many more that we haven't had time to talk about. Do the neutrinos have mass, and if so, what are those masses, and how does that fit into the story? Is there a Higgs particle? Is it real, or is it just a mathematical construct that makes this stuff all tie together? Again, something that we really would like to know the answer to, and we're trying to find out, how about this violation of left-right symmetry? The weak force of nature seems to distinguish between your left hand and your right hand in some fundamental way. They are fundamentally different, as far as the weak force is concerned? Why is that? We can describe it very, very accurately. We can make quantitative predictions; but I can't tell you yet why that's true. And, we would like to know. Why is matter and antimatter not quite the same? Why is there CP violation in the universe? Why are we here? Why is the universe mostly matter, and not mostly antimatter, or actually a mix, a fifty-fifty mix?

You look at that little periodic table, and it's got three generations. There are the light particles, up and down quarks, the electron, and the electron neutrino, and they make up the world, the ordinary, everyday world. Everything. All objects, all materials, all phenomena that we normally deal with in our lives, come from just a subset of all the available, fundamental and elementary particles of nature. Why is that? Why is it that there is a duplicate generation, and then a triplicate generation, that appear to be identical, except they're more heavy? And, why do they have the masses that they do? We just described them. We go out in the laboratory and we measure those masses; however, we don't know why the muon weighs what it does. So, I think that most physicists believe the standard model is elegant and descriptive, but incomplete. And in particular, I can prove that it's incomplete if you allow me to worry about gravity. Quantum mechanics is incompatible with the present theory of gravity that we have, and so far it hasn't mattered because quantum-mechanical experiments deal with little things where gravity doesn't matter. And the experiments—like looking at solar systems, where gravity does matter—quantum mechanics is irrelevant. And so, we haven't had to worry about that; but conceptually, we really would like some theory that ties everything together.

Physicists sometimes talk about the theory of everything. A TOE, the Theory Of Everything. I don't really like that word, but you see it all the time. I don't like the word because, boy, it makes physicists just seem really arrogant. A theory of everything! If you read that physicists have discovered a theory of everything, you think wow. They can explain the weather in three weeks, the stock market next week, they can solve the Middle East crisis, and they can tell me how to make the perfect omelet, because they have a theory of everything.

Well, of course that's not what physicists mean when they talk about this theory of everything. What they mean is a theory of everything at the simplest level. And, we are making some progress towards such a theory.

The standard model is kind of a—well, it's not really a theory of everything, because of all the problems that I've described. What we're looking for is something that ties it all together, at the microscopic level. What are the true fundamental constituents, and what are the true fundamental forces? And then, from that, the hope is that one can then explain the quarks, and the leptons, and their interactions. In other words, one could explain the standard model—wouldn't that be nice—because the standard model explains how atoms are formed. An atom is quarks forming into protons and neutrons, which bind together to form a nucleus, and then electrons, which are electrically attracted. So the theory of QCD, to describe the nucleus, and QED—or actually the electroweak theory—to describe the attraction of electrons to that nucleus, is enough to explain everything you would want to know about an atom. Everything: its size, its mass, its chemical properties and its electrical interactions with other atoms. So, in principle, this underlying theory explains how two hydrogen atoms can bind together and form a stable hydrogen molecule. And, how hydrogens and oxygens can combine to form stable water molecules.

Now in principle, you start from this fundamental theory and work your way up, and now you understand chemistry, deeply. Now the chemists are interested in this, and they occasionally do the quantum-mechanical calculations to make predictions and to understand their systems; and sometimes they've got their own rules and ways of thinking about things that are effective. They work and they don't really always worry about the connections down to the fundamentals. The more complicated of a system that you're looking at, the less likely you are to want to really—in real life—follow this chain all the way down to the bottom. If you're a biologist, studying the structure and properties of DNA molecules and how they replicate, and how errors appear, and how they correct those errors—the kind of stuff that a biologist might really want to know about—it's nice for them to know that there is a standard model of particle physics which is explaining the chemistry, which is explaining the biology. It's nice, from a conceptual framework, but from a practical point of view, it's pretty rare that the biologist will really go down all the way and start to do QCD calculations. In fact, I don't think they ever have to bother doing that.

Ultimately, what particle physicists are studying is the five, sort of conceptual ideas that tie together the physical world: force and energy, matter—what things are really made of—space, and time. Those five ingredients are the ultimate components of particle physics. And, we've been talking about all of those throughout this entire course. Force and energy. I think the core of particle physics is the matter itself, what are things made of; and that's certainly been the focus in this course. But when you're actually working out the mathematical details, all five of those ingredients take pretty much equal billing. Space and time is the framework, in which the particles live, and play, and interact, and we need to understand those. Right now our standard model involves all of those ingredients, but doesn't really unify or tie them together in the most elegant way that you could imagine. And so, science progresses. We continue to learn about particle physics.

We began this course asking, "Why do people care about this stuff?" And I had some answers then, and I'll give you some answers again now; and I hope that at this point you have your own answers. Everybody cares about this for different reasons. It speaks to us in our own personal way. You can think about spin-offs; particle physics is a very, very high-tech field of scientific knowledge. I mean, we are building giant accelerators, some of the most sophisticated, complex machinery ever designed, along with the space shuttle, and the telecommunication grid in the United States. Particle-physics accelerators are really high-tech, and there are spin-offs. There have always been medical spin-offs from this field, right from day one. When Roentgen discovered X-rays, the first of a new kind of radiation, within a year doctors were taking X-rays of people's bones. And this still happens today. Particle accelerators are used by neighboring medical facilities, sometimes for diagnosis, sometimes for treatment. People use proton beams, and pion beams, and anti-electron beams in order to image and to treat various medical ailments.

The magnets that are designed to make these super-high-energy particle beams go around in circles, at a particle accelerator like Fermilab, are themselves very high-tech devices. They're superconducting magnets, which required a lot of development of new materials, and new ideas. Now, I don't want to say that the particle physicists invented or discovered superconductivity; that's a separate branch of physics. But the fact that they're using them and developing them has led to spin-offs, has led to the development of this technology, and you know, this list just goes on and on. The World Wide Web is, in a very real sense, a spin-off of particle physics. It was the desire of particle physicists to have rapid, easy communication of scientific ideas across international laboratories that led to the development of this mechanism for communicating via computer. In fact, a lot of computer technology, both hardware and software, has been very, very strongly developed by particle physicists, who have to deal with enormous quantities of data, perhaps the largest data-storage problem of any branch of anything that I can think of. If you're collecting all these particles that are spewing out into your detectors from one of these modern accelerators, it's an enormous task. You need fast computers, you need big computers; and so there's been a lot of development there.

So those are techno spin-offs, and you can kind of go out and hunt for many, many more. Many of the accelerator public relations folks are interested in letting everybody know what this branch of science is giving us in our everyday lives. But, it is pretty esoteric physics. Particle physics is the most esoteric, the least connected in a direct way to our lives, of any other branch of physics or science that I can think of. Now, we've been talking about quarks, and neutrinos, and everybody realizes that these things are abstract. You can't see them, you can't hold a neutrino in your hand. It is fundamentally mathematical. It is a framework, an abstract framework for understanding the world. So it's no surprise that particle physicists don't have the best toys, or applications, that come from the work that they're doing.

There are many other spin-offs that aren't technological, they're scientific or intellectual. For instance, the biggest one that I can think of right off the bat is the field theory itself. Okay? The field theory, quantum field theory, is a mathematical framework that forms the basis for doing all of these calculations that I keep talking about. And that framework is very general. It just describes interactions when you have a complicated system. The basic idea of field theory is, you've got particle A and particle B communicating through a medium. The medium is the electric field, which can itself create matter-antimatter pairs. But the abstract idea here is, how do you have a system with lots of pieces, where piece A needs to communicate with piece B? And when you think about it that way, you begin to realize that this quantum field theory can be extended to many other situations, and has been over the years. In fact, parts of field theory were borrowed from other branches of science and mathematics, and many have been given back.

So biologists can talk about interacting systems through field theories. Physicists who are dealing with oh, say, liquid crystals, like you might see in a modern computer display, really have a system that has a field of liquid-crystal particles. Where you care about one particle interacting with another. And, they can actually use quantum field theory to help them to understand and describe that system. Even some economists have been trained as particle physicists, and then left the field and went into the stock-market business, and they write computer models in which they try to model stock-market phenomena using principles of field theory, to some limited success. They're dealing with a very complicated system that doesn not have some simple, simple objects right underneath it. The objects underneath the stock market are people, not quarks. And so, you're dealing with an intrinsically more complicated system. The mathematics are useful, but not quite as accurate in its predictive power.

This is one of the lovely things about particle physics, and yet another kind of motivation. It's not a spin-off, but just this kind of puzzle aspect. Particle physicists are solving deep puzzles about what the world is, and what it's made of. These are puzzles that have appealed to humans for a long time. People were asking these questions thousands of years ago and writing about them, and presumably it's a natural question. To look around you, and see all the complications in the world, and ask, can't we understand all this stuff in a simple way? Doesn't it all tie together? And it's wonderful that we've been so successful. Particle physicists are lucky. All right? They deal with the absolutely simplest ingredients; and trying to understand even simple things is hard enough. Then when you try to put that together to understand more complicated things, life just gets even tougher still. So this idea of science as a puzzle—particle physicists are lucky because their puzzle pieces, the building blocks, are really easy to work with.

I can't think of any reason why it had to be this way. The universe could have been a complicated place. You look around, you see all these different phenomena, and each phenomenon might have had a different explanation. I could imagine a universe that was chaotic, and random, and unpredictable. And, I think for a long time, people believed that they lived in such a universe. It's taken a lot of experimentation, and a lot of deep thinking, to realize that everything—everything—can be understood in terms of the interactions of quarks and leptons, via these limited number of forces that's available to them.

And finally, to me, there is this reductionistic pleasure. Okay? It appeals to me, just as a human being, to think that complicated things can be understood in terms of simpler things. So, it's not that particle physics can tell me how to make the perfect omelet, but I get pleasure out of thinking that an omelet is made of a certain set of ingredients. There are eggs, and there's butter, and there's cheese; and in specific ratios, and with a certain method of production, that's how I understand an omelet, as a reductionist. I think of its ingredients, and how they fit together to form this complicated and delicious whole. And then, I can keep asking that, well, so what is butter, after all? You can break butter down into smaller and smaller pieces until you get to a molecule of butter, and then you ask what is that, and why does it feel soft, and look yellow, and taste nice? And, we can understand all of the properties of butter, in principle, by looking at the carbon, and oxygen, and so on. Molecules that form together to make it. Which in turn, are made of protons and electrons, which in turn are made of quarks. I realize it's a kind of an absurd chain when you talk about an omelet and quarks in the same sentence. But nonetheless, I personally get some sense of satisfaction at the idea, just the conceptual idea, that we can understand stuff in this reductionistic way.

I said that was the last, but maybe the really, really last motivation for me is just plain old childlike curiosity. I think we all have this. Why is the world the way it is? I just want to know. I want to go out and do experiments. And to me, it's easier for me to tackle the simple questions. There are many physicists, and scientists, who would rather look at something complicated. They would rather look at an omelet, or a human body, and understand it. Not in terms of its ingredients, but just in all the myriad ways that you can understand a complicated object. That's, you know, absolutely legitimate science, which appeals to me as well. But somehow, for me, I find this basic stuff the most intriguing and the most exciting.

With what should you walk away from this course? You've spent a fair amount of time and mental energy trying to wrap your head around these esoteric concepts. The big, guiding idea here is that the world is orderly. The world is, at its core, made of some simple things with simple laws. And so, when you look around, and you see, either phenomena in your own life—or equally likely, maybe more likely—you read about phenomena in the newspaper, on PBS shows, reading whatever kind of scientific journal articles you might pick up at the newsstand you're going to be hearing about phenomena in the world—now you have a framework. No matter what happens. And, I anticipate great discoveries, right? There have always been great discoveries throughout our lifetimes, and there will surely be many, many more, some of them very deep. Some of them rattling the foundations of the standard model, perhaps. But always, I think you can take what you've learned in this course, and connect what you're hearing to what you know about how the world is made.

The world is made of protons and neutrons, which form nuclei, with electrons around them. That's apparently the way the world works, to the best of all of the data and observations that we've been able to make for 100 years. And, I can almost not imagine that that picture will go away. It will be deepened. It has already been deepened; the protons and neutrons are now understood to be made of quarks. So does that falsify my statement that the world is made of protons and neutrons? Not at all. We just understand now what a proton is, and what a neutron is. So it, similarly, I don't think quarks are ever going to go away, just like Newton's laws that were postulated, written down, in the 1600s have never gone away. We understand them more deeply now. Albert Einstein has extended their realm of applicability from ordinary life, cars and rocket ships and ordinary stuff, to black holes and the early universe. So I would anticipate all sorts of developments which deepen and broaden our understanding of the universe. But, I don't imagine that we're ever going to toss away all this knowledge that we've gained.

It's a wild idea, and it's one that takes people a long time to fully appreciate, that when you hear about exotic stuff, it does fit into this framework. It may extend it. It may deepen it. And that's your job from now on. To ask yourself, when you hear about something on the TV—it will usually be formulated in some sensational way, because that is human nature. Any physicist who makes a new discovery of a supersymmetric particle is going to say, "We've broken the standard model!" and it's going to make headlines. And now, your job is to say, "Ah, supersymmetry, I don't remember exactly what supersymmetry was," but of course the article will give you lots of explanation, which will hook it back into the standard-model framework. How are supersymmetric particles related to ordinary particles? What have they done to the standard model? How have they deepened it? What do we understand now? What of those big puzzles that people have been working on have they now finally understood?

Sometimes you will hear about results that are so sensational that you should be skeptical. One of the values of a course like this is for you to understand what is it that people are worrying about, and what is it that people aren't worrying about? So for example, if you hear a story on the news about somebody who has discovered a perpetual-motion machine, I want all your skepticism radar to come on full alert. That's not just an extension or a broadening of the standard model; that flies in the face of 100 years of data. What you're saying is that everybody was wrong all along; all of the data is wrong. And it's like saying oh, the earth is really flat; or the earth is the center of the universe. That is in direct contradiction with hundreds of years of data, and so—I suppose it could be true; maybe the Earth really is flat, and we've been fooling ourselves all along, but I'm pretty sure that's not the case. So, it's good to be skeptical. In fact, you should be skeptical as all-heck when people talk about the discovery of supersymmetry, or some new data on the top quark. All of this stuff is speculative, and all of it needs to fit together. Science forms a web, and there are always new strands, and there are always deeper layers. But, we can't just throw away what we already know.

So, I think that you are now equipped for this. It's also beneficial that there's a change in climate that I perceive. For example, in the funding agencies now, when I apply for a research grant, they insist that part of what I do with the federal funding from my research is outreach. All scientists and physicists are now being asked to think of ways to communicate what we're learning with the public. It's a wonderful idea. I think for far too long, physicists have been going off into never-never land, working their mathematics, understanding deep truths about the world, forming this lovely, coherent picture;

and, by not articulating it in words that are non-mathematical, we're sort of leaving people in the dark. We understand stuff. It's wonderful. It's great to have this sense that we understand how the world works, and I don't think that you have to be a mathematician, or a physicist, to appreciate these ideas. So I think, when you start to read about supersymmetric discoveries, there will be some effort, more effort than was made in the past, to try to explain what it is that they've discovered; string theory, or dark matter, or dark energy, or extra dimensions. All of these wild, crazy ideas that people are coming up with.

And so, I think that the framework that's set up in this course is going to hook in with the framework that you will be hearing and learning about, and allow you to make sense of all of this exotic stuff. You are equipped to evaluate what's interesting, and why it's interesting. You are equipped to understand, why do we care, and why do we believe in this stuff? Good luck, and enjoy.

Timeline

Useful online source of original papers:
http://dbserv.ihep.su/hist/owa/hw.part1

Prehistory: 400 B.C..... Democritus proposes *atomos*, the indivisible fundamental building blocks of matter.

1861–1868 .... James Clerk Maxwell unifies electricity and magnetism in a series of papers and proposes the electromagnetic nature of light.

1869 .... Mendeleev designs the periodic table of the elements.

1895 .... Discovery of x-rays (Wilhelm Rontgen, Nobel Prize, 1901).

1897 .... Discovery of the electron (J. J. Thomson, Nobel Prize, 1906).

1896–1900 .... Discovery of alpha, beta, and gamma rays (Pierre and Marie Curie, Nobel Prize, 1903; Henri Becquerel, Nobel Prize, 1903; Ernest Rutherford, Nobel Prize, 1908).

1900 .... The concept of quanta, $E = h\,nu$ (Max Planck, Nobel Prize, 1918). J. J. Thomson proposes a "plum pudding" model of the atom.

1905 .... Albert Einstein's "miracle year": special relativity, the photon concept with application to the photoelectric effect, and Brownian motion (Nobel Prize, 1921).

1909 .... Charge of the electron measured (Robert Millikan, Nobel Prize, 1923).

1911 .... Discovery of the atomic nucleus (Ernest Rutherford, with Hans Geiger and Ernest Marsden).

1912 .... Cosmic rays first observed (V. F. Hess, Nobel Prize, 1936, with Anderson). Cloud chamber invented (Charles Wilson, Nobel Prize, 1927, with Compton).

1913 .... Bohr model of the atom (Niels Bohr, Nobel Prize, 1922).

1915 .... General relativity (Albert Einstein).

1918 .... Emmy Noether's theorem relating symmetry to conservation laws.

1919 .... Rutherford observed first nuclear transmutation (alpha on nitrogen gives oxygen + proton). Proton as a fundamental particle is named.

1923 .... Louis de Broglie argues for wave-particle duality (Nobel Prize, 1929). Arthur Compton shows the particle-like nature of x-rays (Nobel Prize, 1927).

1925 .... Pauli formulates the exclusion principle and postulates new quantum property of the electron (Nobel Prize, 1945). This property, the spin, was introduced and quantified by Goudsmit and Uhlenbeck. Quantum mechanics developed in matrix form by Werner Heisenberg (Nobel Prize, 1932), followed by Erwin Schrödinger's wave mechanics (Nobel Prize, 1933).

1926 .... Born introduces the "probability interpretation" (Nobel Prize, 1954). The term *photon* is coined (Gilbert Lewis).

1927 .... Heisenberg's uncertainty principle. Wigner introduces *parity*.

1928 .... Dirac's relativistic wave equation (Nobel Prize, 1933).

1930 .... The neutrino is postulated (Pauli, named by Fermi). Cyclotron invented (Ernest Lawrence, Nobel Prize, 1939, and M. Stanley Livingston). Max Born says, "Physics as we know it will be over in six months."

1931 .... The Van de Graaff accelerator is invented. Dirac predicts antimatter.

1932 .... Positron discovered (Carl Anderson, Nobel Prize, 1936). Neutron discovered (James Chadwick, Nobel Prize, 1935).

1934 .... Beta decay theory written down (Fermi). Yukawa's theory of nuclear force (Nobel Prize, 1949).

1937 .... Experimental evidence for mesotron (now called muon) by Neddermeyer and Anderson, Street and Stevenson (I. I. Rabi later asked, "Who ordered that?").

1938 .... Nuclear fission of uranium observed (Otto Hahn, Fritz Strassmann, Ottto Frisch, Lise Meitner).

1939 .... Muon decay observed (Bruno Rossi).

1945 .... First nuclear weapons detonated.

1946 .... Big Bang theory proposed (George Gamow, named by Hoyle later to mock it).

1947 .... Discovery of pion and pion decay in cosmic rays (Perkins, Lattes, and others). Discovery of V particles in cloud chambers at Manchester (George Rochester and Clifford Butler) (now called *kaon* and *lambda*). Lamb shift measured (hydrogen fine structure) (Nobel Prize, 1955).

1948 .... QED developed by Richard Feynman, Julian Schwinger, and Shinichiro Tomonaga (Nobel Prize, 1965). Pions produced in accelerators (Berkeley synchrotron).

1949 .... Kaon decay observed (Brown et al.). Spark chamber invented (J. W. Keufel).

1950 .... Neutral pion and its decay discovered (Bjorklund, Panofsky, and Steinberger).

1952 .... Delta particle discovered (Anderson and Fermi). Bubble chamber invented (Donald Glaser). Brookhaven cosmotron accelerator opens.

1953 .... Associated production (later understood as strange particles) observed.

1954 .... First "gauge theory" with charged force carriers (C. N. Yang and Robert Mills).

1956 .... Anti-proton discovered (Berkeley bevatron). Anti-neutrinos from reactors observed (F. Reines and C. Cowan, Nobel Prize, 1995, shared with Martin Perl). Strangeness proposed (Murray Gell-Mann and Kazuhiko Nishijima). Parity violation predicted by T. D. Lee and C. N. Yang (Nobel Prizes, 1957).

1957 .... Parity violation observed (C. S. Wu).

1959 .... CERN (in Europe) and Brookhaven accelerator start operations.

1961 .... Kaon "regeneration" observed. Discovery of spin 1 (vector) mesons (rho, omega, eta).

1962 .... Accelerator production of neutrino beams. Muon-type neutrino is a separate flavor (Lederman, Schwartz, Steinberger, Nobel Prize, 1988).

1963 .... Cabibbo theory of weak decays.

1964 .... Quark model introduced (independently) by Murray Gell-Mann and George Zweig (Nobel Prize, 1969, to Gell-Mann). Omega-particle discovered (bevatron). CP violation in K0 decay discovered (James Cronin, Val Fitch, Nobel Prize, 1980). Higgs mechanism proposed (Peter Higgs, Robert Brout, and F. Englert). Color and gluons proposed (Greenberg, Nambu).

1965 .... Cosmic microwave background observed (Arno Penzias and Robert Wilson, Nobel Prize, 1978).

1966 .... Stanford linear accelerator (SLAC) starts operation.

1967 .... Electroweak unification (the *WSG electroweak model*) proposed independently by Steven Weinberg and Abdus Salam, based in part on contributions of Sheldon Glashow (Nobel Prize, 1979).

1968–1969 .... Deep inelastic scattering at SLAC: Bjorken scaling observed, evidence for partons argued by Feynman (Friedman, Kendall, and Taylor, Nobel Prize, 1990). Ray Davis's Homestake experiment first sees solar neutrino deficit.

1970 .... Proposal of charm (Glashow, Iliopoulos, and Maiani: the *GIM* mechanism).

1971–1972 .... Gerard 't Hooft proves renormalizability of electroweak theory (Nobel Prize, 1999).

1972 .... Fermilab begins operations.

1973 .... QCD developed (Gross, Wilczek, Politzer, Fritzsch, Gell-Mann, Leutwyler, Weinberg, and others). Neutrino experiments verify parton = quark (Gargamelle detector at CERN). Neutral weak current observed (Gargamelle detector at CERN). CKM matrix for weak decays (Cabibbo, Kobayashi, Maskawa).

1974 .... J/psi discovered, the "November Revolution" (S.C.C. Ting at Brookhaven, Burton Richter at SLAC, Nobel Prize, 1976). SU(5) grand unified theory proposed (Howard Georgi and Sheldon Glashow) (later shown to be incorrect because of incorrect predictions of proton decay).

1975 .... Charmed baryons discovered. Tau lepton discovered (Marty Perl, at SPEAR, SLAC, Nobel Prize, 1995, shared with Reines). Quark jets seen (at DESY, in Germany).

1976 .... CERN SPS (super-proton synchrotron) starts.

1977 .... Bottom/anti-bottom meson (upsilon) discovered at Fermilab (Leon Lederman). The standard model is now complete.

1978 .... Parity violation observed in neutral current reactions (SLAC).

1979 .... Three jets seen at PETRA (Germany), direct evidence for gluons.

1983 .... Discovery of Z and W bosons at CERN SPS (Carlo Rubbia's group, Nobel Prize, 1984).

1984 .... Superstring theory developed (Michael Green and John Schwarz).

1987 .... Supernova 1987a (detected with visible light and neutrinos!).

1989 .... Z0 copiously produced at LEP and SLC (number of neutrinos = 3).

1990 .... COBE (Cosmic Background Explorer) satellite returns high-precision data on the cosmic microwave spectrum.

1993 .... Gallium experiments confirm the solar neutrino problem. Atmospheric neutrino anomaly discovered in Japan's Kamiokande experiment. Precision Z0 measurements confirm standard model.

1995 .... Top quark discovered at Fermilab.

1996 .... SuperKamiokande neutrino detector begins operations in Japan.

2000 .... Tau neutrino discovered at Fermilab. Cosmic background radiation spectrum results from Boomerang and Maxima.

2002 .... Evidence for neutrino flavor oscillations from SNO detector in Canada.

Glossary

accelerator: Any device that creates high-speed, high-energy particles.

alpha radiation: When a material releases a stream of particles (radiation) that are, specifically, positively charged helium nuclei (two protons and two protons bound together). Caused by the strong force.

angular momentum: A quantitative measure of how rapidly objects turn.

antimatter: Particles that are "opposites" in most respects to ordinary particles; for example, an anti-electron has opposite sign of charge and opposite sign "electron number." However, it has the same mass and the same spin. Matter and antimatter will annihilate, producing pure energy.

associated production: The observation that the strong force conserves strangeness number; that is, in a strong interaction in which two particles are produced, if one has strangeness +1, the other will have strangeness −1.

asymptotic freedom: Quarks that are very close (that is, that interact with very high energy) feel almost no strong force. They are "free."

atom: The smallest building block of *chemistry*, an individual particle of an element. Physically, a heavy nucleus with electrons orbiting.

baryon: A strongly interacting particle with half-integer spin, such as a proton or neutron.

baryon number: A conserved quantum number, +1 for any baryon, −1 for any anti-baryon. No known violation of baryon number has yet been observed but is being investigated.

beta decay: When any particle or nucleus transforms to something else via the weak force, in the process, emitting an electron and (anti) neutrino.

beta radiation: When a material releases a stream of particles (radiation) that are, specifically, electrons. Caused by the weak force.

bevatron: A large nuclear accelerator located in Berkeley, CA. The name came from the beam energy, "billion eV," or BeV. (We would now call that a GeV.) This was the facility where, for example, the antiproton was first discovered.

Big Bang: The theory of the cataclysmic start of the universe. A point of infinite temperature and density, from which the universe was born. Currently estimated to be about 12–15 billion years ago.

boson: Any particle with integer spin (0, 1, 2...). Bosons may be in the same quantum state.

bottom quark: A heavy quark, in the "third generation," similar to a down quark (charge −1/3) but heavier.

broken symmetry: A symmetry of nature that has been hidden by accidental circumstance. For example, a magnet has a direction, even though the underlying forces are truly and precisely symmetrical. The direction is arbitrary, but once chosen, the underlying symmetry is broken and no longer apparent.

Brownian motion: The random "drunken walk" motion of tiny particles (e.g. pollen grains) drifting in a fluid. Observed by Brown in the 1800s, explained quantitatively by Einstein in 1905 as evidence of tinier (invisible) atoms bumping into the grains.

bubble chamber: A device to track charged particles (passing particles ionize a liquid, forming bubbles). Invented in the 1950s.

CERN: European Center for Nuclear Research; home of the largest, highest energy European accelerator.

charm quark: A heavy quark, in the "second generation," similar to an up quark but heavier. First found in the November Revolution in the form of a c-cbar meson.

cloud chamber: A device to track charged particles (passing particles ionize a vapor, forming droplets). Invented in the early 1900s.

color: The "charge" for the strong force. There are three colors.

confinement: The fact that quarks cannot be removed from hadronic matter. They are permanently connected into "colorless" objects.

conservation law: When some quantity remains unchanged during an interaction. For example, charge conservation states that the sum of all electric charges never changes in any particle reaction.

cosmic background radiation: Residual evidence of the Big Bang; low-energy (mostly microwave) photon "bath" we live in, which permeates the universe.

cosmology: The field of physics that studies the structure and evolution of the universe.

CP violation: A symmetry of nature that is slightly broken, effectively a "matter-antimatter" symmetry that is not exactly perfect. A topic of great current interest but not yet well understood or explained.

cyclotron: An older type of particle accelerator.

dark matter: Something that is present throughout much of the universe, carries mass, but does not emit visible radiation; therefore, we don't know what it is. Current estimates are that much of the universe is dark matter!

decay: When a particle transforms, emitting some other lower mass particles as a result. For example, a neutron decays in roughly nine minutes, emitting a proton, electron, and neutrino.

DESY: German high-energy accelerator facility.

detector: Any device designed to identify and characterize the properties of particles.

DIS (Deep Inelastic Scattering): Ultra-high energy particle experiments begun in the 1970s at SLAC. Deep means "very high energy;" the incident electrons come in and go deep into the heart of the nucleus. Inelastic means they give up much of their energy, rather than bouncing, like a rock smashing through a glass window. DIS gave us the first direct evidence for the existence of quarks inside protons and neutrons.

down quark: One of the two light quarks, with spin 1/2 and charge − 1/3. (The proton is two ups and a down; the neutron consists of two downs and an up.)

eight-fold way: An early theoretical model to explain regularities in the particle zoo, invented by Murray Gell-Man in 1964. It was the precursor to the idea of quarks.

electroweak theory: The unified quantum field theory of electromagnetism and the weak force. Coined by Salam; developed by Weinberg, Salam, and Glashow.

emulsion: An old, fairly simple detector technology, effectively just like photographic film.

eV: A unit of energy. 1 eV = 1.6×10^{-19} joules. It is a typical "atomic" energy scale.

family: Another name for a generation of particles; for example, the up and down quarks form the lightest family of quarks.

femtometer: A metric unit of distance, 10^{-15} meters; about the size of a proton. Abbreviated fm; sometimes called a "Fermi."

Fermilab: Highest energy accelerator operating in the United States; location of the Tevatron ring; accelerates protons and anti-protons.

fermion: Any particle with half-integer spin (1/2, 3/2, and so on), such as electrons, protons, quarks, and others.

Feynman diagram: Symbolic shorthand for quantum field theory calculations that resembles a "cartoon sketch" of the particle reaction.

field: The physical manifestation of a force of nature, present throughout space; an alternative way of thinking about forces as opposed to "action at a distance."

flavor: The name for the characteristic that distinguishes certain groups of otherwise similar particles. For example, there are three flavors of neutrino: electron type, mu type, and tau type.

force carrier: A particle which serves as the intermediary for a force of nature. For example, the proton is thought of as a particle, a tiny quantum bundle of energy which allows one charged particle to "feel" another one electromagnetically. The photon is then the electromagnetic force carrier.

gamma radiation: When a material releases a stream of high-energy electromagnetic waves (radiation) of very short wavelength.

gauge boson: The force carrier particle in any quantum field theory, such as the photon in QED, the gluon in QCD, and the W and Z in the electroweak theory.

gauge symmetry: An abstract symmetry of nature present for the three fundamental forces (strong, electromagnetic, and weak). The presence of gauge symmetry in a theory requires the existence of mass-less gauge bosons.

general relativity: Einstein's theory of gravity. Not yet consistent with quantum mechanics but spectacularly successful in all experiments to date.

GeV: A billion eV's, 10^9 eV. (See eV.)

gluon: The gauge boson (force carrier) of the strong force.

grand unification: The idea that, at very high energies, all forces of nature (strong, electromagnetic, weak, and ultimately, gravity) become one. They are different low-energy manifestations of one fundamental force. Not yet an established theory.

GUT: A theory of grand unification.

hadron: Any particle that interacts strongly. (Any object made up of quarks.)

Heisenberg uncertainty principle: A fundamental principle of quantum mechanics that certain observables (e.g. position and momentum) are intimately connected: the better you measure one of these quantities, the more uncertain the other must be. It's a quantitative statement of the idea that observations must affect the system being observed.

Higgs mechanism: The mathematics that makes the Higgs field special, breaking the electroweak symmetry, giving the W and Z bosons mass.

Higgs particle: The physical manifestation of the Higgs field; the last unproven piece of the standard model. Actively being sought.

interaction: A synonym for *force*; a way in which particles transform or perturb one another. For example, the weak interaction causes beta decay.

J/psi: The particle found in the November Revolution of 1974, a charm/anti-charm meson. Simultaneously discovered at SLAC and

Brookhaven. The particle that in some ways clinched the quark model in many physicists' minds.

kaon: A strange meson (see strangeness, meson); heavy relative of the pion.

Lamb shift: A tiny splitting in the light emitted by hydrogen atoms, indicative of subtle QED effects. The experimental push in 1947 to make QED a successful theory.

lepton: A class of spin 1/2 particles that do not interact strongly. The electron, muon, tau, and the three flavors of neutrinos are all the leptons.

meson: Any strongly interacting particle with integer spin. A bound state of quark and anti-quark. Lightest example is the pion.

MeV: A million eV's, 10^6 eV. (See eV).

molecule: A chemical building block that is not fundamental but built up out of a bound state of two or more atoms, such as an H_2O (water) molecule.

muon: A fundamental lepton, in the "second generation"; a heavy version of the electron. (I. I. Rabi asked, "Who ordered that?") Decays weakly into electron, mu-neutrino, and electron/anti-neutrino.

neutrino: A fundamental lepton, with (near) zero rest mass and zero charge. Interacts only weakly. It is under intense current investigation, because it is not known what the mass is or whether the three different flavors can oscillate from one to the other.

neutrino oscillation: When one flavor of neutrino spontaneously (through quantum mechanics) changes into a different flavor. Under current study at many facilities, this is not a part of the standard model.

neutron: Partner of the proton, electrically neutral baryon that is present in essentially all nuclei. Consists of d, d, and u quark.

Noether's theorem: A beautiful and important mathematical theorem relating symmetries of physical theories with conserved qualities.

November Revolution: The discovery of the J/psi particle in November 1974.

nucleon: A generic name for neutrons and protons, the "constituents of nuclei."

nucleus: A bound collection of protons and neutrons; the center of atoms.

parity: Mirror symmetry; the observation that the laws of physics are the same when viewed in a mirror.

parity violation: The breaking of parity symmetry. Only the weak interaction violates parity; for example, the weak interaction will produce "left-handed" particles but not "right-handed" ones in some reactions.

particle physics: The study of the fundamental constituents of nature and their interactions with one another.

Pauli exclusion principle: A quantum mechanical law stating that identical fermions cannot be in the same quantum state at the same time. This principle is responsible, in a very real sense, for much of chemistry.

periodic table: Mendeleev's organization of atoms into a simple "table," in increasing order of weight, which shows the underlying structure of atoms.

photoelectric effect: Explained by Einstein in 1905; when light hits a metal, it can eject electrons. The details can only be understood by postulating some "particle-like" properties to the light.

photon: The spin-1 gauge boson of electromagnetism, the quantum of light, the carrier of the electromagnetic force.

pion: Originally postulated by Yukawa as the carrier of the strong force, it is now simply the lightest meson, a spin-0 quark/anti-quark bound state. Comes in +, −, and zero charges; the charged versions decay weakly into a muon and muon neutrino.

positron: An anti-electron (see antimatter).

proton: The fundamental baryon, building block (with neutrons) of nuclei. Composed of two ups and a down. A stable particle as far as we know (still under investigation, but if it decays, the lifetime is very long).

QCD: Quantum chromodynamics, the quantum field theory describing the color force, the strong interaction between quarks.

QED: Quantum electrodynamics, the quantum field theory describing the electromagnetic force.

quanta: Chunks, of just about anything.

Quantum chromodynamics: See QCD.

Quantum electrodynamics: See QED.

quantum mechanics: The physical theory which tells how microscopic particles behave under the influence of forces.

quantum numbers: Properties of elementary particles that come in chunks; for example, the quantum numbers of a proton are: charge 1, strangeness 0, baryon number 1, lepton number 0, and so on.

quark: The fundamental spin 1/2 constituents of all strongly interacting objects. Quarks come in six flavors: u, d, s, c, t, b (up, down, strange, charm, top, bottom). Never found isolated; they always come as q-qbar (meson) or q q q (baryon). Quarks carry electric charge and color charge and experience all fundamental forces of nature (but the strong force generally dominates). The heavier quarks are not stable.

reductionism: The philosophical principle that complex systems can be understood once you know what they are made of and how the constituents interact.

relativity: Generic term usually reserved for Einstein's theory that describes the motion of particles moving at high speeds. Modifies our conventional views of space time and gravity. (It does not mean that "everything is relative.")

renormalizable: A quantum field theory that can be easily fixed up to yield finite results.

renormalization: A mathematical technique to take a quantum field theory, which generally produces infinite results, and "fix up" a *small* number of formal "bare" quantities so that, after adding the infinite quantum corrections, you match experimental data in the end. Once you do this for the small number of quantities, every other observable is then finite and well determined.

RHIC: Relativistic Heavy Ion Collider. A nuclear physics accelerator in Brookhaven, NY, just recently opened. Produces high-energy, heavy particles to make high-density, high-temperature collisions.

SLAC: Stanford Linear Accelerator Center. A two-mile-long electron accelerator, now up to a maximum of almost 100 GeV. Extremely successful and long-lived accelerator.

solar neutrino: A neutrino emitted from the nuclear reactions in the core of the sun. Generally very low in energy, but there are a lot of them.

solar wind: A constant stream of energetic particles emitted by the sun.

special relativity: Einstein's 1905 theory describing the motion of particles moving at high speeds. Modifies our conventional views of space and time. (*Special* means the theory is limited to observers moving with steady velocity and ignores gravity.)

spin: A quantum property of particles. It is somewhat analogous to "rotational angular momentum," how fast something is spinning, but applies even to point particles. Spin is quantized. Particles can have spin 1/2, 3/2, 5/2, and so on (fermions) or 0, 1, 2, and so on (bosons). (Those numbers are really expressed in units of h/2 pi, where h is Planck's constant, 6.63×10^{-34} Joule × sec.) Spin can also be thought of as describing degrees of freedom of a particle; for example, spin 1/2 particles have two degrees of freedom (up or down).

SSC: Superconducting Supercollider, the failed U.S. mega-project that would have produced protons at extreme energies to search for the Higgs and learn about electroweak symmetry breaking.

standard model: The theory of fundamental particles. It consists of a list of the particles and their properties (the quarks and leptons and the Higgs, their charges and masses) and the theories that describe their interactions, specifically, QCD and the electroweak theory.

strange quark: A second-generation quark, charge −1/3, heavy relative of the down quark.

strangeness: A quantum number of hadrons that effectively just counts how many strange quarks are in the object (times −1, technically). Strangeness number is conserved by all forces except the weak force.

string theory: A tentative fundamental theory of nature in which particles are described not as points, but as tiny strings, living in ten (or more) dimensions. This theory appears to give finite results, unifies all four forces, leads to general relativity, and may also yield the standard model as its "low-energy limit." Under active investigation as the ultimate theory of nature; stay tuned.

strong interaction: One of the four known fundamental forces; binds quarks together. (May also refer to the residual force that binds protons and neutrons together.) Responsible for alpha decays.

superconductor: A metal that conducts electricity with zero resistance. Used to make ultra-powerful magnets; needed in high-energy accelerators to bend particles.

supersymmetry: A hypothesized additional symmetry of nature that relates fermions and bosons. Not yet experimentally verified. If supersymmetry exists, every particle should have a supersymmetric "partner," probably heavier, differing by 1/2 unit of spin. Supersymmetric partners of fermions are named by adding an *s* in front (selectron, squark, and so on), while partners of bosons are named by adding an *ino* on the end (photino, gluino, Wino, and so on).

symmetry: When a system appears unchanged after some specific change is made to it (such as rotating a cube by 90 degrees or replacing a proton with a neutron in a strong interaction).

synchrotron: A circular accelerator using electric fields to speed up charged particles and magnetic fields to make them travel in a circular path. A synchrotron is designed to handle even relativistic particles.

tevatron: The name for the latest accelerator facility at Fermilab, in Chicago. TeV stands for "Terra-eV" or "trillion electron volt," a measure of the highest energies the protons in the ring can achieve. This is the facility where the top quark and tau neutrino were discovered.

TOE: Theory of Everything. The dream of particle physicists, an ultimate theory that unifies all four fundamental forces and all particles. String theory is a candidate. It is still only a theory of subatomic particles, so the name is misleading. You will not be able to figure out tomorrow's weather any better with a TOE.

top quark: The most massive quark of all, the third-generation partner of up and charm. Found at Fermilab in 1995 but predicted and expected since 1975.

translation symmetry: The symmetry of nature which states that the laws of physics are the same at any place in the universe. (Think of "translation" as meaning "moving sideways.") This does not say that conditions are the same—clearly the inside of the sun is hotter than my house, but the laws of nature are still the same there.

unification: The goal of physicists to find a deep connection between forces. Electricity and magnetism were unified by Maxwell in the 1860s; they are both manifestations of one underlying "electromagnetic field."

up quark: One of the two light quarks, with spin 1/2 and charge +2/3. (The proton is two ups and a down; the neutron consists of two downs and an up.)

vacuum fluctuations: The vacuum refers to empty space. Even in empty space, quantum mechanics allows for the bizarre possibility that particle anti-particle pairs can spontaneously spring into a tenuous, "virtual" existence for a brief time before re-annihilating into nothing. The bubbling background, which exists everywhere, is called "vacuum fluctuations."

Van de Graaff accelerator: One of the earliest particle accelerators, this device built up very high voltages (in order of 1 million volts). Often seen today in science museums and physics lecture demonstrations.

W or W-boson: A carrier of the weak force. W's are electrically charged; for example, a neutron can decay into a proton and a W-boson. The W-boson then decays into an electron and an electron anti-neutrino. Weighs about 80 times as much as a proton.

weak boson: A generic term for the W's and Z's.

weak interaction: One of the four fundamental forces of nature, responsible for beta decay, and the only force that neutrinos feel. All particles feel the weak interaction.

x-rays: High-energy electromagnetic radiation. Often as a synonym for gamma rays, although x-rays connote slightly lower energy radiation.

Z, or Z-boson: A carrier of the weak force. Z's have no electric force; they transmit the "weak neutral current." For example, when a neutrino scatters from another particle, it can emit a (virtual) Z particle, much like an electron scatters by emitting a (virtual) photon. Weighs about 90 times as much as a proton.

Biographical Notes

A biographical list of "key contributors" to the development of particle physics is almost impossible, because the number of contributors is huge! Although famous physicists often get sole credit for their accomplishments, the great discoveries are inevitably part of a web of scientific progress. Truly significant contributions come from both brilliant and more mediocre scientists, not to mention the support from graduate and sometimes undergraduate students, technicians, lab assistants, and others. Most of the discoveries in physics have a complex lineage; historians can (and do) quibble about the attributions and origins of almost every idea in the field. Some ideas get "rediscovered" or further developed, then attributed to the one who was better able to spread the word. What follows is an extraordinarily abbreviated list of some of the most famous names in the field. The large number left out is painful to this "biographer"—especially the more recent contributors, whose number is large and growing.

To learn more, a starting point is with Nobel Prize winners. Even among this select group, I have left many out! The Nobel site, www.nobel.se/physics/ laureates, is a good starting place. (Another good site for more biographies is www.gap-system.org/~history/BiogIndex.html.) Of course, many of the reference texts for this course also contain extended biographies of various subsets of key players.

Niels Bohr (b. 1885, d. 1962, Nobel Prize 1922)

A Danish physicist who lived much of his life in Copenhagen, Niels Bohr is known as the first physicist who made the transition from classical to quantum understanding of atoms. He was infamous for his mumbling; many people recount stories of listening intently to the great Niels Bohr, only to have no idea afterward what he said. As a postdoctoral researcher, he worked briefly in Ernest Rutherford's lab starting in 1911. He expanded Rutherford's classical "solar-system" model of an atom into what is now known as a semi-classical, or hybrid quantum model. Quantum mechanics did not yet exist, but Bohr's model of the atom introduced many of the qualitative ideas of quantum physics and helped provide a stepping stone to the more fully developed theory of the 1920s and 1930s. Ten years later, Bohr helped create and direct the Institute of Theoretical Physics in Copenhagen (now known as the Niels Bohr

Institute). Although Bohr himself did not make so many direct significant contributions to the quantitative development of quantum mechanics, his leadership, philosophy, and guidance were of essential and fundamental importance. Bohr helped develop ways of interpreting quantum mechanics; in fact, we now refer to the *Copenhagen interpretation* of quantum mechanics when discussing how to think about quantum physics. His famous debates with Einstein helped further establish quantum mechanics.

Marie Curie (b. 1867, d. 1934, Nobel Prize [physics] 1903, Nobel Prize [chemistry] 1911)

One of the most famous pioneers in the early days of modern physics and inventor of the term *radioactivity*, Marie Sklodowska left her native Poland in 1891 (where opportunities for advanced studies were extremely limited for women) to study math and physics in France. She married Pierre Curie in 1895, a like-minded, similarly energetic and brilliant scientist. Marie became interested in Becquerel's new discovery of "uranium rays" and decided to pursue a Ph.D. in this field. She maintained her fascination with radioactivity throughout her professional career. Curie was the first person to understand, based on her research, that radioactivity was not a chemical phenomenon, but linked to the atomic nucleus. She worked closely with her husband, Pierre (until his untimely death in a street accident in 1906), often in extremely difficult circumstances, arduously isolating, then studying radioactive elements, including polonium (which Curie named after her native Poland). She isolated a tenth of a gram of pure radium from literally tons of raw material, all worked and processed by hand. She received her Ph.D. in 1903, the same year she got the Nobel Prize! She received her second Nobel (the first person ever to do so) in chemistry, for her work in isolating and studying the radioactive element radium. (Her daughter, Irene, would later win the Nobel Prize in chemistry for the discovery of artificial radioactivity.) Marie Curie died of leukemia at the age of sixty-seven, possibly the result of massive exposure to radioactive materials during her career.

P.A.M. Dirac (b. 1902, d. 1984, Nobel Prize 1933)

Paul Dirac was an extraordinarily brilliant man, raised in England with a Swiss father and British mother. He was a man of few words. As a child, his father insisted that only French should be spoken at the dinner table. As a result, Dirac never said much! Acquaintances joked that his vocabulary was "yes," "no," and "I don't know." Still, his papers were beautifully written; he was inspired by the beauty of mathematics. He had eleven papers in print by the time he got his Ph.D. at age twenty-four. Along with developing the new theory of quantum mechanics, Dirac struggled with combining relativity with quantum mechanics; he wanted his quantum equation to satisfy Einstein's special theory of relativity. The Dirac equation is an elegant mathematical marriage of those two theories. This equation predicted the existence of antimatter, which was later experimentally discovered.

Dirac worked briefly with Bohr as a postdoc in 1926 and received his Nobel Prize in 1933 (along with Schrödinger). His mother went with him to Stockholm; he was thirty-one at the time. Dirac made a large number of other significant contributions during his career, including the introduction of an extraordinarily powerful mathematical notation, now called *bra's* and *ket's* for the little brackets he used, which is indispensable in practical quantum mechanical calculations. Dirac held the Lucasian chair of mathematics at Cambridge University (held earlier by Isaac Newton and, currently, by Stephen Hawking) for thirty-seven years.

Albert Einstein (b. 1879, d. 1955, Nobel Prize 1921)

Born in Germany, Einstein is surely the most brilliant and famous physicist of the twentieth century. (There are countless biographies available; I would urge you to read more about this fascinating man. His own writings are often surprisingly accessible, as well.) His contributions to physics are extraordinarily broad and far-ranging and, in several cases, profoundly changed the way we conceptualize the physical world. In 1905 (his "miracle year"), Einstein was a young man working in a patent office, doing physics in his spare time; he had not been able to secure a university position. He published three papers that year, any one of which would have put him on history's top ten list of physicists. One of those papers was on the special theory of relativity, which changed our understanding of the nature of space and time. Another was on Brownian motion, a paper that effectively put to rest the longstanding debate, both physical and philosophical, regarding the existence of atoms. The third was on the photoelectric effect, which was in a real sense the birth of quantum mechanics. That paper extended and generalized Max Planck's ideas. Einstein was the first to appreciate the true depth of the idea that photons are quanta, or "chunks," of energy. (Technological applications of this concept abound today, from electric eyes to solar panels.) Roughly ten years later, Einstein published his work on general relativity, in which he explained and described a theory of gravity that once again revolutionized how we conceive of space and time.

In his later life, Einstein struggled to find a grander "unified theory," with no success. He also argued frequently against the quantum theory that he had helped give birth to, saying famously, "God does not play dice with the universe." This was not a religious commentary, but a statement that he found the random nature of quantum mechanics philosophically unacceptable. Although he was, in the end, demonstrably wrong in this attitude, his constant questioning of the then-young theory of quantum mechanics played an important role in its early development.

Enrico Fermi (b. 1901, d. 1954, Nobel Prize 1938)

Enrico Fermi was an Italian physicist, famous as perhaps the last physicist who was both a brilliant experimentalist and world-class theorist. Fermi paved the path to nuclear power (and weapons) and, along the way, played a central role in the development of both quantum mechanics and nuclear physics. Fermi's self-confident but casual and open style was in sharp contrast with the somewhat elitist approach of German physicists of that era and heavily influenced the following generation of physicists, many of whom worked or studied with him. (Fermi was also famous for his "Fermi problems," realistic puzzles involving logic, numeracy, and basic physics principles; his ability to make quantitative estimates of the solution to such vague but real-life problems was truly impressive.)

The number of physics terms with *Fermi* as an adjective is mind-boggling: Fermi constant, Fermi statistics, Fermions, the Fermi (a unit of length, roughly the size of a proton, 10^{-15} m), Fermi gas, Fermi sea, Fermi energy, Fermi momentum, Fermilab, Fermium (element number 100 in the periodic table), and the list goes on. Fermi named the neutrino and developed the first mathematical theory of the weak interaction (beta decays). He studied the physics of neutrons early in his career and pions, later. He escaped fascist Italy (his wife was Jewish), using his Nobel Prize in 1938 as a tool to emigrate to the United States. Once there, he worked on experiments that led to the first successful controlled nuclear chain reaction (under the sports stadium at the University of Chicago!). After the war, he fought the development of the H-bomb on ethical grounds. Fermi died very young, of cancer, still in his prime as a physicist.

Richard Feynman (b. 1918, d. 1988, Nobel Prize 1965)

Born and raised in New York and one of the most engaging and charismatic figures in recent physics history, Richard Feynman can be characterized, in my opinion, as the greatest physicist of the second half of the twentieth century. Irreverent, egotistical, brilliant, a true scholar and teacher, Feynman made contributions to a wide variety of branches of physics. His Nobel Prize work was for the development of QED, the quantum theory of light. One of the great aspects of that work was his invention of the *Feynman diagram*, a simple cartoon-like sketching device that represents a quantitative mathematical formula. These diagrams are ubiquitous now, not just in QED but in almost any branch of modern physics, allowing one to think qualitatively about complex physical processes while retaining the mathematics "underneath" the pictures. Feynman played a central role in the ongoing development of particle physics after QED, including his insightful interpretation of high-energy data from SLAC (the Stanford Linear Accelerator) in terms of *partons*, later to become quarks.

A number of biographies of Feynman are available (see the Bibliography). His own writings on physics are inspiring and delightful. In the 1960s, Feynman decided to "rewrite the book" on freshman physics. The result, his famous *Feynman Lectures*, is on the shelf of almost any professional physicist. However, by his own admission, the lectures were not a complete success with the CalTech freshmen for whom he had intended them. (His autobiographies may annoy you because of his ego and occasional lack of respect for others, but if you can get past that, they are fascinating and entertaining.)

Murray Gell-Mann (b. 1929, Nobel Prize 1969)

Murray Gell-Mann a professor first at Chicago, then at CalTech, was a prime driver in our understanding of the strongly interacting particles, the quarks. A colleague of Feynman, Gell-Mann's style was quite different; Gell-Mann was literate and a bit sophisticated in his tastes, wearing fine clothes, but still with a great sense of humor and whimsy. His broad interests led one colleague to say, rather facetiously, "Murray has no particular talent for physics, but he's so smart he's a great physicist anyway." He invented the concept of *strangeness*, later understood to signal the presence of a new, heavier form of matter (the *strange particle*). He developed a mathematical framework based on symmetry, which he called the *eight-fold way*, to explain the properties of the rapidly expanding "zoo" of particles being discovered at accelerators in the 1960s. (The name was borrowed from Eastern mystical teachings, a reference that Gell-Mann later came to regret when his rigorous mathematical theories were sometimes misinterpreted as esoteric or philosophically vague.) Gell-Mann's development of the consequences of nuclear symmetries led to his articulation and naming of the *quark model*, which forms the underpinnings of our modern theory of QCD (quantum chromodynamics, the theory of the strong force.) His choice of particle name came from James Joyce's *Finnegan's Wake*, with a passage beginning "three quarks for Muster Mark!"—an appropriate name for what seemed, at the time, like a perfectly absurd particle of nature.

Werner Heisenberg (b. 1901, d. 1976, Nobel Prize 1932)

A German physicist who was the first to create a mathematical theory of quantum mechanics at the young age of twenty-three, publishing the work in 1925. Heisenberg argued that a theory should refer only to quantities that can be *observed*, an idea that played a guiding role in the development of quantum physics. Heisenberg was very much a mathematician; he nearly failed to get his Ph.D. because of his weakness with laboratory work. He joined Niels Bohr's Institute in 1926 for a productive year. In 1927, Heisenberg developed his famous *uncertainty principle*, which states that one cannot, in principle, have precise simultaneous knowledge of the momentum and position of a particle. (This principle is, in fact, a rigorous, mathematically derivable statement that contains useful quantitative, predictive power. It is far more than just a curious philosophical idea.) During World War II, Heisenberg spent five years directing the unsuccessful German atomic bomb project, a period in his life which remains somewhat controversial. (There has even been a recent Broadway play about this.) He was imprisoned by the allies briefly after the war but was returned to Germany in 1946, where he established the Max Planck Institute and served as its director until his retirement.

James Clerk Maxwell (b. 1831, d. 1879)

A Scotsman, born without privilege or high social rank, Maxwell worked in the field of mathematical physics, and electricity and magnetism, during the 1800s, when the scientific community was tackling this "exotic" field with great vigor. Maxwell was especially intrigued by the discoveries of Michael Faraday (himself a man with humble beginnings) who had introduced the concept of *force field* as a physically relevant entity. Maxwell succeeded in mathematically describing *all* phenomena of electric and magnetic origin in a set of four relatively simple equations, now called *Maxwell's equations*. Most of those had been developed over the previous decades by others, but Maxwell organized and formalized them, adding a key component based not on experiment, but on his own aesthetic mathematical sense of symmetry, intimately and permanently unifying electricity and magnetism. Maxwell discovered that these equations led to the phenomenon of *traveling electromagnetic (EM) radiation*—moving at the speed of light—and with this, realized the deep connection to optics, as well.

Today, Maxwell's equations and the corresponding unification of forces are regarded as one of the grand highlights of human intellectual achievement. They form the basis of electrical engineering and modern optics and have survived the discoveries of modern physics in the twentieth century essentially unscathed. They paved the way for the discovery of relativity (being fully relativistic equations, even though Maxwell didn't appreciate that!) and form the classical underpinnings of QED, the quantum theory of light. The study of Maxwell's ideas generally forms the second half of any standard college-level introductory physics course.

Isaac Newton (b. 1643, d. 1727)

The father of physics, indeed of all modern science. In many ways, I can think of few individuals of the last 1000 years who had more direct and profound influence on the human condition. Isaac Newton's masterwork, the *Principia*, articulated not only a number of physical laws, but also the scientific method itself. Newton's laws describe and explain motion and gravity. When faced with the need to solve the equations he developed, Newton *invented* the calculus required to solve them. Newton's central laws are *universal*, applicable to any system in any circumstance. Even today, their accuracy and power is extraordinary. Although Newton's laws must be extended under extreme conditions (such as for objects traveling near the speed of light), they still form the basis for much of modern technology. Newton did both theory and experiment; his research touched and formed the roots of many branches of modern physics, including optics, thermodynamics (heat), fluids, and more. Students in freshman physics learn about Newton's work in their first semester (then repeatedly, with further depth, as they progress). The metric unit of force, the *Newton*, is named in his honor. Newton was not a pleasant or easy man. He had a big ego, never married, and had many disputes over intellectual priorities during his life. However, in an uncharacteristic but famous quote, he said, "If I have seen further, it is by standing on the shoulders of giants."

Emmy Noether (b. 1883, d. 1935)

Although not a physicist, this mathematician played a significant role in the early conceptual understanding of modern theoretical physics. Born and raised in Germany, Noether persevered in a system heavily biased against women in academia. She studied mathematics at university but was only allowed to sit in on classes unofficially. Even then, professors had to give permission individually. She studied under some of the great mathematicians whose names are also linked with developments of modern physics: Hilbert (whose work is now applied in quantum mechanics), Klein (general relativity and field theory), and Minkowski (special relativity). Noether later did her Ph.D. work with a mathematician whose work would also become closely tied to future physics developments, Paul Gordon (quantum mechanics and gauge field theories). Normally, such a brilliant and promising student in Germany would get a still higher degree ("habilitation"), but this was forbidden for women at the time. Noether helped her father, also a mathematician, and continued working, doing research, and supervising doctoral students, all without pay. (Hilbert, in attempting to get her a faculty position, said, "I do not see that the sex of the candidate is an argument against her admission as Privatdozent. After all, we are a university and not a bathing establishment.") Noether's publication list and reputation grew rapidly, but it took twelve years until she successfully petitioned to obtain the habilitation.

In 1915, she published the work that is most directly relevant to particle physicists, now known as *Noether's theorem*. Albert Einstein praised this work, calling it "penetrating mathematical thinking." The bulk of Noether's further research was in a field known as abstract algebra, which has also played a role in quantum mechanical theory. By 1922, she started receiving a small salary but was still without tenure. (Noether was also a Jew, a Social Democrat, and an outspoken pacifist, none of which was much help in that regard.) She left Germany in 1933 for the United States, as a result of Nazi dismissal of Jewish faculty. She spent several years teaching and working as a visiting professor at Bryn Mawr in Pennsylvania. Emmy Noether died quite young, of complications after a surgery. Albert Einstein, in a tribute to Noether in the *New York Times* on May 5, 1935, wrote:

> In the realm of algebra, in which the most gifted mathematicians have been busy for centuries, she discovered methods which have proved of enormous importance... Pure mathematics is, in its way, the poetry of logical ideas... In this effort toward logical beauty, spiritual formulas are discovered necessary for deeper penetration into the laws of nature.

Wolfgang Pauli (b. 1900, d. 1958, Nobel Prize 1945)

Born in Vienna, Wolfgang Pauli was in many respects the theoretical leader of the development of quantum mechanics in the 1920s and 1930s. Pauli even impressed Albert Einstein when, in his sophomore year in college, he published a brilliant review article explaining special relativity for a mathematical encyclopedia. Pauli spent a year with Bohr in Copenhagen (1922–1923) and, soon after, developed his famous "Pauli exclusion principle," which states that no two quantum particles (of spin 1/2) may exist in the same quantum state. This law of nature has tremendous applications. It explains, among many other things, the chemistry and properties of the periodic table of the elements and the structure of atomic nuclei. In 1931, Pauli predicted the existence of a new particle of nature, later called the neutrino, although it was several years before he would actually publish a paper about it. Pauli was always a sharp thinker and, ever skeptical, able to poke holes in anyone's theory. He was quite intolerant of sloppy thinking, striking fear in the hearts of visiting speakers when he sat in the front row. He is famous for his quips, such as stating that a paper was "not even wrong." To a postdoc, he once said, "I don't mind your thinking slowly. I mind your publishing faster than you think." Still, for his brilliant, critical, and honest thinking, Pauli has been called by some "the conscience of physics."

Max Planck (b. 1858, d. 1947, Nobel Prize 1918)

A German physicist who started his career studying thermodynamics (heat), a branch of physics that was well established by the late 1800s. When Planck entered university at age sixteen, he was told that physics was essentially a complete science with little prospect of further developments. Fortunately, he decided to study physics despite the bleak future for research that was presented to him! He got his Ph.D. by age twenty-one. Planck's fame arises from his work on the question of electromagnetic radiation emitted by hot objects. It had been established that classical physics (Maxwell's equations, combined with thermodynamics) not only couldn't explain the data but also gave nonsensical, infinite results. After what Planck called "the most strenuous work of my life," he was able to describe the data by postulating that electromagnetic radiation was *quantized* in its interaction with matter, following a characteristic formula he derived. ($E = hf$, which states that the energy of a bundle of light is a constant, h, times the frequency of the light). This was the birth of quantum mechanics. The idea that energy comes in chunks, or bundles, *quanta*, was a stroke of genius, a thoroughly nonclassical and unexpected concept. Interestingly, Planck's contributions to quantum theory didn't continue after this and, in fact, he was not convinced by the developments in quantum theory that arose from his work. The constant h that appears in the equation he developed, and in essentially all quantum mechanics formulas since, is now named *Planck's constant*, in his honor.

Ernest Rutherford (b. 1871, d. 1937, Nobel Prize 1908)

Born in New Zealand but living his life in England, Rutherford was a brilliant experimentalist, the first of the modern breed of particle physicists. He was a bear of a man, with a loud voice and a strong personality. Working at the Cavendish Laboratories, Rutherford was the first person to identify the types of radiation emitted by naturally radioactive substances. He recognized that radioactivity represented the transformation of elements from one type to another. Rutherford's experiments with Hans Geiger and Ernest Marsden (an undergraduate) helped him formulate the classical but thoroughly modern picture of an atom as a composite object with a tiny, heavy nucleus at the center and electrons in orbit. His famous quote about this experiment is: "It was quite the most incredible event that ever happened to me in my life. It was as if you fired a 15-inch artillery shell at a piece of tissue paper and it came back and hit you." Rutherford later showed that he could send alpha particles onto nitrogen and convert atoms into oxygen, the first deliberate "transmutation of elements" accomplished by humans. In his later life, Rutherford remained active, administrating the Cavendish Labs and guiding many future physicists in their early careers. Shortly before his death, Rutherford said, "Anyone who expects a source of power from the transformation of these atoms is talking moonshine." (The first nuclear chain reaction was constructed shortly after his death.)

Abdus Salam (b. 1926, d. 1996, Nobel Prize 1979)

Born and raised in Pakistan, Abdus Salam was a mathematically precocious child, getting his Ph.D. by age twenty-five. His major work and contributions were in the mathematical development of what is now called the standard model, in particular, the unification of the weak and electromagnetic forces of nature. He coined the phrase *electroweak theory* and made significant contributions to issues in modern quantum mechanics. Salam predicted, on the basis of his theories, the existence of the weak neutral current (a new form of fundamental interaction) and of W and Z particles (carriers of the weak force), before they were experimentally identified. In many aspects, his work paralleled, but was independent of, the theoretical efforts of Steven Weinberg. Salam left Pakistan in 1957; spent many years as a professor in Imperial College, London; and later went on to direct the International Center for Theoretical Physics in Trieste, Italy, where he made great strides in improving the connections and opportunities for third-world physicists to participate in world-class research. A pious and devout Muslim, Salam also worked for many years with various UN committees to encourage the advancement of science and technology in developing nations.

Erwin Schrödinger (b. 1887, d. 1961, Nobel Prize 1933)

An Austrian with broad intellectual interests and a distinctly unconventional personal style, Schrödinger is most famous for the equation that bears his name, the fundamental wave equation of quantum mechanics. Schrödinger served in the German army in World War I and submitted two theory papers from the front. As a young physicist, he was asked to give a colloquium on the thesis of de Broglie, and a physicist in the audience commented that he thought this way of talking was rather childish: "To deal with waves, one has to have a wave equation." Schrödinger found that equation in 1926. He is said to have developed the ideas when on holiday with a Viennese girlfriend. (He had many lovers, not always secret from his wife.) Although his work on quantum mechanics followed Heisenberg's, it was in a form that was mathematically more accessible to other physicists. His equation is still the way that quantum mechanics is generally first taught to students today. (He later proved that it is mathematically equivalent to Heisenberg's methods.) Schrödinger's equation was spectacularly successful and opened the way to quantitative (versus qualitative) calculations with the new theory of quantum mechanics. He left Germany in 1933 because of his discomfort with the growing Nazi presence, later returned to Vienna, and ended his career in Dublin. Interestingly, Schrödinger, too, had a hard time with the philosophical implications of the theory he helped develop. He said, "Had I known that we were not going to get rid of this damned quantum jumping, I never would have involved myself in this business."

Steven Weinberg (b. 1933, Nobel Prize 1979)

Steven Weinberg was one of the central figures in the development of the electroweak theory and the standard model. He made the first quantitative prediction of the mass of the W and Z bosons, well before their experimental discovery. His work has spanned the broadest spectrum of issues in particle physics, including strong and weak interactions, neutrino physics, astrophysics, cosmology, and grand unification. He has written several books aimed at the general public and has been a passionate, articulate, and prominent spokesman for support and dissemination of high-energy physics. He is currently a professor at the University of Texas in Austin.

Bibliography

Essential Reading

Barnett, R. M., Muhry, H., Quinn, H. R., *The Charm of Strange Quarks*, New York: Springer-Verlag, 2000. Very readable and up-to-date; a great collection of pictures, anecdotes, and well-organized summaries and explanations. A few symbols and equations, on a level roughly similar to Cindy Schwarz's book (college level but not overly technical; perhaps a slightly higher assumption about the reader's tolerance for "light" math).

Kane, Gordon, *The Particle Garden: Our Universe as Understood by Particle Physicists*, Cambridge: Perseus Publishing, 1996. An excellent text that summarizes many of the central ideas of contemporary particle physics without getting into technicalities. Well written, aimed at a general audience.

Schwarz, Cindy, *A Tour of the Subatomic Zoo*, New York: AIP, 1996. Used as a textbook in an undergraduate course for non-science majors with no physics background, this book is perhaps not quite so entertainingly "readable" as some others, but it is accessible and contains some *slightly* more technical details for the reader who wants to go a little beyond the purely descriptive, qualitative, story level.

't Hooft, Gerard, *In Search of the Ultimate Building Blocks*, Cambridge: Cambridge University Press, 1996. A firsthand account from one of the key theorists who helped create the standard model ('t Hooft won the 1999 Nobel Prize for these contributions). He has tried hard to write a book without math or technical detail and succeeds for the most part; the level is accessible (perhaps on a par with Krauss), although I can't call it easy (especially the last few chapters). But he has a great talent for making analogies with real-world (and, thus, comprehensible) phenomena to explain esoteric ideas.

Weinberg, Steven, *Dreams of a Final Theory*, New York: Vintage Books, 1993. A firsthand account from a key theorist who helped create the standard model (Weinberg won the 1979 Nobel Prize for his contributions). This book is certainly not a textbook (no equations or math whatsoever), nor a typical "summary of particle physics," but it waxes a bit more philosophical about the goals and ideas of modern physics. You may find Weinberg philosophically provocative, but this is a highly literate and pleasurable book.

Recommended Reading

Bodanis, David, $E=mc^2$, New York: Walker and Co., 2000. Bodanis is not a physicist, and this book is not about particle physics, but it is a more personal tale of Einstein's famous equation, which of course plays a central role in our understanding of particles and their dynamics. The book is *far* from technical; it's not really even centered on the physics, but rather on the stories, characters, and history leading up to (and following) the development of the equation. The guide for further reading at the end is a good one, with nice descriptions.

Bromley, D. Allan, *A Century of Physics*, Heidelberg: Springer, 2002. This lovely book consists of very short (paragraph-long) discussions of key events and people in the development of physics over the last 100 years, with lots of great pictures. It's a "tour book," beautiful to look at and fun to peruse.

Calle, Carlos, *Superstrings and Other Things: A Guide to Physics*, Bristol: IOP, 2001. Very readable text at a level accessible to a non-science undergraduate. It covers a lot of physics, not just particles. Calle very occasionally uses numbers and equations, at a similar (or slightly higher) level than the Schwartz or Barnett texts, but still nowhere approaching a "physics text" in terms of math requirements. Nice summary boxes and interludes, good selection of illustrations and explanations.

Close, Frank, *The Cosmic Onion*, College Park: American Institute of Physics, 1983. A slightly older book and one of the earlier attempts at "popularizing" particle physics, this book is a bit more terse and technical than the others I've described. It is explicitly intended for "prospective science undergraduates" or "[any] non-scientist prepared to think." It's somewhat tougher going than, for example, Cindy Schwarz's book or Gordon Kane's, but if you want to go a little further into the details, this is an excellent choice.

Close, Frank, Marten, Michael, and Sutton, Christine, *The Particle Explosion*, **Need City**: Oxford University Press, 1987. A colorful book, great pictures, nontechnical, complete, lots of history, very descriptive and detailed.

Davies, Paul, *The Last 3 Minutes*, New York: Basic Books, 1996. The title is a takeoff from Steven Weinberg's *The First 3 Minutes*. This book covers a readable selection of topics in modern cosmology (as modern as a decade-old book can be now).

Ferris, Timothy, ed., *The World Treasury of Physics, Astronomy, and Mathematics*, New York: Little, Brown and Company, 1991. A collection of articles by and about scientists. Not all particle physics (even ranges to math and astronomy, of course!) but very readable and interesting, a nice selection of essays. Not technical at all, but because it is a collection, each article has a different style and level. Some of the short biographies are charming.

Feynman, Richard, see sample list of titles below. If you become interested in Feynman (it's nearly impossible not to!), I recommend just about anything written by Feynman himself. For entertainment, you can't beat his "autobiographies." Start with *Surely You're Joking, Mr. Feynman: Adventures of a Curious Character*, 1985 (Norton and Co.), followed by *What Do You Care What Other People Think? Further Adventures of a Curious Character*, 1988. For some real physics from the master, I recommend *6 Easy Pieces*, Helix Books, 1994, a compilation of six lectures about topics in modern physics Feynman gave to his freshman students at CalTech. These are truly brilliant. Another similar text, this time about more classical questions in physics, is *The Character of Physical Law*, MIT Press (1985). Feynman also wrote *QED: The Strange Theory of Light and Matter*, Princeton University Press (1985), in which he attempts to explain QED to non-experts. An interesting book, but I believe it's still a little hard. I'm not sure if Feynman completely succeeded with his goal on this one, but it's definitely worth a look if you really want to dive deeper.

Franklin, Allan, *Are There Really Neutrinos: An Evidential History*, New York: Perseus Books, 2003. This book is different from most in this list, being written by a historian and philosopher of physics (also a particle physicist). It focuses on the history of neutrinos, addressing the fundamental question: Why do we believe in the reality of particles like the neutrino? Could the neutrino be a social construct rather than something real? An interesting perspective. Mild warning: The book is technical in many places, definitely aimed above the "novice general public" in my opinion.

Fraser, Gordon, *The Quark Machines: How Europe Fought the Particle Physics Wars*, Bristol: Institute of Physics Publishing, 1997 (paperback). Nontechnical summary of more recent developments, with an unusually international perspective, a good deal of discussion of the people involved, good list of references for further reading.

Gamow, George, *Mr. Tompkins in Paperback*, Cambridge: Cambridge University Press, 1993. A whimsical book, very amusing, although a bit dated. Mr. Tompkins is an "interested layperson" who attends lectures on modern physics for the public, but alas, he inevitably falls asleep partway into the lecture. This book describes his ensuing dreams, in which the laws of physics being discussed are "visualized" in some dramatic way. For example, when Mr. Tompkins falls asleep while learning about relativity, in his dream, the speed of light is only about 25 miles/hour; thus, relativity effects become "visible" as he walks around town or gets in his car. In the lecture about quantum mechanics, Planck's constant (which tells the strength of quantum effects) is huge, and billiard balls on Tompkins's pool table suddenly "fuzz out," then tunnel off the table. Very creative way of presenting physics, although the topics covered are not exactly the most "modern" particle physics.

Glashow, Sheldon, *Interactions: A Journey through the Mind of a Particle Physicist and the Matter of This World*, New York: Warner, 1988, and *The Charm of Physics*, College Park: AIP Press, 1991. Two books by a Nobel Prize winner, both light in style, entertaining, filled with stories, from a somewhat personal perspective. Both books also contain a great deal of particle physics. Recommended.

Gleick, James, *Genius: The Life and Science of Richard Feynman*, New York: Pantheon Books, 1992. Not about the physics, but a biography of Richard Feynman, well written, a good glimpse at this remarkable character.

Greene, Brian, *The Elegant Universe*, New York: Vintage Books, 2000. Greene has tried to meet a great challenge—to write a "popular" book about the most abstract and mathematically complex physical theory of them all, string theory. He does a great job, but it's not always the easiest going. I suspect that the casual reader will often be left a little dizzy. Still, Greene manages to "return to reality" enough to allow you to continue reading and continue getting a lot out of the book right up to the end. This is hard stuff, and Greene does an amazing job of presenting it without getting technical.

Hawking, Stephen, *A Brief History of Time* and *The Universe in a Nutshell*, New York: Bantam 2001. Stephen Hawking is one of the most celebrated and well-known contemporary physicists. His books (sometimes considered "coffee-table books," in the sense that some people buy them but don't actually read them) are comprehensive, up-to-date, and full of wonderful ideas about modern physics.

However, I often find that when I get to material about which I'm not an expert, Hawking can lose me; I imagine this could be a problem throughout for the non-physicist reader. I also find that Professor Hawking has some strong ideas that sometimes reach well beyond particle physics, to the realm of philosophy and interpretation, which the reader should be aware of. Interesting books nonetheless.

Kevles, Daniel J., *The Physicists*, Cambridge: Harvard University Press 1995. History of particle physics, more focused on the earlier years. A little dry and dense, but lots of interesting details and anecdotes. I found the introduction/preface on the rise and fall of the SSC especially interesting.

Krauss, Lawrence M., *Fear of Physics*, New York: Basic Books, 1993. Delightful book. Not about particle physics per se (although that's clearly his focus). More a book about how physicists think, how they approach problems. As the book progresses and Krauss gets more into the details and explanations of modern particle physics ideas, the reader may become a little lost because of the completely nontechnical approach (all examples are analogies or simple pictures), but it's a creative and insightful book. Definitely recommended. I just loved the opening chapters.

Landsberg, Peter T., *Seeking Ultimates: An Intuitive Guide to Physics*, Bristol: IOP Publishing, 2000. A popular-style account of many of the fundamental ideas of physics, not limited to particle physics. Some personal philosophy is also mixed in with the book; the author believes deeply that physics is, and always will be, incomplete, but that it is the journey that is most important. Quite readable and a little broader in scope than many of the other books I have included.

Lederman, Leon, *The God Particle*, Boston: Houghton Mifflin, 1993. Whimsical, with a light style and lots of bad puns, a Nobel Prize-winning experimentalist's take on the significance, content, and meaning of particle physics. This is not a book filled with technical explanations or details; it's more a collection of stories and insights, with lots of history and fascinating introduction. Very entertaining reading and still up-to-date. (I find his curious renaming of the Higgs to be completely inappropriate and somewhat annoying, but then, he's the one with the Nobel Prize.)

Leighton, Ralph, *Tuva or Bust*, New York: W.W. Norton and Co., 1991. A less scholarly but more personal work about Richard Feynman. A breezy and delightful story of Feynman as a friend and human being.

Pais, Abraham, *Inward Bound*, Oxford: Oxford University Press, 1988. A slightly more technical book, aimed at scientists (though not necessarily physicists). It's a little dense, very comprehensive, but quite readable if you are comfortable with a few equations and a little mathematical reasoning.

Park, Robert, *Voodoo Science*, Oxford: Oxford University Press, 2000. This book has nothing directly to do with particle physics, but it's a fascinating story of "the road from foolishness to fraud." It's about "bad science," with thoughts on how to distinguish real science from the marginal. The author, Robert Park, is strongly opinionated; if you disagree with him, you may find his strength of conviction challenging, but I think it's a good representation of where most working physicists stand. Great reading, very interesting, entertaining, and thought provoking.

Riordin, Michael, *The Hunting of the Quark*, New York: Simon and Schuster, 1987. A historical narrative focusing on the 1960s–1970s, with many anecdotes and stories about the people and events, as well as the physical ideas. No math but occasional overuse of jargon. The chapters on the November Revolution are among the best of the lot, though.

Taubes, Gary, *Nobel Dreams: Power, Deceit, and the Ultimate Experiment*, New York: Random House, 1987. The "human side" of particle physics, with all the hubris, ego, deceit, confusion, and passion exposed. Much more entertaining reading than most of the other references I've provided, although by its nature, less physics and more soap opera!

Wearth, S., and Phillips, M., eds., *History of Physics: Readings from Physics Today*, Heidelberg: Springer, 1987. A variety of articles, although nothing really state of the art. I especially enjoy "The Birth of Elementary Particle Physics" (Laurie Brown and Lillian Hoddeson, from *Physics Today*, April 1982.)

Weinberg, Steven, *The First 3 Minutes*, New York: Basic Books, 1993. An excellent introduction to the Big Bang and the origin of our universe. Although there have been some important theoretical developments since this book was written, it is still relevant. The level of the book is above the "purely popular," a bit more on the level of an undergraduate text (but suitable for a non-physics major).

Wilczek, Frank, and Devine, Betsy, *Longing for the Harmonies*, New York: Norton, 1987. Although the book is fifteen years old, it is still quite relevant, because the authors do not try to teach the details of modern physics, but rather, to give a taste of the type of aesthetic and intellectual issues involved. They focus on the "musical metaphors" of science. The authors believe that modern physics is not commonsense, but neither is it mystical or incomprehensible. This book is chock full of gems, lots of wonderful insights about the world that help clarify what modern physics is about. I recommend it highly.

Web Sites

http://www.nobel.se/physics/laureates/index.html. The Nobel Prize page for physics, with detailed links if you're curious to follow up on any of the people or ideas.

http://press.web.cern.ch/pdg/particleadventure/other/suggestedreading.html. An excellent collection of additional readings from CERN, the European center for particle physics. Very comprehensive.

http://www.pparc.ac.uk/Ed/ppres_books.asp?Pv=1. PPARC is a particle physics site from the United Kingdom. This site offers a collection of links with many book suggestions (with summaries and "level descriptions"). A useful source for finding further readings.

http://www.fnal.gov. Fermilab's central Web site; this is the premier particle physics experimental facility in the United States. The facility has a solid public outreach program, and its Web site is well organized and interesting, with lots of material aimed at the non-physicist. If you are interested in getting some K–12 students involved in learning about particle physics, the link http://quarknet.fnal.gov is a great resource.

http://www.slac.stanford.edu. SLAC (Stanford Linear Accelerator Center) is the "other" premier U.S. particle physics experimental facility. This site has a great deal of information for the public, and the www.slac.stanford.edu/history/ link is a nice one.

http://particleadventure.org/. Comprehensive and educational site, highly recommended. Created by the Particle Data Group. The site is aimed at, perhaps, the high school level, but I find it informative and educational for any interested readers. Another related link is http://www.cpepweb.org/ particles.html.

http://public.web.cern.ch/Public/. This is the Web site of CERN (the premier European particle physics facility) aimed at the public. Lots of easily readable information about particle physics here.

http://pdg.lbl.gov/cpep.html. The "wall chart" of particle physics. This is from the Particle Data Group. The links to the group's more technical Web pages contain an incredible summary of all the detailed quantitative knowledge we have accumulated regarding all fundamental particles and the laws of physics.

http://dbserv.ihep.su/compas/contents.html. A chronology of particle physics ideas, with links to original papers. Very comprehensive for those interested in historical aspects.

http://www.aps.org/resources/particle.html. American Physical Society page with many links (and descriptions of those links), heading to a variety of resources appropriate for everyone from students in grades K–12 to interested members of the public to working physicists.

http://www.hep.ucl.ac.uk/~djm/higgsa.html. In 1993, the then U.K. Science Minister, William Waldegrave, issued a challenge to physicists to answer the questions "What is the Higgs boson, and why do we want to find it?" on one side of a single sheet of paper. Here is David J. Miller's prize-winning "qualitative layperson's explanation." Other replies can be found at http://hepwww.ph.qmw.ac.uk/epp/higgs.html.

http://scienceworld.wolfram.com/physics/. Eric Weisstein's "World of Physics," with short biographies of just about every physicist I've ever heard of. Nice historical/biographical reference, although rather brief in most cases.

http://www.aip.org/history. Excellent site, very readable, with a small (but growing) collection of historical hypertexts of some key physicists and physics topics.

http://www.powersof10.com/. Not exactly particle physics, but a wonderful site to help think about the world at different distance/size scales.